THE
GREAT
TECH
GAME

'As one of the first early-stage VCs in India, Anirudh's journey has coincided with the massive boom in India's tech journey. He has been witness to it all. In this book, Anirudh has combined his ringside view with insightful historical and systemic perspectives. His global, multi-disciplinary perspective of the Great Tech Game is unique. And in urging that technology be designed in sync with the values we wish to uphold, he has hit the nail on the head. This book will definitely change the way you will view the world of tech … a must read!' **Nihal Mehta,** CO-FOUNDER, ENIAC VENTURES

'*The Great Tech Game* is an insightful account of the multiple and sometimes surprising ways in which technology and geopolitics interact to create our world. Anirudh Suri has given us a jargon-free and accessible book dealing with an issue that will determine our future. It deserves to be widely read by layman and scholar alike.' **Shivshankar Menon,** FORMER NATIONAL SECURITY ADVISOR FOR INDIA AND AUTHOR OF *INDIA AND ASIAN GEOPOLITICS*

'A fascinating look at the entire gamut of the tech world, with very interesting references to history. I learnt so much about the background to many of the recent events. Anirudh has spent a lot of time researching for this book and the list of people he has talked to is very impressive. Policymakers in India should read this to understand the opportunity we could lose if we don't focus on making it easier to do fundamental, long-term R&D in India and building local talent and businesses.' **Luis Miranda,** CHAIRMAN, INDIAN SCHOOL OF PUBLIC POLICY AND CENTRE FOR CIVIL SOCIETY

'In *The Great Tech Game*, Anirudh Suri unpacks the enormous impact of the unfolding technological transformation on our individual and collective lives. Combining his rich experience as an entrepreneur in the technology sector with a close reading of history, politics and international relations, Anirudh Suri makes sense of the multiple emerging fault lines between the citizen, corporation, society, state, and the global system. Suri's deep insights coupled with lucid writing makes this important tract accessible to all.' **C. Raja Mohan,** DIRECTOR, INSTITUTE OF SOUTH ASIAN STUDIES, NATIONAL UNIVERSITY OF SINGAPORE

'Anirudh Suri's timely book highlights why it's essential that we as a society make better choices. As the book rightly argues, it is critical that women have the opportunity to compete in the Great Tech Game as players on an equal footing. The rules of the game must not continue to put them at a disadvantage. Anirudh Suri's book is a brilliant and compelling read.' **Reshma Saujani,** FOUNDER, GIRLS WHO CODE AND MARSHALL PLAN FOR MOMS

'The next thirty years will be very different. More liberalization, while necessary, will not be sufficient to lift hundreds of millions out of poverty. A new playbook is needed. This book outlines this playbook for India. It presents the context, outlines the "great game" that shapes today's geopolitics and frames the issues before us. It is a wonderfully easy read, and yet it brings important counter-intuitive insights to life. This is a terrific agenda-shaping book for our times.' **Sharad Sharma,** CO-FOUNDER ISPIRT FOUNDATION

'In his book, *The Great Tech Game*, Anirudh Suri offers a fresh perspective on how technology has invaded our lives and is affecting everything we do, as individuals, corporates and governments. Today, technology and innovation are key to how economies grow, how competitive they are and decisions they make regarding how they align with other nations economically and militarily.

'The scope of the narrative is comprehensive and multi-disciplinary, encompasses historical, global and social perspectives, geo-politics and international dynamics. This is something I feel has never been done before.

'Suri truly comprehends how the game has changed and to what extent technology will be all prevailing in our engagements in the future. From a practitioner's point of view, Suri stresses on the need for dialogue on the impact of technology, and the decisions and choices that follow. The book is an easy read and an engaging discourse even for those who are not technically oriented.' **S.D. Shibulal,** CO-FOUNDER, INFOSYS

'Digital technologies have transformed the geopolitical landscape, elevating platforms to the stature of nation states while leading us into a deeply uncertain phase of human history. Anirudh Suri's book is the best guide so far to navigating this new world order. Rigorous yet readable, with piercing insights from history. You'll devour it in one sitting, then return to it again.' **Arun Sundararajan,** NEW YORK UNIVERSITY PROFESSOR AND BESTSELLING AUTHOR OF *THE SHARING ECONOMY*

'*The Great Tech Game* is an inspiring read that describes growth as a complex phenomenon which requires politics, economics, sociology, global events, contingencies—everything—to come together. It demonstrates the important role of science, technology and human choices in shaping the future. The real examples and insights also provide a moment to contemplate and examine how and what India can do to participate in this evolutionary journey.' **K. VijayRaghavan,** PRINCIPAL SCIENTIFIC ADVISOR TO THE GOVERNMENT OF INDIA

THE GREAT TECH GAME

SHAPING GEOPOLITICS
AND THE DESTINIES
OF NATIONS

ANIRUDH SURI

HarperCollins *Publishers* India

First published in India by HarperCollins *Publishers* 2022
4th Floor, Tower A, Building No. 10, Phase II, DLF Cyber City,
Gurugram, Haryana -122002
www.harpercollins.co.in

2 4 6 8 10 9 7 5 3 1

P-ISBN: 978-93-5489-426-8
E-ISBN: 978-93-5489-428-2

Cover design: Saurav Das
Cover image: Getty Images

Typeset in 11/14.3 Adobe Garamond Pro at
Manipal Technologies Limited, Manipal

Printed and bound at
Thomson Press (India) Ltd

❶❶◎❷HarperCollinsIn

In loving memory of my father, whose love for books will always stay with me;

for my mother, who has always been my guide;

and for my wife, who has been a true partner through it all.

'Adapt or perish, now as ever, is nature's inexorable imperative.'

—H.G. Wells, *A Short History of the World* (1922)

Contents

Preface

In May 2020, while most of the world was paying attention to the spread of the novel coronavirus COVID-19, an armed standoff between India and China developed in Ladakh. During the course of this standoff, shots were fired between the two armies for the first time in forty-five years. Though the Ladakh standoff seemed an isolated border incident, it came in a series of odd events relating traditional geopolitical concerns to new questions about technology, power and humanity. In June 2020, the US would launch the Clean Network initiative, meant to bring friendly countries together to create a global 5G network infrastructure independent of Chinese state-affiliated companies such as Huawei. And then, in July 2020, India banned several Chinese mobile applications for national security reasons—leaving some Indian tech founders delighted and others distressed.

Something was afoot. I wondered what was really going on.

~

My journey towards writing this book has been a long-winded one. I grew up in Delhi, a city where daily life is replete with the signs of the influence of history, trade and geopolitics. Irish Catholic schools sit in the heart of Delhi's army garrison, and large refugee communities of Punjabi trader families still live where they were placed by a Partition effected by the colonial power. But I, as a regular kid, didn't pay much attention to these signs. Cricket, soccer and debating kept me busy, and the once-a-week computer lab sessions barely left an impression.

I left Delhi as a teenager to finish high school in Singapore, along with about thirty other starry-eyed, mostly middle class Singapore Airlines scholarship winners from all over India. It was there, separated from family for the first time, that I began to notice the impact of the internet on our lives. The ability to send e-greeting cards to my family, or chat with them and old friends on online chat platforms, made the transition much easier for my fifteen-year-old self.

I applied to college using paper forms and mailed them the good old way through the Indian Postal Service. I got my admission and scholarship letter from Haverford College, a small private liberal arts college in Pennsylvania, via mail too. My first brush with the mobile phone (and Facebook) happened at Haverford. During my undergraduate years, I spent a year at the London School of Economics, and also several months at Beijing Foreign Studies University in Beijing.

Upon graduating from Haverford, I worked in Washington DC at the Carnegie Endowment for International Peace. There I worked on, among other things, the nuclear non-proliferation programme with George Perkovich, the US–India civilian nuclear deal and India–China relations with Ashley Tellis, Iran–India relations with Karim Sadjadpour and with French South Asia scholar Frédéric Grare. Looking back, the US–India nuclear deal was a harbinger of the realignments and geopolitical changes in the world order.

During my time at McKinsey & Company in New York and Washington DC, I was exposed to the ramifications of technological advancement for corporates. Technology was impacting sectors as diverse as retail, healthcare, publishing and consumer. From close quarters, I saw the players in the emerging digital economy challenge the established players in these sectors.

At the Harvard Kennedy School (HKS), I delved deeper into the policy implications of technology. I got a glimpse of the emerging complexities of the world of cybersecurity while working closely with researchers at the Berkman Klein Center for Internet & Society. Extensive research on internet and politics, cybersecurity, diplomacy and national security—with Professor Jack Goldsmith at the Harvard Law School and Professors Nicholas Burns, Nicco Mele and Eric Rosenbach at HKS—helped me see how this new domain would shape global politics, diplomacy and international cooperation. Across the Charles River, at Harvard Business School (HBS) and Harvard's Innovation Lab (I-Lab), I experienced a wholly different dimension: the power of technology to drive innovation, the significance of emerging digital platforms and the potential of entrepreneurship to transform economies.

Later, as I worked as a policy advisor in the IT ministry of the Government of India, I got a ringside view of how technology was penetrating the various sectors of India's economy but also the complex policy challenges it presented. The opportunities technology offered for India to meet its socio-economic goals was evident from the work I did on the Common Service Centre (CSC) programme—an initiative to bring the internet and e-governance services to the villages of India that has seen great success.

All these experiences—at the Carnegie Endowment, McKinsey, Harvard and in government—cemented my belief that the technology sector would shape the world yet bring with it a new set of opportunities, challenges and complexities. While I was completing my MBA at the Wharton School, I met Nihal Mehta who along with other Penn/ Wharton alums had started a US-focused early-stage fund called ENIAC Ventures. Driven by the belief that the tech scene in India was about to take off in the same way that it had in the US, Nihal and I raised an India-dedicated technology venture capital fund, India Internet Fund, backed by HNIs and family offices. And so, after over a decade in the United States, I moved to Mumbai to set up India Internet Fund's first India office.

Over the past decade, we've invested in several successful (and some not so successful) technology start-ups across various sub-sectors. I also founded a tech start-up, Findable, focused on hyperlocal commerce. Along with our sister fund, ENIAC Ventures, we also helped several cross-border start-ups (India to the US, and the US to India) scale across these two geographies that we operated in.

In the process, I have witnessed the transformation of India's tech start-up ecosystem. From the early days, when three or four early-stage funds would share our deal flow and pipeline over a Google Drive sheet, the Indian tech ecosystem has come a long, long way. From early rounds of a few hundred thousand dollars, tech founders are now raising rounds of hundreds of millions of dollars. The India arms of the global venture capital funds such as Accel and Sequoia were followed by the arrival of the big boys, like Tiger Global and Softbank.

In 2016, I found myself in the imposing Plenary Hall of Delhi's Vigyan Bhawan, where the Indian Prime Minister was launching the 'Startup India' initiative with much fanfare while hugging founders of Indian tech start-ups. Old friends, such as Vijay Shekhar Sharma and Bhavish Aggarwal, with whom I had shared car rides, conference stages and even offices, were suddenly the poster boys of the Chinese- and American-funded Indian tech start-up ecosystem. At TiE, TechSparks and NASSCOM start-up events, Indian entrepreneurs were suddenly mingling with young representatives of the 'new money', the Chinese Big Tech firms. The game had changed.

As I immersed myself in the world of technology, start-ups and venture capital, I was always watching the larger world as well. I had kept in touch with friends and colleagues from the world to which I had been exposed by my time at the Carnegie Endowment and HKS, earlier stints at think tanks in India and China, and as a policy advisor in the IT ministry at the Government of India. Along the way, I had also advised some large traditional industrial businesses in India on their digital transformations. Again and again, I was struck by how fundamentally different the agricultural, industrial, political and technology worlds were. Yet, they were co-existing, and in India and around the world, they were colliding in unexpected ways.

Where did this crazy spaceship of a ride in the technology sector fit into the larger scheme of things? What was going on in the world? As India and China locked horns in battle over the peaks of Ladakh, it was clear to me that the technology sector—of which I had been intimately part for a decade—was now more than just a hot new sector. It was starting to shape our politics, our foreign policy, our society, our world. But, despite that, we didn't quite grasp the scale, depth and breadth of its impact. The conversations in the technology world were very narrowly focused on valuations, the new hot sectors and the new unicorns. A broader, macro view of how technology was shaping our world was mostly, and very unfortunately, absent.

～

This book puts together all the pieces that have been cumulating in my head, through my personal and professional experiences, but also through the extensive research and scholarship on technology and society that already exists. While much has been said on these themes, it has often been written with an eye towards tech's impact on the US and Europe. Perspectives from the rest of the world, especially Asia, have not often been offered.

Further, most existing writings tackle technology's impact on geopolitics, but rarely attempt to put all the pieces together. Even those that did often failed to put the impact of technology within the appropriate historical context. On the economic front, much has been written about the need for traditional corporate firms to embark on digital transformations, but few discuss the need for nation-states to purposefully embark on similar transformations of their economies.

In this book, I have therefore attempted to provide, first, a multi-disciplinary view. The book evaluates technology's impact by weaving in perspectives from across history, economics, politics, international relations, sociology, behavioural psychology and philosophy.

Second, I hope to view technology's impact not from the perspective of one region or nation but a truly global view. Over the last year or so, I have conducted hundreds of interviews with historians, economists, management consultants and thinkers, venture capitalists, business leaders, sociologists, psychologists, lawyers and policy-makers from literally every continent. Their wisdom has informed my thinking on every facet of this book.

Third, I have written the book from a practitioner's perspective. I have been a technology entrepreneur and venture capitalist for over a decade, and have seen the developments within the global technology world from very close quarters. But I have also worked in academia and think tanks across the US, UK, India, Singapore and China; as a policy advisor; and as a management consultant with McKinsey & Co. in the US and Europe. Here, I have brought my experience from the academic, business, technology and policy worlds together to provide a holistic, yet practical, perspective in this book.

Most importantly, my effort has been to ensure that these perspectives are easy to understand. The book is decidedly not technical. Rather, it provides familiar conceptual frameworks and the relevant historical contexts and analogues to make it easier for everyone to understand what is going on today in the world of technology, and how that will impact what goes on everywhere else.

At the same time, the book also highlights the key practical choices that we need to make as individuals, nations and societies, and suggests ways to adapt to the new world. Technology is driving fundamental changes not only in our societies and nations, but also in our personal and work lives. We are at a digital crossroads, with key choices to be made in each of these dimensions.

Research for this book has led me to identify connections between seemingly disparate events. What ties the Ladakh standoff to the global technology wars? Is there a link between the investment of billions of dollars in Reliance Jio, an Indian telecom firm promoted by an oil baron, at the height of the COVID crisis and the US–China trade and technology wars? And how does all of this matter to any of us? Will it affect our personal lives, our jobs and our future?

I've written this book to help people see and make those links for themselves—hopefully even links that I have not yet seen. Making the connections is, of course, never easy, especially when they're not obvious. But as I spoke with experts in the fields of history, law, space, genetic engineering, cybersecurity, cyberwarfare, internet technologies, start-ups, venture capital, domestic and foreign policy, some of these connections emerged quite clearly.

For this reason, the research I have done for this book has been the most rewarding part of the project. Though the world is always changing in ways we don't understand, clues and harbingers of change can always be found. With the help of many, many others, I have attempted to put some of those clues together to begin to reveal a larger story. Though I cannot claim to have all the answers, I do strongly feel that a much broader and deeper conversation needs to take place about the impact of technology on our world and the choices we need to make, urgently.

This book is an attempt to kick off that conversation.

Introduction

'The specialization which belongs to technology makes it difficult to see the larger picture. The fragmentation of knowledge proves helpful for concrete applications, and yet it often leads to a loss of appreciation for the whole, for the relationships between things, and for the broader horizon, which then becomes irrelevant.'

—Pope Francis, *Laudato Si'* (2015) [1]

When humans began practising agriculture, little did they know the fundamental changes it would trigger. A similar story would play out thousands of years later, in the mid fifteenth century, with the invention of the Gutenberg press. There was no way of knowing the scale or duration of the changes these new inventions would create. We are now beginning a series of changes with similar sweep. Technology is shaping our destinies: as individuals, as families, as nations, as societies, as a world and, increasingly, as humans.

And that, quite simply, is what this book is about: how is technology shaping us? And not only our lives, how is technology shaping nations and their destinies, the world order and the future of humanity? How can we start to make sense of the epochal changes we seem to be living through? How can we understand the ways technology is changing us and what might we do about it?

The scale of the changes associated with what I call the Era of Technology is extraordinary. Some have termed it 'the most profound transformation in our information environment since Johannes Gutenberg's invention of printing in circa 1439'. [2] But history shows us it can be extremely difficult to think clearly about such profound transformations while living through them. Just as no one in the mid fifteenth century could have known that the Gutenberg press would fuel socio-religious movements such as the Reformation and undermine the mighty Catholic Church, it is hard for us to understand and predict the changes the current technology revolution will spur.

Thinking about technology, we are often like the blind men trying to describe the elephant: though everyone from schoolchildren in Delhi to undergraduates in Pennsylvania to graduate students in Beijing has a partial view, nobody can quite assemble the full picture. Even well-placed tech professionals find this bigger picture hard to paint. As former Google CEO, Eric Schmidt, and Jared Cohen point out, 'the Internet is among the few things humans have built that they don't truly understand', even as we all are witnessing how 'mass adoption of the Internet is driving one of the most exciting social, cultural and political transformations in history'. [3]

This book, then, attempts to paint the big picture of how technology is changing our world—and what we might do about it. And while I am no expert in all the individual domains—history, economics, politics, sociology, psychology or culture—I strongly believe a holistic framework is needed, and that is the goal of the book.

Where might such a holistic framework begin? One answer lies in the ways humanity has reacted to past changes. In past eras, like our own, new developments have had profound impacts on the shapes of human lives. We discovered fire and tools; mastered agriculture and eventually trade; greedily sought empire and colonies; organized production within industrial processes; embraced the unprecedented economic growth of capitalism. At each stage, humans first wielded new technologies to shape their lives—but soon found that tools shape their wielders as well. This book will look into the patterns that have emerged in those past changes, and what they might illuminate about the changes yet to come.

And at each stage the changes brought by new ways of living and producing have created new winners and losers. Nations have risen and fallen, and within those nations, ideologies and systems of governance have assembled and dissolved—sometimes peacefully and other times not. By thinking through the changes we are facing, this book also hopes to understand the challenges that states—both incumbent powers and those seeking to develop their tech industries—will face, and how they might best navigate those challenges.

The Great Tech Game—this global contest for technological, economic and geopolitical dominance—is starting to shape the world political and economic order, and underlines what experts have called 'a major shift in the arena of geopolitical rivalry to technological competition'.[4] The Great Game of the nineteenth century saw Britain and Russia battle it out for dominance of Central Asia. But this time, the battle for dominance is global, both in its scope and the ambition of the various players involved. The Great Tech Game—the defining contest of the twenty-first century—is unfolding in front of our eyes.

~

They say the deeper you look into the past, the further you can look into the future. As Brad Smith, the president of Microsoft and author of *Tools and Weapons*, says, 'For every current challenge that seems unprecedented, there is often a historical counterpart that, while distinct, has insights for our day.'[5] Part 1 of the book, therefore, delves deep into history to look for clues to help us understand what we are living through today. I consider the lives of hunter-gatherers and agriculturists, and travel all the way through to the modern day. I examine the impact of key shapers—agriculture, trade, colonization, industrialization and capitalism—which have transformed our world in the past. In doing so, I find that many themes, conflicts, problems and trends that seem uniquely characteristic of our times are not so novel after all. We've been through much of it before.

Yet it is clear that, as Jamie Susskind, British author of *Future Politics*, says, 'we are not yet ready—intellectually, philosophically, or morally— for the world we are creating'. [6] He also points out: 'If mainstream predictions about the future of technology are close to the mark, then the transformation on the horizon could be at least as important for humankind as the industrial revolution, the agricultural revolution or even the invention of language.' [7] The next few decades are likely to witness the birth and expansion of new socio-political movements and ideologies, new debates, new geopolitical actors, new power struggles and some new existential questions that humanity will need to grapple with. The old forms of thinking and old frameworks for understanding the world are not going to work.

We are already witnessing a sneak preview of that world. That is the journey that Parts 2 and 3 take you on. In Part 2, I look at how technology is beginning to transform the economic destinies of nations. As the digital economy outpaces the industrial economy, the nature, and rules, of the economic game are also changing. Technology, I argue, is the new wealth of nations. Technology firms are replacing the manufacturing and industrial-era firms in all key indices of size, productivity and profitability. Technology has become the key driver of productivity and economic growth. Not surprisingly—as in every other transformative era in history—we are seeing a new set of winners and losers emerge. Nations can't expect to win the future by playing the game of the earlier eras. Nations that want to win in this new era must learn the rules of the Great Tech Game and develop tailored strategies to compete in the digital economy.

Part 3 looks outside the confines of the nation. How is technology shaping the relations between nations and the world order? What are the new emerging geopolitical battlegrounds? How is the quest for technological dominance driving great power rivalry and alliance formations today? New enemies and friendships are being made, as nations ready themselves for the new world order. I evaluate whether fears of a new form of colonialism—digital colonialism—are justified.

Part 4 looks at how the rules of the Great Tech Game are being set. I examine whether new forms of global governance principles and institutional frameworks will be needed, or whether existing global institutions like the UN can reform themselves for a new era. And the key battle in shaping the political destinies of nations is the big battle of our times: Big Tech versus the state. Even as this technological transformation brings new, exciting benefits to our civilization, technology will also come to control and shape us and our political, economic, societal and moral systems in powerful yet seemingly unimaginable ways.

In recent history, the world has lived through *Pax Romana*, *Pax Islamica*, *Pax Mongolica*, *Pax Britannica* and *Pax Americana*. We are now living through what could be termed as *Pax Technologica*, though the period of relative peace for this era might soon be coming to an end. Great power rivalries seem to be heating up, new forms of war and attacks are appearing, the authority of nation states is being challenged by some of the largest, richest corporations and individuals in history, the known frameworks for economic competitiveness and upward mobility are being completely upended, and we as humans are under threat of being edited out of our millennia-old bodies and minds. And yet, we don't seem to quite grasp the enormity of change, let alone be prepared for it.

Technology is the real 'great game' going on behind the scenes today. And this is where the overarching frame of the book—*The Great Tech Game*—helps us understand this better. In each era, the shaper or the new technology or trend of the time changed the 'great game'. New winners and losers emerged each time, and they in turn shaped the nature of the great game, how it was played, who it favoured and how it shaped society, economics and politics. I do not use the word 'game' lightly or to suggest that the consequences are not serious. Quite the contrary. For those individuals, corporations and nations that do not understand the contours and the rules of this great game, it'll be a tough road ahead.

In Part 5, I lay out what could change or go wrong with the Great Tech Game. As inequality permeates societies and creates impenetrable divides between the tech-haves and the tech-have-nots, there is a serious possibility of social, political and economic movements arising in response to these growing divides. The game could also entirely change. I highlight two key wild cards in this game: climate and biotech. Climate change and disruption caused by it could change the contours of the Great Tech Game completely, as could developments in genetic engineering and biotechnology. I end by evaluating technology's impact on human behaviour, human relationships, our values and by extension, our culture. I argue that technology is fundamentally re-shaping many aspects of our decision-making and altering, in complex ways, how we think. Its impact will be no less than the cultural impact of the industrial, colonial or the capitalist eras.

~

My goal in writing this book is to make it easy for everyone to appreciate one of the most important, consequential and long-standing drivers of our individual and collective destinies: technology. It demystifies technology, and shows just how broad and deep its impact is. It is easy to say that technology is shaping our world, but it is much harder to unpack and take a long-term, big-picture view of just how technology is shaping the economy, politics, society and the individual.

To many people who are not immersed in the world of technology, Silicon Valley and tech firms globally are held in mixed regard—a mystique laced sometimes with contempt. My book hopes to demystify technology, offering an accessible framework through which to understand what is going on today in the world of tech. In addition to using historical analogies and present-day events to understand how tech is transforming the world, this book also offers many concepts, heuristics and ideas that the readers—no matter their particular context—can use to make sure that they emerge intact from this fundamental transformation of our world. But more importantly, it provides a compelling vision for how we can bridge the digital divides, both among and within nations.

There is so much happening in the world of technology that most of us do not understand or control. But this must not be reason to fear technology, but rather to better understand its various facets. We must learn to make sense of what's going on, and develop guidelines for how to navigate the technology-shaped future.

Throughout the book, I also lay out the critical choices that we face today, so we do not repeat mistakes of the past. The outcomes in all of the previous 'great games' depended on the choices that people made at that time. And we are standing, I believe, at the same crossroads again. The present digital crossroads offer a moment of opportunity, but require responsibility and mindfulness. We must not sacrifice one for the other. What choices we make—as individuals, as families, as nations, as societies, as a world and as a race—in this era will similarly determine not just the outcomes or how we fare in this game, but the nature of the game itself.

The book is therefore also a clarion call to governments, businesses, societies, families and individuals to understand and actively shape the rules and contours of the Great Tech Game to build a kinder, more inclusive, equitable and sustainable world. We must take better decisions that reflect the values we want our world to reflect. The design of technology and our policies and attitudes towards it must similarly evolve with consideration towards the values that truly matter to us.

This book has largely been written from the famous Doab of north India—the area between the Ganges and the Yamuna rivers of north India—in the heart of one of the oldest civilizations in the world. Cognizant of the rich history of this region, yet humbled by how much we still do not know, I hope that this book is useful for those who are inclined—as I am—to place one eye on the past, and the other on the future.

Notes

1. Pope Francis, *Encyclical Letter Laudato Si' of The Holy Father Francis on Care for Our Common Home*, The Vatican (May 2015), https://www.vatican.va/content/francesco/en/encyclicals/documents/papa-francesco_20150524_enciclica-laudato-si.html#_ftnref92, accessed on 15 July 2021.

2. John Naughton, 'The Goal Is to Automate Us', *The Guardian* (20 January 2019), https://www.theguardian.com/technology/2019/jan/20/shoshana-zuboff-age-of-surveillance-capitalism-google-facebook, accessed on 1 October 2021.

3. Eric Schmidt and Jared Cohen, *The New Digital Age: Reshaping the Future of People, Nations and Business* (John Murray Press, 2013), Kindle.

4. Smita Purushottam, 'US–China Geotechnology Race and the Lessons for India', ICS Occasional Paper No. 24 (2019), https://www.icsin.org/uploads/2019/02/05/b57720af41345138ec4a73830943bc8f.pdf, accessed on 1 October 2021.

5. Brad Smith and Carol Ann Browne, *Tools and Weapons* (Hodder & Stoughton, 2019), Kindle. This is the first book by Microsoft CLO Brad Smith, exploring the biggest questions facing humanity about tech.

6. Jamie Susskind, *Future Politics* (Oxford: Oxford University Press, 2018), Kindle.

7. Ibid.

PART ONE

~

INSIGHTS FROM THE GREAT GAMES IN HISTORY

'Our fascination with our own day and age, and our preoccupation with both the promise and peril of new technology, often leads us to think that we are experiencing something entirely new. Seen through the lens of the long record of human history, however, this seems unlikely to be true.'

—Carl Benedikt Frey, *The Technology Trap* (2019)

'It made me realise that change is normal, that big shifts in the global centre of power are quite common, and that this chaotic and unfamiliar world is perhaps not so strange and unusual after all.'

—Peter Frankopan, *The New Silk Roads* (2018)

The future of our world will be determined by the choices we—as a species, as nations and as citizens—make about technology in the coming decades. Understanding this Great Tech Game—in which outcomes of all kinds might depend on how intelligently, ethically and assertively we relate to the changes brought by technology—is as difficult as it is essential. How are we to think through the rapid and profound changes that the Great Tech Game will bring?

One set of answers lies in the Great Games of the past—how nations and peoples related to the defining forces and economic drivers of their periods. In this section, I will consider how human history was shaped during periods defined by agriculture and trade, colonialism and industrialization and, finally, capitalism and technology. By understanding how these forces shaped the world—and how nations won and lost in addressing them—I believe we can gain valuable insight into how the Great Tech Game might develop, and how we can plan for it.

Agriculture, beginning around 10,000 BCE, marked the first great revolution in human economic activity—some would say the invention of economic activity as we understand it today. It did so by creating surpluses far larger than the species had previously experienced. These surpluses drove prosperity and trade, creating flows between groups and nations. These flows, in turn, created both interdependence and tension—while well-placed trade intermediaries became wealthy and influential, critical choke points for trade flows (often including those same intermediaries) often became flashpoints for geopolitical conflict and war. Partly in response to these conflicts, world trade and political systems were developed—often to the advantage of those who controlled the flows.

In this section, we will examine many of these themes—surpluses, flows and intermediaries, geopolitics and conflict, monopoly and world trade, and the rise of trade entrepots—in order to understand the basic shapes that have created and settled global conflicts in the past. As we will see, many of these shapes are as influential today as they were millennia ago—Amazon's contemporary strategy has much in common with the strategies of ancient Byblos or Dilmun, and today's American hegemony mirrors in many ways the systems created by Roman or Mongol governance. By understanding the patterns of power present in the Great Games of the past, we can learn valuable lessons about how to navigate the complexities of our current Great Tech Game.

1

The Great Agri and Trade Game

The Genesis of Geopolitics (10,000 BCE–1500 CE)

Over 10,000 years ago, when human beings began to engage in agriculture, little did they realize that it would end up shaping the economic systems, drive economic competitiveness, prop up civilizations across the world and lead to the genesis of geopolitics as we understand it today.

While we do not know where human beings first discovered fire, we do know that the major agricultural civilizations and the earliest urban settlements came up around rivers, whether it was Mesopotamia (the Tigris and the Euphrates), the Indus Valley civilization (the Indus River and its tributaries), Egypt (the Nile River delta), the Indo-Gangetic plains (the Ganges and the Yamuna) or China (the Yellow River).

Agriculture introduced to humans the concept of high yields, or in modern terms, high productivity. The presence of rivers, rainwater and generally cultivable fertile land was the prerequisite for most large civilizations. It was the Fertile Crescent in Mesopotamia (modern-day southern Turkey, Syria, Jordan, Israel and Iraq) that witnessed the first farmers and the first urban settlements. The dark, moist and rich soil of the wonderfully complex delta of Mesopotamia (the land between the Tigris and Euphrates rivers) would drive higher agricultural yields.[1]

Economic strength during the agricultural era came down to one key capability: controlling the water flows to improve yield. In civilizations that did succeed in controlling the water flows, the results were remarkable. For example, while Neolithic farmers in that region farming on rain-watered land would hope to get four to five grains of barley for every grain of barley planted, the river valley farming in the Fertile Crescent would yield up to forty grains, if given the right amounts of water at the right time.[2] A tenfold improvement in yield would change the dynamics and attractiveness of farming altogether.

The increased yields had other significant spillover effects not just in that region but all over the world. Harvard archaeologist Ofer Bar-Yosef has argued that while agriculture took root in parts of the Fertile Crescent first, other parts of the Crescent eventually also started to take farming seriously upon seeing the effectiveness and high yields associated with the combination of crops and livestock, and the technology to manage them. Scientists have called this combination the 'Neolithic package'.[3]

Over the next two to three millennia, the farming communities of the Fertile Crescent, armed with the Neolithic package, would spread out to span three different continents: Eastern Africa, Europe and South Asia.[4] As they searched for more territory to farm, they encountered more hunter-gatherers (especially in Europe), but seized the territory to start farming on larger and larger tracts of land. This original land grab will turn out to be eerily similar to the colonial-era land grab and the data grab that Big Tech firms are engaged in today (more on that later).

While Egypt and the Indus Valley seem to have been inspired or influenced by the Fertile Crescent, other civilizations—in China, Mexico and Peru—would also develop extensive agricultural set-ups. On the plains beside the Yellow River in China, Neolithic farmers were by the fourth millennium BCE leveraging similar channels, reservoirs and embankments to control the river's natural rhythms. The thousands of villages along the Yellow River's floodplains would become the cradle of Chinese civilization.

In the early rounds of this Great Agricultural Game, then, advantages fell not only to those groups most blessed with natural resources but to those who most energetically and inventively maximized their local advantages—and found ways of compensating for disadvantages in the form of flooding. This pattern, however old, is also an essential one for understanding how the Great Tech Game might proceed.

Food surplus (the first surplus humans had known)

With increasing yields came food surplus. For the first time in history, human beings had the ability to produce food in excess of what they needed. This would have key implications for human society. First, societal structures and hierarchies would start to form. To control water flows, the collective action needed meant that thousands of people had to work together, presumably under the supervision of a few. This would lead to the creation of organized societies with established hierarchies, in stark contrast to the more egalitarian societies of the hunter-gatherers.

Second, the food surpluses caused the world population to rise rapidly and led to the rise of sustainable civilizations with elaborate cultures and monuments. People stopped moving around as much and started building villages, which would gradually grow into towns. Each unit of farmed land could support as much as ten times as many people as each unit of land covered by hunter-gatherers. Women in hunter-gatherer groups could only carry a limited number of children, but in settled communities, that was no longer a constraint.[5]

The Great Agri Game set in motion significant changes in human society. Not all people had to be engaged in farming, which in turn meant that those people could take up other occupations. People could start specializing as farmers, craftsmen, architects and soldiers. Complex societies—or civilizations—would arise in those places where 'controlling water was the key to producing surpluses of food that could support an elite class of warriors and priests and those who served them as traders, artisans and servants'.[6] Ancient Egypt, Mesopotamia, India and China—all civilizations that have lasted for thousands for years—stand testament to the monumental changes set in motion at that time by a simple development: food surpluses. Ultimately, as Joseph Henrich, a professor of human evolutionary biology at Harvard University, has argued, 'the spread of food production—agriculture and animal husbandry—shaped our social worlds and institutions'.[7] As I will explain later in the book, technology is today similarly shaping our social worlds and institutions.

Food surplus leads to trade flows

A final momentous outcome of agricultural surpluses was the rise of trade. A country or civilization producing a great surplus of food, beyond the needs of its population, could now choose to trade with neighbouring regions. For example, Greece, due to its topography, could not grow any grain but could grow olives and grapes. So, the traditional Greek farmer would produce olive oil and wine to exchange for grains such as wheat and barley from elsewhere. For several millennia post the advent of the agricultural revolution, the world would simply be governed by agriculture and trade, which would yield increasingly complex organizations and civilizations around the world, and greater interaction amongst them.

Metals would play an important role in boosting cross-border trade as well. By approximately 3500 BCE, human beings had started to discover metals as well and begun to experiment with processes like smelting. For countries that had agricultural surpluses, trade with countries that were surplus in metals but lower in soil fertility would provide them the raw materials required to boost their agricultural productivity. Metals would help regions defend themselves against aggression or attack, not to mention that silver and gold would become major sources of revenue and serve as the currency for trade.

Settlements also gradually turned into mercantilist towns, which further enabled trade by affording a ready market for the surplus agricultural and metal produce. This further encouraged greater cultivation and improvement in productivity. This formed a virtuous cycle of greater surpluses and higher productivity. This, in turn, would increase the real wealth and revenue for that society. Even today, cities serve as the clearing house for the agricultural and other produce from the rural regions. It all seems so obvious and intuitive in retrospect, but the key thing to note is that this process required surpluses to be kick-started.

The other requirement for trade at that time, in addition to the surpluses, was for infrastructure or trade routes to allow the surpluses to flow between regions. The earliest Mesopotamian records show, for example, that grain and cloth were being exported from Mesopotamia, and strategic metals such as copper were being imported. These trade routes would evolve rapidly from their early beginnings. Soon, rivers, overland routes and sea routes would all be viable options for trade to take place. A significant technological development helped this increase in trade: the invention of the sail. The reason that around 3000 BCE, merchants, were able to start travelling long distances was that the sail boats could travel ten times further than the ancient row boats. These boats could traverse stretches of rivers and the open sea that were previously not accessible easily to traders. Trade via the sea was becoming a much faster and more cost-efficient way of transporting goods over long distances.[8]

Trade flows lead to prosperity

That trade flows were beginning to lead to riches is illustrated by the example of Dilmun or modern-day Bahrain. Ancient Sumerian mythology talks about Dilmun as the land of milk and honey, celebrated for its prosperity. Dilmun was not rich in agricultural produce but instead derived its wealth from its strategic location as a trading post along the Persian Gulf. By 2000 BCE, Dilmun was estimated to be as big as Ur, the largest Mesopotamian city of the time and an agricultural production hub. This illustrates an early rule that we will see repeated throughout the history of trade and our story of surpluses and flows: that trading hubs can become as prosperous, if not more prosperous, than the production hubs. Similarly, the Old Kingdom period for Egypt, with a strong central government and its leadership of international trade in the region, witnessed unprecedented economic prosperity as a result.

Economic prosperity, in turn, would boost trade beyond the essential trade of necessities. The elites began driving an international trade in luxury goods, as they looked for ways to stand apart from the lower classes in their societies. Social hierarchy, which presumably began with the advent of agricultural surpluses as discussed, was now already starting to look similar to how we know it.

Over the centuries, the profits generated from trade—either from trading itself or from taxing the goods flowing through their territory or trade routes controlled by them—would fuel rapid economic development of nations. By taxing the imports and exports of goods passing through their territories, the governments could fund large infrastructure projects such as the construction of roads and ports, which in turn would help boost trade further. Some cities would even form massive empires based on their active participation, even leadership, of the trade networks.[9]

Agriculture and Trade Shaped the World Order and Geopolitics

Trade created dependencies and pivot points

With trade and complexity of needs came dependency. And with dependency would come the initial strains of trade-driven geopolitics. The United States worries about its dependency on unstable regimes for key materials such as oil. The situation was not much different for ancient Mesopotamia. Mesopotamia was definitely an agricultural superpower in its own right. However, as the importance of other strategic materials such as metals, timbers and stone arose,

Mesopotamia's strategic positioning became more dependent on others. As author William Bernstein concluded, 'The very survival of Mesopotamia's great nations—the Sumerians, Akkadians, Assyrians, and finally the Babylonians—hinged on the exchange of their surplus food for metals from Oman and the Sinai, granite and marble from Anatolia and Persia, and lumber from Lebanon.'[10]

Trade flows also meant that various pivot points on the trade routes, or the arteries of trade, would benefit greatly. By 3000 BCE, the Persian Gulf was already playing the role of a major trade route for commerce. As various civilizations began to develop in Egypt, Greece, Phoenicia and the Indus Valley, the Red Sea would also start to serve as a strategically important maritime route. And this would continue for several thousands of years since then till today. As a result, countries or civilizations, such as Egypt, located on these routes also benefitted greatly over this period.

As they benefitted from trade across these maritime routes, the Egyptians would begin to seek control and security of these routes. During the Third Dynasty, around 2600 BCE, the Egyptians sent the first Royal Expedition to turquoise-rich Sinai to 'dominate the source of turquoise rather than import it'. This would be the beginning of a key pattern of the geopolitics of trade: 'As trade continued to develop, securing important trade routes became an increasing concern for Mediterranean powers, which often sought political control of specific areas that provided crucial imports to ensure that supply lines remained open and accessible.'[11]

The state vs private players (traders and pirates)

As these maritime trade routes got busier, especially with ships carrying precious stones, metals and oils, pirates were also starting to see opportunities to plunder and raid these ships. For countries like Egypt, where the centralized government controlled all the trade, this was the only avenue for private individuals to 'participate' in global trade directly. Over time, this would necessitate the societies controlling these maritime trade routes to develop naval military capabilities to protect the trade routes from the increasingly active pirates as well as potential rivals.

As the power of the Egyptian state began to decline during the New Kingdom (roughly 1500–1000 BCE), piracy began to flourish in the region. At the same time, the wealth and power of the Egyptian state would inspire other enterprising cultures in the region to take control of the ever-growing trade in the region. By 2000 BCE, the control of long-distance Mesopotamian or Sumerian trade had been assumed by private players such as the Ea-Nasir, though the state continued to control the trade in Egypt.

While in some cases, the state continued to control all the trade, in other regions, like Mycenae, trade was no longer controlled by a central power but was increasingly the domain of enterprising traders, who were willing to not just explore new territories and travel far and wide, but also assume much of the risk that was inherent in such trade. The governments, in this case, began to restrict their role to taking a percentage of the profits both on import and export of goods through taxation. Even then, we saw differences in government policy towards trade.

The early colonies and new winners

The mantle of controlling the Mediterranean Sea trade would be taken over subsequently by the Minoans, Mycenaeans and then the Phoenicians during the second and first millennium BCE. The Minoan civilization, centred in Crete, while still considered mysterious, is believed to have been a regional sea power during roughly 2700–1500 BCE. Their sea empire is believed to have spread from Spain to Syria and Egypt, with colonial cities established around the eastern Mediterranean Sea and the Aegean Islands. Like Egypt, the Minoans exercised sole authority over the Cretan trade till about the end of the second millennium BCE. This idea of sole authority over trade was unknown (and, if known, not practised) a few thousand miles across in the civilizations of the Indian

Ocean. That itself would have implications about which nations would seek to colonize and monopolize trade versus others that looked to simply promote trade.

But unlike the Egyptians, whose empire was largely a land-based empire, the Minoans, with their primarily sea-based empire, not only dominated the maritime trade but also used this strength to build one of the world's first navies to effectively police the waters. They prioritized the safety of the trade routes, and their navy was capable of patrolling the Aegean waters. The Minoans are also believed to have another first to their credit: they were believed to be the first to establish colonies along the critical maritime trade routes to serve as stopping points and also help secure their trade interests. These 'colonies' would not only use the same language as the Minoan court, but also the same Minoan systems of weights and measures, which helped facilitate trade as well.

The Minoan dual strategy of a strong patrolling navy and the establishment of colonies at critical trading points was innovative thinking at that time, as economic considerations were starting to drive political policy. Other countries had not exerted power in the ways that the Minoans started to. They sent out Minoan colonists to establish cities, live on these foreign islands for the entire year and set up political systems that helped the central Minoan government to control the governments of these places. This innovation would inspire many empires and nations and have ramifications for centuries to come.

Before this period, there had been neither the motive nor the desire to take over new places or secure geopolitically advantageous positions along critical trade routes. But it attests to the profitability of the international trade that it drove rulers like the Minoans to view this strategy as a key pillar of their overall political and economic strategy. In effect, the Minoans 'set the stage' for the way trade and geopolitical relationships would evolve not just in the Mediterranean but the entire world.[12]

After the Minoans, the Mycenaeans are believed to have physically taken over the Minoan trade networks, starting sometime around 1450–1400 BCE. The Mycenaeans would extend the sea-trade routes established by the Minoans, but also go deeper into south-eastern Europe. The regional supply chains were also being developed. Much like the Sumerians had started to do with copper-tin alloys, the Mycenaeans sourced raw materials like ivory, tin, copper, gold and glass from parts of Europe and the Middle East, and these were turned into value-added, finished goods by local craftsmen in Mycenaean settlements, before being exported back to foreign countries.[13]

Trade gets intertwined with geopolitics

That trade was getting intricately intertwined with geopolitics already is evident not just from the strategies of colonization and naval policing, but also very simply from the wars that were starting to break out.

The legendary Trojan War, dating back to the second half of the second millennium BCE, illustrates this intertwining perfectly. Troy, situated at the mouth of the strategically important Hellespont channel linking the Near East to the Mycenaean world, was very significant for the smooth passage of goods. Despite the story revolving around Helen of Troy being stolen away by the Trojan prince, it has been argued that 'it is more likely that the Trojan War was started because Mycenaean traders sought to take over this key area from the Hittite rulers who controlled it in the 14th century BCE'.[14] Increasingly, trade was becoming important enough that people were willing to go to war and die for it. This is equally true today.

After the Mycenaeans, it was the turn of the Phoenicians, who were based in modern-day Lebanon.[15] Phoenician cities such as Tyre, Sidon and Byblos grew prosperous based on the Phoenicians' expansive control of the trade routes.[16] After the Phoenicians, in the subsequent millennium, the Greek city-states, the Macedonians (led by Alexander and his generals), the Romans and the Persians would continue to battle for the regional and global trade and access to markets. Many wars—including more famously the Peloponnesian Wars and the Persian Wars—would be fought to wrest or maintain control of the strategic trading centres and trade routes, whether over land or via sea. Rulers such as Alexander would pledge the freedom of the seas for Greek shipping as a way to maintain support of key constituencies in these states. Trade was as great a unifier as it was a divider.

Over the next millennia, everything around trade would expand: the routes, the navigation technology, the size and technology used by the fleets, the size and riches of the various civilizations and the empires, the range of goods being traded, and the number and diversity of merchants or traders facilitating that trade. In today's world too, geopolitical tensions and alliances often arise around control of the key flows—of data and expertise in addition to physical goods today.

The strategy of trade monopoly

The Romans went a step further than their predecessors in ensuring their primacy in trade. The Romans decided to completely eliminate any competition whatsoever that might arise to their trading empire from any other major regional trading powers, such as the Corinth and Carthage. These cities, for example, had earlier enjoyed great prosperity as trading powers, but the Romans were intent on not just controlling these centres, but actually destroying them to prevent the possibility of any threat to the Roman supremacy in the future as well. This strategy—of complete annihilation of enemies, current and future, and of establishing a clear monopoly of trade backed by force— would also continue to be replicated by powers, long after the Roman empire had fallen.[17]

Of course, trade would enrich many across the entire supply chain. Within this value chain, every people, nation or empire would build its own competitive advantage. For example, the Chinese fiercely guarded their knowledge and production of silk to try and monopolize that luxury trade. The elites of the Roman empire, for example, wanted tea, spices, porcelain and silk from Asia, but had nothing much to offer to those largely self-sufficient nations. This led to the one-way flow of gold and silver to India and China.

Building their competitive advantage was not enough. States or empires were also very keen to protect their competitive advantages. Intermediaries such as the Arabs and the Genoese merchants—like contemporary platforms such as AirBnB and Amazon—would prevent direct contact between the buyers and sellers. These intermediaries understood that profits were to be made by denying such access.

The most illustrative—if also a bit ludicrous when looked at in retrospect—example of the success of the producers and intermediaries to withhold their trade secrets was evident from the fact that for a long time, the Romans did not even know where silk came from, or how it was made. Today, that competitive advantage—both the building of it and protection of it—remains a key policy priority for successful nations and major firms.

From regional geopolitics to global: The rise of the world trade systems

In addition to the Mediterranean trade system, the first millennium BCE also saw the development of major trade systems in China and India. By the first century CE, these regional trade systems were also connected with each other, forming a truly world trade system (with the exception of the Americas).

The relative stability and peace provided by *Pax Romana* on one end and the Han empire in China on the other encouraged commerce, albeit indirect, between Rome and China in the first two centuries. After the disintegration of the Roman empire, trade would also suffer, though obviously not stop completely. The lesson was clear: political stability, guarantee of security and predictability of rules would lead to greater trade, while political instability, uncertainty and insecurity would inhibit trade. The world of trade would learn this lesson from time to time: great empires allowed trade to flourish and their disintegration would lead to decreased trade.

Pax Islamica: Islam takes over global trade

By the sixth and seventh centuries CE, a new religious and political force would take over the global trade routes: Islam. Islam's spread was intricately linked with trade, starting from the fact that its founder, the Prophet Mohammed, was himself a successful trader. It is widely believed that the lightning speed with which Islam spread in the centuries after the birth of the Prophet Mohammed had much to do with its emphasis on promoting trade.

As the European states weakened due to internal strife and other reasons, Islam stepped in to control the trade routes by shutting out the Europeans from the Persian Gulf and the Red Sea. Islamic armies would fight various key battles to wrest control of these routes, extending a pattern that had now become quite common in the region. The first order of business for the Caliph was to secure grain for the masses. Egypt, the long-time granary of the Mediterranean, was the obvious target. Control of the ancient version of the Suez Canal was next. The grain that used to flow north from Egypt to the Roman and Byzantine empires would now flow south-east. The loss of this granary contributed to the decline of the Byzantine empire. The goals of today's technology wars—where countries are seeking to deny technologies and their core components such as semiconductors—are not very different.

The sea routes between Europe and India and China had been severed, and their control shifted into the hands of the Caliphate. Over the next few centuries, the early Islamic empires (the Umayyad before 750 CE and the Abbasid after 750 CE) would extend their naval dominance of the Red Sea, the Persian Gulf and the Mediterranean, by conquering various strategic islands in the Mediterranean, such as Cyprus, Crete, Malta and Sicily. Control of trade and commerce would be the primary driving force in the choice of these conquests.

With the sea routes in hand, the Islamic empires turned their focus to the land routes. Less interested in the backwaters of Europe, they focused on control of Central Asia, with its abundant opportunities of controlling the Silk Route trade and hence further riches. In 751 CE, the Muslim armies finally succeeded, after multiple failed attempts, in defeating the Tang Chinese at Talas (modern-day Kazakhstan) and gained control of the caravan routes that they had eyed for so long.

These Muslim conquests, and control of the trade routes, would essentially seek to create *Pax Islamica*, and in that context, recreate on a grander scale the *Pax Romana*, that had been the golden age for trade until a few centuries ago. The Umayyad and Abbasid empires were recreating a global system of trade that would include the three great routes between southern Europe and Asia: the Red Sea, the Persian Gulf and the Silk Road (which itself consisted of multiple routes that ran east–west).

The Islamic empires of the time decided to further boost the integration of the sea and land trade. Prior to the rise of Islam, trade was still poorly integrated, with goods having to pass through multiple lands and the hands of merchants following different trade practices and different legal traditions. Islam sought to change all that. Islam would 'sweep away this fragmented and pluralistic pattern of trade in the ancient world'.[18] Arabic became the lingua franca of trade, and Muslim navies patrolled the seas from Gibraltar to Sri Lanka.

The entire known world was now knit into a vast Islamic trade world. As the well-known traveller in the Muslim world of this time, Ibn Battuta, described, the Muslim traders and importers—whether in Cairo or Tangiers—followed the same religious, ethical and commercial customs and rules as the suppliers and exporters in Gujarat, Cambay or Malacca. The Muslim rulers—whether in Arabia or India or Malaysia— implemented the same tax and import–export rates. Uniform rules for trade made for more predictable trade, which led to greater trade.

Importantly, Islamic empires controlled the trade now to the exclusion of all the European powers. After the victories that gave them control of the key entry and exit points such as Bab el-Mandeb and the Suez Canal of the time, Islamic forces would prevent any Greek ships from sailing towards India. None of the great Italian trading states would have any access, either, to these trading routes. By the turn of the millennium, Muslim trade with China would also grow both via the maritime route and the Silk Road.

Rome, which had been the centre of world commerce, and its descendant states had been turned into a backwater, with no direct access or control to the trade routes. Just like the Roman and Han empires had encouraged long-range, albeit indirect, trade in the first and second centuries CE, the Islamic and Tang empires would foster trade between the Islamic empires and China during the seventh and ninth centuries. Trade in this period would, however, become a lot more direct, and evidence suggests that Muslim merchants—Persian, Arab and Byzantine—were actively present in China.

Pax Mongolica: The Mongols take over

In the thirteenth century, many geopolitical events would completely upend this Islamic trade order as well. When the Mongols led by Genghis Khan ransacked Baghdad, a new geopolitical force had arrived on the Eurasian landscape. They revolutionized warfare, leveraging a combination of Chinese siege technology, fast cavalry and heavy artillery that allowed them to overrun the defences of any existing militaries in the region.

The Mongols—while not having any religious or political ideology to propagate—believed in promoting trade through the vast Eurasian empire that they came to control in the thirteenth and fourteenth centuries. As Robert Kaplan has also pointed out, the 'Mongols' grand strategy was built on commerce, much more than war', and that 'it was trade routes, not the projection of military power, that emblemized the Pax Mongolica'.[19]

The Mongols supported merchants with low taxes, financing, partnerships and large merchandise orders. Most importantly, they focused on logistics and transport infrastructure in order to promote trade and also ease the supply of goods from newly conquered territories. They built roads and bridges, protected from potential robbers by soldiers. They built ten thousand postal stations, spaced a day's walk apart, which were enabled with messenger services to relay news from one post to the other. Their continent-wide networks would serve, much like the British-built rail networks in India, to both transport the spoils of war and also facilitate trade. Not driven by political or religious ideology, the Mongols were mainly interested in amassing wealth (and legacy). So, they tolerated a diverse set of religions, cultures and ideologies as long as the wealth flowed freely to the Mongolian centre.

Pax Mongolica, which lasted almost a couple of centuries, also meant that the trade barriers between the Mediterranean and China were removed. The intermediaries in the region around the Levant and the Fertile Crescent—who would otherwise have captured a lot of the value of the great trade by imposing high taxes on both sides—were no longer able to. Merchants from various nations from as far away as Italy, North Africa and India were allowed to set up trading sections in China, and vice versa. This deep integration of Eurasian trade and unprecedented governance meant that unlike in previous eras, when the Silk Road routes were almost always less preferred than the sea routes due to the risks they entailed, the Silk Road finally began to emerge as 'a well-guarded conveyer belt of goods, people, and ideas'.[20]

Of course, beyond the free flow of trade of goods, people, ideas, knowledge and technology flowed much more freely too. As the twain between East and West seemed to finally be meeting, the thirteenth and fourteenth centuries would come to be called 'the first golden age of globalization'.[21] This flow of knowledge and technology from East to West would have significant geopolitical implications in the centuries to come, when the inventions of the East, including gunpowder and navigational instruments, would ultimately help shift the balance of influence in Eurasia to Europe. But more on that later.

Trade across southern and eastern Europe, the Middle East and Asia followed a largely standard set of rules promoted by Islam and later by the Mongols. However, the Indian Ocean trade still remained largely decentralized, yet still surprisingly safe for navigation by traders and merchants. States whose political institutions were best suited to trade and commerce thrived, while those whose institutions were not, declined.[22] This lesson—of the need for adaptability of governments and institutions to compete in the world arena of trade and commerce— has continued through the ages.

Malacca, near modern-day Singapore, presents a fascinating example of a trading entrepôt from that era. Founded in 1400 by Parameswara (one of the last princes of the sea-faring empire of Srivijaya), Malacca grew rapidly in wealth, prosperity and prominence. While its location was strategic, so was the case for the neighbouring trading cities on the Malay and Sumatran coasts. But it was Parameswara's 'institutional genius' (laws, institutions and trade policies) and focus on commerce that helped Malacca outcompete them in the global trading game.

What exactly did the Malaccans do to get there? One, they imposed duties and taxes that were lower and less onerous than that prescribed by Islamic custom of that time, with 6 per cent being the maximum. However, certain groups would pay half of that, while others would pay no import duties at all. A well-defined and well-known and well-understood legal architecture, combined with an efficient trade administrative structure, allowed trade to run smoothly. All goods were traded via multi-party auctions and bids, again using well-described and well-known rules. The government ensured that the participants in these auctions were considered 'honest and reliable'. Furthermore, the Malaccan rulers kept open lines of communication, through regular visits, with their largest trade partners, such as China.

A Portuguese apothecary traveller, Tomé Pires, described how in the early 1500s, one could count eighty-four languages being spoken in Malacca—all courtesy of the merchants who assembled at the point that would connect India, the Arab world and Europe in the West to China and the legendary Spice Islands in the East. Malacca was in many ways not unique. It was simply following the essential formula that many other trading entrepots before it—Venice, Canton and Tyre—had followed, to become a prosperous coastal trading centre of the world.

In the twelfth century, Venice, for example, invented new forms of contracts called *colleganzas* to facilitate greater risk-sharing between investors and merchants. Often thought of as the precursor of the joint-stock companies[23] (that we will see in the next chapter), such institutional innovation helped trading entrepots such as Venice to remain at the forefront of the Great Trading Game of the era. In their unstinting focus on capturing a lot of value as part of the global trading supply chain, entrepots such as Malacca and Venice were to the Middle Ages what Singapore, Dubai and Hong Kong are to the modern world. They understood the Great Trading Game of that era, and mastered it—and proved that winners in Great Games need not have the largest armies, richest soils, or most expansive territories. They may just be the parties that most swiftly grasp the defining forces and flows of their time, and act to position themselves accordingly.

A Few Lessons

Agriculture and trade were the key shapers of the world for the period between 10,000 BCE and 1500 CE. As I argue, they constituted the respective Great Games of this era. They shaped not just the economic destinies of the nations and civilizations of the time, but also led to the genesis of many economic and strategic concepts that are very familiar till today. In many ways, what we see today is nothing new. Wars over trade supremacy and control of strategically important trade routes go back at least 3,000 years. Furthermore, many of the strategies deployed by these countries and peoples in history have continued to be replicated and built upon by those who have come since. As you will see, many of these patterns are being repeated and utilized in the Great Tech Game as well.

This era taught us about man's continuous quest for domination of the various elements of nature. It is surpluses—food surplus, trade surplus (and in today's world, data surplus)—that drive trade and prosperity. Controlling the flows—whether of river water or of trade (or today, of data), therefore, becomes critical for countries hoping to capture value, whether by becoming Malaccan entrepots or Minoan monopolists. With expanding trade, countries or regions become dependent on each other, and this dependence becomes leverage for power. Critical choke points for trade flows often become the sites or reasons for geopolitical conflict and wars.

Trade had especially created the concept of the intermediary between the producer and the consumer. Venice, for example, mastered that game by being the trading intermediary between the East and the West. As you'll see, this quest to replace the incumbent intermediary often lies at the core of economic competition. Even in the Great Tech Game, Big Tech firms such as Amazon are becoming the new intermediaries, replacing the traditional traders or retailers.

Adaptability and the establishment of innovative institutions, tailored to the needs of the Great Game in play in that era, often distinguishes the winners from the losers. Ultimately, in each era, new winners emerge by mastering the dominant trend-shapers or the 'great game' of that time better than the incumbents. And these great games—whether agriculture or trade—transform the world's societal, economic and political systems, while also giving birth to new societal structures, cultures, values and ideologies.

Notes

1. Andrew Marr, *A History of the World* (Pan Macmillan, 2012), Kindle.
2. Ibid.
3. Carl Zimmer, 'How the First Farmers Changed History', *The New York Times*, October 2016. https://www.nytimes.com/2016/10/18/science/ancient-farmers-archaeology-dna.html, accessed on 1 October 2021.
4. Ibid.
5. Andrew Marr, *A History of the World* (Pan Macmillan, 2012), Kindle.
6. Daniel R. Headrick, *Humans versus Nature* (Oxford University Press, 2019), Kindle.

7. Joseph Henrich, *The Weirdest People in the World: How the West Became Psychologically Peculiar and Particularly Prosperous* (Penguin, 2020), Kindle.

8. Charles River Editors, *Ancient Mediterranean Trade: The History of the Trade Routes throughout the Region and the Birth of Globalization* (Charles River Editors), Kindle.

9. Ibid.

10. William Bernstein, *A Splendid Exchange* (Grove Press/Atlantic Monthly Press, 2009).

11. Charles River Editors, *Ancient Mediterranean Trade*.

12. Ibid.

13. Ibid.

14. Ibid.

15. Bernstein, *A Splendid Exchange*.

16. Mark Cartwright, 'Phoenician Colonization', World History Encyclopedia (14 April 2016), https://www.ancient.eu/Phoenician_Colonization/, accessed on 1 October 2021.

17. Ibid.

18. Bernstein, *A Splendid Exchange*.

19. Robert D. Kaplan, *The Return of Marco Polo's World: War, Strategy and American Interests in the Twenty-First Century* (Random House, 2018), Kindle.

20. Jeffrey E. Garten, *From Silk to Silicon: The Story of Globalization Through Ten Extraordinary Lives* (Westland, 2017), Kindle, 35.

21. Ibid.

22. Bernstein, *A Splendid Exchange*.

23. Henrich, *The Weirdest People in the World*.

2

The Great Colonization and Industrialization Game

The West Outflanks the East (1500–1945 CE)

Just as outcomes in the Great Agricultural and Trade Games were sometimes surprising—driven not only by natural advantages but insightful and decisive positioning—so too would the outcomes of the next Great Games, those of colonialism and industrialization. These recurring surprises in history—in which once-dominant powers failed to adapt to new world-shaping forces, and saw themselves supplanted by newer entrants—offer a valuable lesson for our times. As fixed as current power arrangements may seem, new forces always offer both opportunity and risk for players of all sizes.

At the dawn of the sixteenth century CE, several changes were underway in the world. Islam and the Mongols had suffered from internal strife and other such issues that eventually plague most large successful empires. The actual plague had also served to weaken the Mongol empire that had, between the thirteenth and fourteenth centuries, governed *Pax Mongolica*. This left the ground open for a new geopolitical power to emerge: Western Europe.

Until now, power and affluence lay in the south and east of Europe: Greece, Italy and parts of the Byzantine empire. Trade and geopolitics remained as intertwined as ever. During the period of Islamic and Mongol domination, Italian merchant-states like Genoa and Venice had still managed to remain relatively prosperous by controlling the intra-European trade routes. The Venetians' alliance with Egypt helped them continue a very profitable spice trade by purchasing spices from Egypt and then distributing them all over Europe.[1] (Both the Mamluks governing Egypt and the Venetians considered the Turks their enemy.) If the Mongols and the Islamic empires had been the gatekeepers of Asia, the Venetians were the gatekeepers of Europe.

Meanwhile, Western European nations such as Britain, Spain, Portugal and the Netherlands had been on the periphery. The Islamic Caliphate and the Mongols, for almost a thousand years, kept them away from the control of the most important trade routes of the world. Therefore, they had not accumulated any significant riches compared to other trade-centric nations.

But the Western European nations had been itching with envy, waiting for their moment in the sun. A few key developments had started to level the playing field for Western Europe. One, the plague and internal strife had hit the Mongol empire and weakened its grip on the Eurasian landmass. Two, the openness afforded by the Mongol empire for innovations to flow from East to West had helped Western Europe adopt and improve on these innovations from the East. Three, complacency had started to set in for the Islamic empires that survived after the Mongol era.

Europe builds on technology and innovation from the East

Between roughly 800 and 1200 CE, technological and trade supremacy lay solely with the Islamic empires. The control of the key trade routes, access to the wisdom of the East and West, and technological advancement, lay at the heart of Islamic dominance. Islamic empires would learn, compile, synthesize and adapt ideas from the known world—stretching from Europe to Africa to India and even China.

By around 1200 CE, however, the Western European nations had learnt most of the techniques used by the Islamic empires. Around this time, the general flow of technology and inventions was from East to West, that is, from Arabia, Persia, India and China to Europe. Through translations of Arab writings, Europe learnt Hindu–Arabic mathematics (replacing the abacus), the Chinese use of magnetism and the Indian ideas of perpetual motion.

Further, the Europeans demonstrated the ability to improve upon those ideas and techniques by adapting them and applying them in novel ways. This, as historian Joel Mokyr argues, helped them advance much further than the East. Economic historians such as Mokyr and Donald Lach point out that by 1500, 'Europeans already controlled more energy, machinery and organizational skill than any civilization, ancient or contemporary.'[2]

If the Islamic world had mastered civil engineering and built some of the most impressive civil works the world had ever seen, the Europeans were intent on mastering mechanical engineering. By the sixteenth century, the European clockmakers, for example, were master craftsmen, using advanced technology in scientific instruments. Mastering the dynamics of mechanical power would underpin the Industrial Revolution in Europe eventually.[3]

Similarly, Europe demonstrated an increasing ability to build upon the navigational technology developed by others. Innovations, such as the ability to determine the longitude at sea, allowed them to carry out a new wave of long-distance explorations.[4] This ability had evaded explorers for centuries, and would help the Europeans drive maritime exploration over bodies such as the Pacific Ocean. Learning how to prevent scurvy, a disease that would take the life of many a sailor, also meant that the Europeans could survive for months at sea.

By the seventeenth century, the Western European nations, for the first time in history, were now able to explore all the oceans of the world that were navigable by ships. Before this wave of European-led oceanic exploration, the seafaring nations had all operated within limited or bound maritime environments. Historian Daniel Headrick has concluded that 'this discovery of the oceans from the fifteenth to the eighteenth centuries ranks as one of the greatest epics of humankind'.[5]

In doing so, Western Europe had achieved another technological milestone in human history. Much like other prosperous civilizations of earlier eras, the Europeans had developed a technological edge over the others. If the agricultural powers had mastered the water and earth elements of nature, the Europeans were beginning to master the oceanic winds—or the air element.

Portugal had long been peaceful and politically stable but excluded from traditional trade routes. Other rival European states were too busy, struggling either with internal strife or with foreign rival powers, to contemplate any further highly risky exploratory voyages. Given its geographic proximity to Africa, it had made sense for the Portuguese to continue to go down its west coast, and not necessarily confront all the other established maritime powers in the Mediterranean. (This, on the face of it, ties in perfectly with the typical start-up-incumbent analogy. As the late HBS Professor Clayton Christensen would argue, instead of fighting the incumbent where it is strongest, start-ups or challengers should find an altogether new niche to actually gain sufficient market share first.) The Portuguese knew that Bojador on the African coast had been a point of no return for Iberian and other European explorers seeking to find the source of the West African gold trade. They, therefore, focused on getting past Bojador.

Two developments would help Portuguese voyages break that barrier. One, an increasing understanding of the trade winds blowing in the north and mid Atlantic. The Portuguese navigators around the 1400s would come to master their understanding of the North Atlantic *Volta do Mar*, much like the Greek and the Arab seafarers had mastered the navigation of the monsoon winds in the Indian Ocean.

Two, the Portuguese further significantly improved ship-building technology. At the time, ships in the Mediterranean were heavy, slow-moving cargo ships, or Italian galleys. The Portuguese invented the caravel, a fast, light sailing ship that could sail windward and also achieve remarkable speeds for that time.[6]

After these developments and innovations finally enabled the Portuguese to cross the psychological barrier of Bojador, successive voyages would continue to go further down the African coast and around the Cape of Good Hope. Finally, towards the end of the fifteenth century, this would allow the trans-oceanic voyages of Columbus (two of the three ships used by Columbus were caravels). In 1498, Vasco da Gama would reach India with a Gujarati trader accompanying him to India from the coast of Africa. The Portuguese mastery of ship-building and the oceanic wind patterns of the Atlantic would help Magellan navigate across the Pacific in the early sixteenth century and to circumnavigate the globe.

Colonialism and Industrialization Would Shape the Economic Destiny of Nations

Europe begins to colonize

Colonization is often understood as a seventeenth to twentieth-century phenomenon. But as we saw in Chapter 1, the Mediterranean Sea—faring 'colonial powers' such as the Minoans and the Phoenicians had been creating colonies and trading posts and fighting for the control of wealth-generating trade routes.

The objectives of each wave of colonization are related to the prevailing economic game at the time. For example, agriculturists colonized territories to get more land under agriculture. The Minoans, the Phoenicians and the Romans colonized outposts in the Mediterranean and elsewhere to control trade. The wave of colonization that began with the voyages of explorers such as da Gama and Columbus in the last decade of the fifteenth century would, similarly, be for trade and natural resources.

The Europeans believed that great riches lay beyond the trade centres of the Mediterranean and Central Asia, and that the best way to secure these riches for themselves required them to go straight to source. (As you'll see, the desire to replace established intermediaries remains strong today as well. Amazon, for example, has replaced existing intermediaries in Europe and the Middle East and allowed Chinese manufacturers to sell directly to America. Shopify is now seeking to replace Amazon by facilitating the growth of Direct-to-Consumer brands, while blockchain technologies are also attempting to replace institutional intermediaries.)[7]

As the European powers explored and conquered these countries, they also developed the means. They accumulated great wealth from all the trade monopolies they established, not to mention just the plain looting and extraction of resources and wealth. As historian Richard Webster has pointed out, the European powers' exploration phase would be followed by conquest and settlement before they finally established themselves as exploitative colonial powers.

The military superiority, especially gunnery, of the Europeans over their Eastern peers also allowed them to unleash military force at unprecedented speed and scale with minimal costs. As Adam Smith has argued, 'The superiority of force happened to be so great on the side of the Europeans, that they were enabled to commit with impunity every sort of injustice in those remote countries.'[8] The European powers had seen a long, highly fractious period in their continent with lots of wars, conflict and competition, whereas the Islamic empire and countries like India and China had become complacent. The vicious competition of Europe, the argument goes, also served as superior training when it came to winning battles and wars.

The Western Europeans, having been on the periphery for so long, seemed hungrier for power and wealth. The social revolutions in countries such as Portugal, and later among the Dutch and the English, in the decades prior, had allowed for upward social mobility. The agents that the trading companies sent to these colonies were brutal and ruthless in establishing monopolistic trade domination at any cost as a way to garner riches and move up in society.[9] They were often more cunning and devious in their quest for dominance as well.

Certain financial and structural innovations would also aid Europe's quest for trade dominance. First was the development of the joint-stock corporation. This allowed limited liability for the investors, so any losses or debt would not have to be borne by the investor, but in case of profits, the investor would get his share. This opened up a lot of capital for new trading corporations being set up in Europe. Along with private investors, the sovereigns of these nations would often also sponsor these voyages, in return for anywhere between 20 per cent and 50 per cent of the profits gained.

As the American business historian John Gordon argues, 'Next to the nation state itself, the joint-stock company was the most important organizational development of the Renaissance and like the nation state, made the modern world possible.'[10] (As you'll recall from the previous chapter, Venice had also introduced contractual innovations such as the *colleganza*, considered to be one of the first joint-stock companies, which also allowed a much larger part of the population to engage in international trade.)

Second was a series of Dutch financial innovations, which by many was considered to be their 'most potent weapon'. The Dutch, by the early seventeenth century, had built the finest political, legal and financial institutions that were oriented towards increasing trade. The Dutch innovations were focused on decreasing risk by essentially dividing or spreading the risk. To ensure that their low-lying farmlands could be farmed, for example, the Dutch had built a culture of local churches and municipal councils raising loans to build dikes and windmills. This made it very normal for Dutch citizens—peasants, merchants and elites—to invest some of the capital towards ownership of shares in trading vessels.

To make such investing widely accessible, the Dutch allowed the concept of fractional shares as well. As author William Bernstein points out, widely distributing ownership and risk in this way was the essence of Dutch finance.[11] As more and more investors provided capital for these adventures, the high availability of capital, in turn, lowered the interest rates, which made capital even more attractive to entrepreneurs.

In addition to fractional shares, the Dutch further propagated the use of futures markets and maritime insurance, both of which would also help decrease risk. Though these concepts were likely known to the Muslim world as well as earlier trading empires, the Dutch scaled up the use of these financial innovations. The result was Dutch interest rates would be 4 per cent compared to English companies which would need to borrow at 10 per cent.[12]

Prior to this, most of the wealth would have remained confined to the feudal lords of Europe, tied up in real estate or other such asset classes. But the development of the joint-stock corporation and various financial innovations would make it possible for large amounts of capital to be directed towards risky yet very financially rewarding projects.[13]

Of course, the other source of capital for such exploratory voyages over time was these voyages themselves. When a successful voyage like the one to the Americas yielded large quantities of silver, that silver could be used to further the colonialism project elsewhere in the world. Historians believe that the silver from the Americas would end up fuelling colonialism and industrialization as well as provide the fuel for capitalism. (This bears parallels with today's quest for accumulation of data to fuel what has been called surveillance capitalism and data colonialism.)

Colonialism built upon agriculture and trade

The Europeans knew that excellence in agriculture was a prerequisite for boosting trade and economic prosperity. Whether it was cod for Captain John Smith in New England, tobacco for the Virginia Company, rice in the Carolinas or sugar in the West Indies, extracting agricultural surplus would remain a key objective of the early colonizers. In the earliest exploratory voyages to South or North America, for example, the Spanish and the Portuguese were looking for gold or silver mines.

Those would be considered easy wins by the explorers. Europe needed this gold and silver to pay for its own imports from Asia. However, when they did not discover gold or silver mines in the territory, they turned to agriculture. This agricultural surplus could then be traded for other goods, courtesy of the global trade market.

Soon the colonial powers had evolved a clear strategy to master both the great games of the previous era, agriculture and trade. The strategy was simple: find and colonize new territories, especially those that could fetch them great levels of agricultural surplus, produce these crops at the cheapest cost using slave or cheap labour, and then supply them to their home markets if there was domestic demand, else trade those commodities in the international markets.

The Europeans would do this with sugarcane, rice, tea, coffee and many other such agricultural commodities. The Europeans would end up introducing sugar, for example, to the Americas (the Caribbean and Brazil, in particular), and rice to the Carolinas in America. The British empire added about a million pounds sterling to its economic output this way.

Soon, these Western European colonial powers had become agricultural superpowers, replacing the river-based civilizations of the world at the top. At the apex of this massive agricultural surplus, the Europeans developed the largest global trade networks in human history. These networks were critical because these cash crops and plantations would yield such heavy profits precisely because they could be sold into the global trade networks. Furthermore, it was only through global trade networks that Europeans could bring crops from Asia and plant them in the Americas, and vice versa. The Western Europeans had finally become the centre of the world.

This then offers us one of the key learnings of the book: Each new shaper-trend, or great game, of the world builds upon the previous one. It was only by excelling at agriculture and trade that the colonial powers were able to become the winners in the colonial era. The surpluses and advantages gained by mastering agriculture and controlling trade set the foundation for them to become the winners at the new emerging great game, colonialism. And not just that, the next great game, industrialization, would also build upon colonialism. It would be the colonial superpowers who would also become the industrial superpowers.

Industrialization built upon colonialism

Many arguments have been put forth by economic historians for why industrialization began in England. The Glorious Revolution in Britain in the 1680s, which reduced the power of the monarchy and devolved more power to the Parliament, is considered by many a crucial turning point in the economic history of Britain (and not just its political history). With greater security that the rewards of their efforts could not be arbitrarily drawn by a monarch, the British people are believed to have become more incentivized to be more productive.[14] And this desire for greater productivity would, according to some, lead to the innovations that led to the Industrial Revolution.

Eric Jones, writing in his book *The European Miracle,* has argued that the Asian empires, in contrast, did not incentivize many to engage in productive investment. Merchants were viewed as necessarily inferior to warriors in many Asian societies, even if the merchants grew extremely rich. And unless the merchants themselves became landed officials, the public officials could always confiscate their wealth. The emperors in Asia never needed to rely on the support of merchants 'as impecunious European kings did' and therefore merchants never gained the kind of influence as a class as they did in European states. Jones concludes, 'they never succeeded in hollowing out the Asian empires into bourgeois states'.[15]

Jones has therefore identified structural and systemic incentives, and political and social systems and hierarchies as a potential reason for why the Industrial Revolution happened in Europe, and not in Asia. He argues that it was not a switch that was turned on; rather, the conditions that developed over a couple of centuries allowed for political competition. The limits thus imposed on arbitrariness were key for the breakout economic growth experienced by Europe. This would stand in contrast to the large, centralized empires of Asia, where arbitrariness ruled large.

Importantly, having access to colonies gave the colonial powers a major leg up in the industrialization process as well. As countries such as England embarked on industrialization, they realized their colonies could now be even more useful as a source of raw materials for their manufacturing set-ups. By building further rail lines into the interiors of their colonies, the colonial powers, especially the British, were able to dig deep into their colonies' rich natural wealth. With full political and economic control of their colonies, the colonial powers extracted the natural resources at nominal rates. That, along with better, more productive technology, and the low wages initially given to the labour, ensured profitability for the industrial ventures in Britain. But more importantly, it would make sure that they could offer their finished products for cheaper prices than most competitors globally. This would allow them to price out most competitors, who just could not compete.

There was a second advantage that accrued from having colonies. The industrial powers ramped up their production—with abundant labour, better technology and cheap raw resources—leading to an abundance of finished goods. Supply now greatly exceeded domestic demand. In a scenario without colonies, as Adam Smith would have argued, the prices of these goods would have fallen sharply. But the colonies again came to the rescue. They began to also serve as the markets for their finished goods.

Third, the colonial powers actively discouraged and even prevented industrialization from taking root in the colonies. They did this through a range of unfavourable trade and other economic policies, which essentially made any industrial goods made in the colonies highly uncompetitive in the global market. So incumbent industries, such as the Indian textile industry, would, as a result, be completely destroyed in the face of cheap British cotton textiles and extremely high tariffs.

The Great Divergence

One of the biggest and longest-lasting economic and geopolitical implications of colonialism and industrialization was the Great Divergence. The Great Divergence or the European Miracle refers to the socio-economic shift in the world, in which the economic growth of the Western European nations greatly exceeded that of the Asian powers. While some believe that it began in the sixteenth or seventeenth century, the massive divergence began in the nineteenth century with the advent of the Industrial Revolution (chart 1.1).

Chart 1.1 The First Great Divergence, 1500–1950

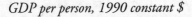

GDP per person, 1990 constant $

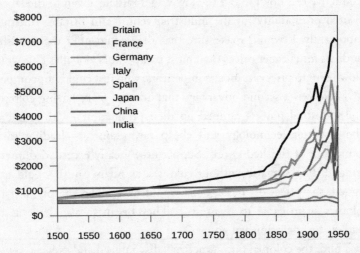

Source: Angus Maddison, *Contours of the World Economy 1–2020 AD: Essays in Macro-Economic History* (Oxford University Press, 2007), p. 382

Several theories have been put forth to explain the Great Divergence, ranging from access to high levels of coal deposits and trade with the Americas to the open science movement in the sixteenth and seventeenth centuries on the back of the Gutenberg press which led to the scientific revolution in Europe.[16] Industrial technology built upon the invention of the steam engine, combined with access to coal deposits as fuel, caused the productivity of the industrial nations to skyrocket. The individual in industrialized Britain could now turn raw cotton into thread so much faster than individuals hand-spinning it in India. Leveraging the industrial technology, the factories in Britain would also scale up much more.[17] The 'virtuous cycle' of industrialization and colonialization worked beautifully, and the results were there for all to see.

Colonialism and Industrialization Would Tilt the Balance of Power and Shape the Geopolitics of the Era

Colonialization and then industrialization paved the way for an astonishing reversal of fortunes, creating a whole new set of economic winners and losers on the world stage. In that process, it tilted the balance of power as well. The share and influence of Eurasian powers— be it China, India or the countries in the Ottoman empire—in the global economy began to decline quite rapidly. As power, wealth and influence shifted from Eurasia to Western Europe, nations such as England and France became the dominant powers. The fulcrum of the world moved from the East to the West, from Eurasia to Western Europe and from the Indian Ocean to the Atlantic Ocean.

The new European colonial powers, when they entered the Indian Ocean, would find a bustling if decentralized trade system extending from the Red Sea to the Spice Islands. The Western European colonial powers, however, were coming to the Indian Ocean game, having learnt from the Mediterranean Sea–faring powers. The Portuguese and the Dutch were seeking monopoly of the trade routes, and would not hesitate to use military force to achieve it.

The incumbents, on the other hand, did not anticipate this monopolistic, militaristic quest. After all, even though certain trade points were controlled by larger empires such as the Ottomans, the Indian Ocean trade was not actually militarized or monopolized. In the early exploratory days of colonialism, the Asian empires were, in fact, at the peak of their strength and influence. If the Egyptians, Ottomans, Indians or Chinese had recognized that the colonial powers' success would lay the foundation for the economic and political system for the next 500 years, they could also have been active participants and leaders and shapers of those systems, instead of being on the receiving end and watching from the sidelines.

But these incumbent powers, victors in the old game of agriculture and trade, did not realize that a new Great Game was underway, nor did they attempt to become active colonists themselves. In history, Indian, Chinese and Egyptian empires had extended beyond their immediate boundaries and shores, so it was not that there was no precedent. But as Adam Smith pointed out, the policies of Egypt, India and China continued to favour and emphasize agriculture over all other avenues.[18] In continuing to focus on agriculture and regional trade, they ended up focusing on the wrong game, a typical folly of an established incumbent. Not surprisingly, the balance of power tilted heavily towards the new colonial powers.

Rivalry between the European powers, and new winners and losers

For almost the entire sixteenth century, the Iberians (the Portuguese and the Spanish) dominated global trade routes—specifically via the sea—to Asia. By the beginning of the seventeenth century, their monopoly was beginning to be threatened by the emergence of the Dutch and English under the auspices of their respective East India Companies.

Advancements in ship and naval technology would help the Dutch and the English take over from the Iberians (who, as you might recall, had themselves gained through the invention of the caravel). By 1700, the Dutch and English East India Companies would come to dominate the trade between Europe and Asia, edging out the Spanish and the Portuguese, who eventually shifted their focus on the Americas instead.

This was an age marked by rising rivalry and frequent wars among the European powers.[19] Not only were there direct wars among the European powers, but the states were also leveraging corsairs (pirates or privateers), who would be authorized by states, sometimes clandestinely, to conduct raids on the ships of nations at war with their home states. (This would today be akin to the cyber-hackers used covertly by states to conduct cyber operations on their behalf.)

Much like the modern-day nation states' obsession with economic espionage, the colonial powers were always attempting to—often clandestinely—learn from the techniques of their peers. For example, the Dutch gained much of their knowledge about the oceans by espionage. They used Dutch residents of Lisbon to learn the secret techniques of the Portuguese, who had become experts at ocean navigation.[20] Today, the US accuses the Chinese of economic espionage of their industrial, trade and technology secrets.

In addition, these rivalries actually deepened the urge for colonialism and imperialism. Until 1880, the Europeans had been content to get local African rulers and merchants to represent European mercantile interests.[21] The intense rivalries amongst the European powers would end up placing virtually all of Africa under European colonial control between 1880 and 1900. Even countries like Germany, where at first Otto von Bismarck did not view colonies as important, ultimately would enter the ranks of imperialist powers due to domestic pressures. As Bismarck said, 'All this colonial business is a sham, but we need it for the elections.'[22] In today's context, the rivalry between Big Tech firms—and not just the major national powers—has parallels with the colonial rivalry, and may similarly lead to unintended pressures for market capture and data colonialism.

The battle between states versus corporations

Just as Britain was achieving global pre-eminence, though, it found itself facing new scenarios at home. The largest trading corporations of the time—such as the British East India Company (EIC)—became intertwined with the domestic politics of their own nations, as much as they did with the politics of the colonies. These trading corporations, in their search for profitable investments and access to new markets, influenced the state in various ways.[23] Since the decision-makers in government were often made investors and shareholders in the trading companies, the latter's interests would be protected if and when matters came to a head.

The trading corporations would also stitch together alliances with those who had a vested interest in continued imperialist expansion for any reason. For example, for some groups of politicians, imperialism served to divert public energy and attention away from domestic agitation to external employment in the colonies.[24] (I will return to this idea of alliances between the state and private firms in a later chapter when I discuss the ongoing battle between Big Tech and governments.)

The imperatives of colonialism and industrialization eventually led the governments of the colonial powers to take over complete control of the colonies from the trading corporations. The British East India Company, for example, initially started off as a monopolistic trading corporation. With time, it went on 'to act as a part-trade organization, part-nation state' and, at its peak, was 'by far the largest corporation of its kind'. [25] At one point, the East India Company commanded a private army of 260,000 soldiers, twice the size of the standing British army of that time.[26]

But as the company started assuming political control of provinces such as Bengal in India through military action, the British government intervened. Through the Regulating Act (1773) and the India Act (1784), the British government took over control of political decisions first, and then eventually commercial ones as well. By 1834, it had been reduced to merely an agent for the British Crown in India, and ceased to exist as a legal entity in 1873. The state had emerged victorious in this battle between corporations and states, a theme I will return to later in the book.

Pax Britannica

Despite intense rivalries, Britain would emerge as the leading colonial and industrial power. The nineteenth century would be 'pre-eminently Britain's century' and, especially after emerging victorious in the Napoleonic wars, the British became the 'arbiters of the world's affairs'. [27] The emergence of *Pax Britannica* transformed the world in a multitude of ways. English became the lingua franca of the world, granting English speakers a competitive advantage that continues to this day. The British empire came to control the trade routes of the world, the communication networks, the political and economic destinies of nations, and, of course, the wealth of the world.

What might have started as a haphazard accumulation of possessions suddenly was starting to fit into a broader pattern and force. This new force, the New Imperialism, described as 'an expansionist, sensational concept of Empire', would make the British feel that 'they were riding a wave of destiny'. This might not be unlike the tech optimism or tech-utopianism prevalent in many parts of the world today.

The shipping and cable routes that underlay Pax Britannica

The British built the most extensive trade and communications infrastructure the world had ever known. This infrastructure consisted of trading choke points such as the strategically critical Suez Canal; island ports and maritime fortresses such as Gibraltar, Malta, Aden, Mumbai, Singapore and Hong Kong; and communications and military intelligence infrastructure in the form of undersea telegraph cables. Like in previous eras, continued control and protection of this infrastructure, especially in light of increasing competition between the colonial powers as well as from domestic rulers, led to heightened geopolitical activity.

For example, the British saw the Suez Canal as their 'lifeline to India' and therefore moved aggressively to take control when it was threatened by the Egyptian army.[28] Similarly, the islands, maritime fortresses, trading outposts and pit stops, such as Gibraltar, Malta, Aden, Singapore, Hong Kong, St. Lucia, Halifax and Bermuda, were consistently placed under 'the protection of British guns'. [29]

The British had invented submarine cables and depended on them for military and political intelligence and centralized control. With the electric telegraph cables being laid globally in the nineteenth century, the whole empire was suddenly accessible and connected, and much easier to control. As Morris explains, 'the electric telegraph and the steamship had transformed the *Pax Britannica*'.[30] This globally connected empire stood in stark contrast to the self-contained Roman empire and a continental Russian empire in the past.

The British were also preoccupied with keeping the control over these telegraph networks overwhelmingly in their own hands.[31] The immense focus of the British on the control of the submarine telegraph cable network has several parallels to the US obsession today to control and monitor the undersea fibre-optic data cable network. As Morris concludes, 'All this vast expertise, of ships and mails and cable stations, had made the British prime masters of international movement.'[32] With such monopolistic control of such a vast imperial trade and communications infrastructure, the British empire was truly a global one. As I discuss in later chapters, control of the technology infrastructure today—the global network of undersea fibre optic cables—also has significant geopolitical implications.

The world wars

As the system of nation states emerged in Europe, competition, not cooperation, became the dominant dynamic. The rivalries over colonies in Asia and Africa, and control of trade networks, drove this competition into what can be described as an 'age of frenzied nationalism and imperialist expansion'.[33]

The two world wars were ultimately also the outcome of the forces and rivalries unleashed by industrialization and colonialism. Whatever the reasons might have been for the final sparking of the Great War, later called World War I, it was probably one of the most significant geopolitical consequences of the economic and social restructuring and rivalries driven by the Industrial Revolution and European colonialism. World War I severely damaged the rational, liberal societies of Europe, not to mention the death toll of almost ten million people. Progress over the previous decades seemed to have been reversed in a few years.

Governments increased their power and control over the lives of citizens and curtailed freedom of the press and speech under the pretext of national security. Strong, central authority became a fact of life in European societies.[34] Even after the end of World War I, the churning in Europe's political systems continued. While in some quarters, the end of World War I was seen as the triumph of democracy, the post-war events would lead to the rise of fascism and totalitarianism in certain states such as Italy, the Soviet Union, Germany and many other European states.

World War I had massive economic implications as well, which in turn often led to some of the geopolitical implications referred to earlier. After the end of World War I, Europe was beset with severe economic problems, with certain countries facing the brunt of it. During and right after the war, Britain, for example, ceded many of the markets for its industrial products and its enormously advantageous trading rights to the new emerging economic powers of Japan and the United States. The decline of the British coal, steel and textile industries that began during the war led to increased unemployment and unrest.

Similarly, Germany, suffering due to its defeat in the war, was also beset with serious economic problems. Plans for economic revival led instead to heightened inflation levels. With extremely high inflation in the 1922–23 period, social unrest in Germany was heightened, as 'widows, teachers, civil servants, and others who lived on fixed incomes all watched their monthly incomes become worthless, or their life savings disappear'.[35] While the economic situation in certain parts of Europe got better during the 1924–29 period, the ensuing Great Depression in 1929 made matters much worse, bringing misery to millions and sparking even further social unrest.[36]

The Great Depression, and the social and economic chaos and suffering that accompanied it, led masses to be attracted to leaders who would offer simple yet decisive solutions. This, in turn, led to dictatorial leaders emerging in various countries around the world. The rise of these authoritarian leaders, such as Hitler, Mussolini, Stalin, Franco and others, would combine with the socio-economic ramifications of World War I to lead to the Second World War.

For several centuries through the colonial and industrial era, Western Europe had been the economic, political and cultural leader of the world. However, the world wars and the ensuing events led to that position being greatly weakened as a whole. What was a loss for the incumbent powers would end up becoming a major gain for the emerging powers such as the US.

The world was witness to great uncertainty and, to some extent, a vacuum in global leadership. That vacuum, as we will discuss in the next chapter, would be filled by a fast-emerging United States. This had larger geo-economic and geopolitical ramifications for Europe. Loss of economic strength, often due to the decline of certain industries, is a leading indicator of transitions of power between nations, a lesson that is as relevant today in the context of the economic war between the US and China.

Colonialism and Industrialization Would Shape Societal Structures and Drive Large Socio-Political Movements

As European nations competed in the Great Games of Colonialism and Industrialization, this competition had a transformative impact on societal structures and class relations. In the process, it also inspired and drove large sociopolitical movements that continue to shape our societies, our ideologies, our politics and our world today. This process offers many lessons for today's era, which I discuss in detail later in the book.

Class relations and societal structures were transformed by the forces unleashed by industrialization and colonialization. One, it led to the creation of a new industrial working class. This working class was primarily made up of rural migrants in industrial townships, and included a large number of women and children. For example, around 1830 in Britain, women and children made up almost two-thirds of the cotton industry's workforce.[37] These workers worked in wretched, often inhumane conditions such as harsh coal mines and high-temperature mills for twelve to sixteen hours a day, six days a week. Worse, they had no employment security or minimum wages (not unlike the cab drivers or delivery executives of today, some would argue).

Two, a new industrial middle class also emerged. This new industrial middle class provided various services and products for industries, such as building factories or manufacturing and selling machinery. Like commercial capitalism or the mercantilist system of trade in the Middle Ages helped create the bourgeois class comprising merchants, lawyers, artists and intellectuals, industrial capitalism led to the creation of the new industrial middle class.[38] (Think the 'techies' of today.)

Three, colonial rule prevented the local social structures in colonies from changing or evolving in the way it happened in the European states during this era. This had the effect of pushing back societal or class reform by several decades or worse, centuries. For example, indirect rule in African nations kept the old African elite in power, limiting the opportunities for ambitious, talented and driven young Africans from outside the existing elites. This would lay the foundation for continued class and tribal conflict in Africa for many decades even after the African nations gained independence.[39]

Four, a new elite took over during the industrial era, which created social hierarchies that were not much different from the feudalist structures they sought to replace. Industrial capitalism was also based effectively on a distinction between two classes, just like its predecessor, feudalism.[40] At the core of feudalism lay an antagonistic relationship between the noble feudal landlords and the subservient peasant farmers.

Similarly, in the case of industrial capitalism, there emerged an antagonistic class relationship between wage workers and capitalists. The wage workers, the producers in the industrial era, were the equivalent of the peasant farmers. The unequal power dynamic amongst classes would continue, and lead to socio-political movements of a massive scale.

The beginning of capitalism

Capitalism, or more specifically the accumulation and use of capital to drive concentration of wealth and economic power, predated industrialization. Economic historians have argued that industrialization was able to achieve its full productive capacity only 'thanks to the slow accumulation of capital which began three centuries earlier'.[41] As Thomas Piketty writes in his magnum opus, *Capital in the Twenty-First Century*, capital would see increasing returns in the 1840s as industrial profits grew, while labour incomes would stagnate.[42]

Industrialization gave Western capitalism the boost it needed to emerge as the dominant form of economic production. As historian Henry Heller has pointed out, 'It was not until the Industrial Revolution that Western capitalism forged ahead of the economies of the rest of the world.' Fuelled by this capital-driven industrialization, the Western economies were able to race ahead of the economies of the rest of the world. Not surprisingly, the Great Divergence between the capitalist West and the rest of the world began after the beginning of industrialization around the 1800s, and not around 1500 CE when the seeds of capitalism are believed to have been laid.[43]

Heller has also argued that colonialism played a major role in the emergence of capitalism. A major chunk of capital was accumulated by the colonial powers by extracting greater value from the natural resources of colonies and the labour of slaves than they paid to the colonies or the slaves. As we saw earlier, just the American colonies ended up contributing over a million British pounds annually. Moreover, the availability of markets in these colonies and the profits that colonial powers accumulated also contributed to capitalism's rise.[44] Moreover, the global triumph of capitalism, combined with the economic revolution unleashed by industrialization and colonization, would underpin the subsequent two centuries of Western dominance.[45]

New economic ideologies and sociopolitical movements emerge in response

The global ascendance of industrialization and capitalism, however, led to a backlash in the form of movements and ideologies such as communism, socialism and Marxism. With growing inequalities between the capitalists and the working class and the stagnating incomes and pitiable conditions of the workers, the communist and socialist movements started to take shape. To again quote Thomas Piketty in *Capital in the Twenty-First Century*:

> The central argument was simple: What was the good of industrial development, what was the good of all the technological innovations, toil, and population movements if, after half a century of industrial growth, the condition of the masses was still just as miserable as before, and all lawmakers could do was prohibit factory labor by children under the age of eight? The bankruptcy of the existing economic and political system seemed obvious. People therefore wondered about its long-term evolution.[46]

Such arguments would form the intellectual underpinning of socialism, an alternative economic system of production in which society, through governments, would come to own and control the means of production, such as factories.[47] Socialist thought, including the Marxian ideology, would not only become the rallying cry of the proletariat, or the working class, but also drive many of the conflicts the world witnessed in the twentieth century.

Ideologues such as Marx and his disciple Lenin would rise to prominence due to their opposition to capitalism and what they saw as the perpetuation of a world order and class hierarchy dominated by capitalists and capitalist nations of Europe and North America.[48]

Marxism would end up playing a significant role in both the anti-colonial national independence movements, as well as post-independence movements in the twentieth century.[49] Based on the political and ideological frameworks provided by Marx and Lenin, major offensives, such as the Chinese, Korean, Cuban and Vietnamese revolutions and wars, were launched against Eurocentrism and imperialism after the Second World War. These uprisings often brought together national liberation movements with anti-colonial and anti-capitalist overtones. And in the post-world war era, leaders such as Mao Zedong, Ho Chi Minh, Fidel Castro, Ernesto Che Guevara, Kwame Nkrumah, Achmed Sukarno and Abdel Nasser emerged as the most important political leaders of these movements.[50]

That such movements were triggered by the impact of the shaper-trends of that era, colonialism and industrialization, offer a few learnings for today's era. As technology and capitalism combine to create some of the same structural inequalities and class conflicts, new sociopolitical movements might evolve over the next few years or decades. We must not forget the lessons from the rise of the industrial era-derived movements, as I discuss later in the book.

Cultural and societal implications of industrialization

Colonial rule, of course, had significant cultural implications. The cultural implications of colonialism—especially the use of cultural imperialism as a tool of colonization—has been written about with great depth and insight by world-renowned scholars such as Edward Said.[51] The colonial elites were often fuelled by a belief in their cultural and racial superiority. Therefore, they used a wide variety of tools—such as laws, education, military force, constant denigration and monetary incentives—to impose various aspects of their own culture and values onto the colonized population. Of course, with the advent of radio and movies, culture was much easier to spread as well. The shrewd colonial administrators also often knew that 'the best way to mitigate resistance by the colonized was to eradicate as far as possible all traces of their former way of life'.[52]

Eurocentrism was another major implication of the rise of Europe and its colonial and industrial success. The white European middle-class male was the chief protagonist of all scholarly disciplines, even during the Enlightenment, but the European colonial conquests and the Industrial Revolution provided a powerful affirmation of Eurocentric thinking and ideology.[53] The rich African and Asian cultural histories and technological achievements were de-emphasized, if not completely ignored, by Eurocentric thinkers and historians. European conceptions of space, time, philosophy, politics and thinking were imposed on the rest of the world. And, as Jack Goody writes in his book, *The Theft of History*, this, unfortunately, 'shaped and distorted the consciousness of both Europeans and non-Europeans'.[54]

Industrialization, similarly, would have a major dual impact on culture and communities. Even as it enabled social mobility, the existing patterns of life and identity and cohesiveness—as had evolved over centuries—were dramatically and rapidly transformed. Often the pace of change was such that many were left without the social safety net that had been provided by existing communities. The patterns and structures of rural life were transformed as people started migrating to cities and industrial towns to work in factories. The social safety net provided by the extended family structure in villages was removed. Nuclear families and urban wage labourers—and the resulting poverty and homelessness for many—increasingly became more common. The disintegration of family networks had a disproportionately adverse impact on children, many of whom were forced into workhouses from orphanages.[55]

The impact on women was mixed. For the first time, women were able to find employment opportunities outside of home, especially in textile production, which helped improve their financial situation. However, they were still excluded from a vast majority of jobs, which meant that their marginalization continued, and in some cases, even increased. Many women who had earlier worked in agriculture and domestic households were forced out of the workforce, often because their husbands did not want them to work within factories.

To its credit, the Industrial Revolution unleashed the power and opportunities for social mobility for many. While factory life was pitiful, for many, it was worth the trade-off as it provided them with a once-in-a-lifetime chance at social mobility and financial independence. But the inequalities within nations—not unlike today—also became that much starker and more visible.

This visible and stark inequality, counter-intuitively, would actually end up sowing the seed for social progress through reform movements. These reforms would ultimately push children 'out of factories and into public education' and labour reforms with policies such as minimum wage, safe working conditions and an eight-hour workday among others. That said, these reforms often did not make it to the colonies, where the colonizing powers such as Britain would continue to put people to work to extract raw materials in harsh conditions.[56]

The Industrial Revolution also transformed the living spaces for many. As people migrated to cities in search of work, cities began to grow rapidly. Often this rapid growth of cities was unplanned and, as we still continue to see in still-industrializing nations like India and others, unsustainable. This rapid urbanization brought with it its own share of economic, social and political issues, as cities grew rapidly and required a whole new set of ways to manage the mixing of people from all over the country (often the world).

Furthermore, educational systems were also transformed, as British education, books and style of teaching would often be imposed on the colonies. Schools and educational systems were designed for that era's requirements. It is no wonder that there are increasing signs that those education systems will be turned on their heads to cater to the requirements of the current technology era. Similarly, health and medical systems such as traditional Chinese medicine or Ayurveda would be similarly overshadowed by British conceptions of modern medicine, which became yet another channel for exerting cultural influence and wiping out indigenous systems and beliefs.[57]

Environmental, biological and ecological impact of industrialization

The environmental impact of industrialization also deserves a mention. The invention of the steam engine, coal-powered industrialization, the increase in productivity and the prosperity that it brought, at least to certain classes, led the industrialized world to make a certain set of energy choices that we continue to live with today. There developed a deep disregard of the environment, which came to be seen as a resource to be exploited to the hilt for the greater cause of industrialization, especially in the colonies. In addition, colonialism led to a monocrop and monoculture strategy, where large plantations of crops such as sugar, rubber, tea and palm replaced what had been biodiverse ecosystems that had evolved over millennia.

The economic impact of this biodiversity loss—a phenomenon that gathered unimaginable pace during the Industrial Revolution and continues till today—has also been estimated by some, including the Dasgupta Review in the UK.[58] Moreover, the ramifications of those energy choices and disregard for ecological balance continue to dictate and shape many of the critical global issues the world is grappling with today, such as climate change, pollution and destruction of the habitat of millions of species on the planet. The famous natural historian David Attenborough has mourned our 'mechanically ingenious' ability to destroy the most species-rich ecosystems and replace them with plantations of single species, 'apparently neither knowing or caring what the consequences might be'.[59] We shall discuss the climate and ecological issues in greater length later in the book.

Through all of these examples—whether cultural, societal or ecological—we see that there is more to Great Games than simply 'winning' by outcompeting a neighbour or foreign adversary. The choices made in the course of these competitions have real and essential impacts on the lives of individual citizens. Both from a competitive and ethical perspective, then, we have learned many times that the

Great Games must be played with consideration for human lives and principles—elements that will prove particularly important as we consider the broader impact of the Great Tech Game in the coming decades.

A Few Lessons

A few key lessons emerge from a survey of how colonization and industrialization impacted and shaped the world. One, new winners and losers emerge as major trend-shapers—or great games—start to shape the world. Western Europe outflanked the Mediterranean and Eurasian powers through a combination of better navigational technology, societal and political reforms, financial innovations, superior military technology, and hunger for wealth and power. Even amongst the Western European nations, rivalry played a big role in driving innovation and helped shape which nations became the dominant ones during different phases of this era. Any disruptions in the world order today will also need the challenger nations to leverage a combination of factors. No one factor alone is likely to uproot the geopolitical superpower of today.

Two, large commercial corporations of this era did not have military conquest or colonization as their primary objective in the beginning. But conflicts with established powers, or competitors and rivals, led them to get pulled into military and geopolitical battles. As you'll see in the next chapter, America would undergo a similar evolution and get pulled into geopolitical quagmires. The worry would be for this story to repeat in the case of Big Tech firms of today.

The ramifications of the churn and changes brought forth by the great games of a particular era are much more complex, long-lasting, and multi-layered than we often can anticipate or understand. This is evident from just the brief survey of the societal, cultural, economic, political and geopolitical implications of industrialization and colonization that we have covered. Of course, a deeper, broader and more systematic study could throw up even more lessons and insights for us today. The Great Tech Game, as we will discuss during the course of this book, has the ability to similarly set off a chain of events with massive geopolitical, economic and social implications.

Major social, political and economic movements and ideologies can develop and grow rapidly during the churn that such trend-shapers spark. Communism, socialism and Marxism continue to impact modern-day politics, alliances, foreign policy and economic decision-making, even though they are centuries-old now. These movements often combine to provide the ideological underpinnings for major conflicts and ideological divides that can continue to shape the foreign and economic policies of countries around the world, not to mention sparking geopolitical conflict between the major powers.

The many parallels with modern-day issues are evident as you read about the changes unleashed by industrialization and colonization. History's lessons are ignored at your own peril. The harsh lessons learnt—by retrospectively looking at both the positive and catastrophic consequences of these trends—can be extremely instructive for the future. By the end of World War II (WWII), the balance of power in the world had begun to tilt away again. The tide, and the era, and the game that needed to be learnt and played skilfully to succeed, were all changing. Again.

Notes

1.   Adam Smith, *The Wealth of Nations* and *The Theory of Moral Sentiments* (Titan Read), Kindle, 508–9.

2.   Joel Mokyr, *The Lever of Riches: Technological Creativity and Economic Progress* (Oxford University Press, 1990).

3.   Donald Lach, *Asia in the Making of Europe,* Vol. II: *A Century of Wonder,* Book 3: *The Scholarly Disciplines* (1977), p. 406.

4.   Daniel R. Headrick, *Power over Peoples,* The Princeton Economic History of the Western World (Princeton University Press, 2012), Kindle.

5. Ibid.

6. 'Caravel', Britannica, https://www.britannica.com/technology/caravel, accessed on 1 October 2021.

7. Benedict Evans, *The Great Unbundling* (January 2021), https://www.ben-evans.com/presentations, accessed on 16 Sep 2021.

8. Giovanni Arrighi, *Adam Smith in Beijing: Lineages of the Twenty-First Century* (Verso, 2007). http://digamo.free.fr/adambeijing.pdf, accessed on 1 October 2021.

9. C.R. Boxer, *The Dutch Seaborne Empire*, 107. Quoted by Bernstein, *A Splendid Exchange*.

10. John Steele Gordon, *An Empire of Wealth* (HarperCollins, 2009), Kindle.

11. Bernstein, *A Splendid Exchange*.

12. Ibid.

13. A side note: The link between those 'early day adventurers' and today's venture capitalists is obvious. Those who invested in these risky enterprises but stayed back in their home nations would be called 'adventurers' (the equivalent of today's venture capitalists) and those who would actually embark on the journey to an unknown land would be called 'planters' (the equivalent of today's entrepreneurs or early start-ups hires who are employee stock option holders). The planters would get shares in the venture or the joint-stock company, in what would be considered to be the equivalent of 'sweat equity' today. As Bhu Srinivasan points out, the term of these agreements would be seven years. At the end of the seven years, the assets of the venture would be distributed amongst the shareholders. The similarities, of course, do not end there. Because they were entering new or 'virgin' territories, the incentives for the planters were high. The colonists would be given land free by the trading companies, in the hope of getting more men to migrate and settle. The system, known as 'head rights', would in many ways be similar to the ESOP systems of today, which could generate a lot of wealth for the risk-takers in the future.

14. 'What Was the Great Divergence?', *The Economist* (September 2013), https://www.economist.com/free-exchange/2013/09/02/what-was-the-great-divergence, accessed on 1 October 2021.

15. Eric Jones, *The European Miracle: Environments, Economies and Geopolitics in the History of Europe and Asia* (Cambridge University Press, 2003).

16. Paul A. David, 'The Historical Origins of "Open Science": An Essay on Patronage, Reputation and Common Agency Contracting in the Scientific Revolution', *Capitalism and Society* (De Gruyter, October 2008), 3(2): 1–106, https://ideas.repec.org/a/bpj/capsoc/v3y2008i2n5.html, accessed on 1 October 2021.

17. Bhu Srinivasan, *Americana* (Penguin Publishing Group, 2017), Kindle.

18. Smith, *The Wealth of Nations*.

19. Ibid.

20. Ibid.

21. Ibid.

22. Jackson Spielvogel, *Glencoe World History* (McGraw-Hill, 2009).

23. John Hobson, *Imperialism, a Study* (1902), http://www.users.miamioh.edu/dahlmac/DG/imperial-geopolitics/4-john-hobson-1902-from-imp.html, accessed on 1 October 2021.

24. Ibid.

25. Emily Erikson, *Between Monopoly and Free Trade: The English East India Company 1600–1757* (Princeton University Press, 2014).

26. Ibid.

27. Jan Morris, *Pax Britannica* (Faber & Faber, 2010), Kindle.

28. Spielvogel, *Glencoe World History*.

29. Morris, *Pax Britannica*.

30. Ibid.

31. Ibid.

32. Ibid.

L

33. Spielvogel, *Glencoe World History*.

34. Ibid.

35. Ibid.

36. Ibid.

37. Ibid.

38. Ibid.

39. Ibid.

40. Henry Heller, *The Birth of Capitalism: A Twenty-first Century Perspective* (Fernwood Publishing, 2011), https://www.econstor.eu/bitstream/10419/182429/1/642724.pdf, accessed on 1 October, 2021.

41. Ibid.

42. Thomas Picketty, *Capital in the Twenty-First Century* (Harvard University Press, 2017), Kindle.

43. Heller, *The Birth of Capitalism*.

44. Ibid.

45. Ibid.

46. Piketty, *Capital in the Twenty-First Century*.

47. Spielvogel, *Glencoe World History*.

48. Heller, *The Birth of Capitalism*.

49. Ibid.

50. Ibid.

51. E. Saïd, *Culture and Imperialism* (Vintage Publishers, 1994).

52. Theresa Weynand Tobin, 'Cultural Imperialism', *Britannica*, https://www.britannica.com/topic/cultural-imperialism, accessed on 1 October, 2021.

53. Heller, *The Birth of Capitalism*.

54. Ibid.

55. Bennett Sherry, 'The Global Transformations of the Industrial Revolution', Khan Academy, https://www.khanacademy.org/

humanities/whp-origins/era-6-the-long-nineteenth-century-1750-ce-to-1914-ce/62-industrialization-betaa/a/read-the-global-transformations-of-the-industrial-revolution-beta, accessed on 1 October 2021.

56. Ibid.

57. M. Bell, R.A. Butlin, Michael J. Heffernan, *Geography and Imperialism, 1920–1940* (Manchester University Press, 1995).

58. P. Dasgupta, *The Economics of Biodiversity: The Dasgupta Review.* (London: HM Treasury, 2021), https://assets.publishing.service.gov.uk/government/uploads/system/uploads/attachment_data/file/962785/The_Economics_of_Biodiversity_The_Dasgupta_Review_Full_Report.pdf, accessed on 1 October 2021.

59. David Attenborough, Foreword to P. Dasgupta, *The Economics of Biodiversity: The Dasgupta Review.*

3

The Ascent of Modern Empire

Capitalism and Technology in the American Era (1945–)

arly developments in each successive Great Game are largely determined by the outcomes of the previous Great Game. Incumbent powers—those that thrived in the previous game—often enter these new scenarios with economic and political advantages. They may also, however, begin the new Great Games in positions of comfort—and sometimes complacency for adapting to the new shaping forces of the next Great Game. This creates the space for new powers to improve their positions by acting purposefully and decisively.

Just as European nations profited from the flow of ideas and technology from the East, so too would the United States' enthusiastic adaptation of industrialization and capitalism set the stage for its emergence as the great power of the modern capitalist period. Several factors would combine to help the US emerge as the dominant global power of the twenty-first century. As the previous chapter concluded, the world had become too complex for any single factor to drive the rise of a new superpower. To better understand this convergence of factors that led to the ascent of the US as the modern empire, we have to delve, not surprisingly, into history.

The great inventions fuelled the rapid industrialization of the US

The Industrial Revolution would reach the United States around the 1840s, soon after its beginnings in Britain, but the US would take to industrialization like fish to water. Steam power, based on coal, began to replace traditional sources of energy such as wood in economic production. Transportation was transformed through the steam-powered rail engine, while communication ended up being transformed by the electric telegraph and telephone. [1]

Even as the British focused on mercantile trade policies and defending their Indian possessions (the 'jewel in their crown'), the Americans would begin to out-compete them in manufacturing and in the applications of various technological innovations. Post the Civil War, economic growth and life began to improve exponentially in the United States. Robert Gordon, author of *The Rise and Fall of American Growth*, attributes this improvement to the 'Great Inventions', which included electricity and the internal combustion engine, and their various applications. [2]

These inventions greatly transformed life, 'transferring human attention and energy from the mundane to soaring skyscrapers and airplanes'. [3] Homes in the United States began to have electricity, heat and sewage systems. The cleaner water and better medicines would lead to a massive drop in infant mortality. Electric elevators allowed buildings to extend vertically, which in turn changed the nature of land use and created the urban density we see today in New York City or Chicago. In factories, small electric machines replaced gigantic steam boilers, while other machines replaced human labour. Motor vehicles, not horses, now plied in American cities. The list is endless. [4]

Rifkin highlights, in particular, the transformative impact of electricity:

So powerful was the new medium that scientists and engineers of the day predicted that its widespread use would make the cities green, heal the breaches between the classes, create a wealth of new goods, extend day into night, cure age-old diseases, and bring peace and harmony into the world.[5]

In the 1920s, the internal combustion engine (ICE), driven by another fossil fuel, petroleum, would shake things up once more. Productivity would increase substantially, with the growing number of automobiles and trucks speeding movement within cities and outside. With the invention of the ICE, 'the Industrial Age reached its full fruition'.[6] Along with the ICE, the railways and the electric telegraph facilitated much faster and more reliable flows of information.[7]

Taken together, these Great Inventions enabled the US industrialization efforts to catch up with those of the UK (and Germany), as it moved rapidly in its quest to become the leader of the emergent Industrial Revolution. Across the country, small makeshift shops were constantly tinkering with countless mechanical and electrical machines, hoping to improve efficiency.

Gordon, in fact, has argued that the recent advances in telecommunications cannot transform society the same way this clustering of post-Civil War innovations, the Great Inventions, did. According to him, these telecommunication advances are largely transforming only 'a narrow sphere of human activity having to do with entertainment, communications, and the collection and processing of information'. As a result, the other concerns of human beings—food, clothing health, transportation, quality of air and water, pollution, etc.—have largely remained outside of the domain of information technology.

Yet, the descriptions of the impact of the invention of electricity bear a striking resemblance to the impact that the internet and other emerging general-purpose technologies (GPTs) such as Artificial Intelligence (AI) are expected to have in our lives today. (GPTs are fundamentally innovative and transformative technologies that have immense applications across a variety of fields.[8]) The relentless innovation being driven by technology start-ups in garages and basements today is similarly reminiscent of the constant tinkering in makeshift shops in the US in this era.

Ubiquitous start-ups are also leading to a new set of Great Inventions today; basis GPTs such as the internet and artificial intelligence, enhancing productivity and efficiency, boosting connectivity, trade and commerce in the process. Excellence or competitive leadership in the applications of these GPTs could offer leapfrogging opportunities for countries today, just the way electricity did for the US vis-à-vis the UK back then.

Staggering pace of adoption of technology

Scholars of technological history have often argued that it is not so much the invention of the technology that matters in our modern world, but the adoption and penetration of it. And the United States took that lesson to heart.

As chart 3.1 shows, the pace of the spread and adoption of technological innovation was staggering in the US. From no electricity-wired households in 1880, the US went to almost 100 per cent of urban homes being wired by 1940. As Gordon describes it, 'The 1870 house was isolated from the rest of the world, but 1940 houses were "networked," most having the five connections of electricity, gas, telephone, water, and sewer.'[9]

The societal transformation the Great Inventions spawned in the half-century after the Civil War was awe-inspiring. The United States would go 'from an agrarian society of loosely linked small towns to an increasingly urban and industrial society with stronger private and governmental institutions and an increasingly diverse population'.[10]

Chart 3.1 Share of US households using specific technologies, 1860 to 2019

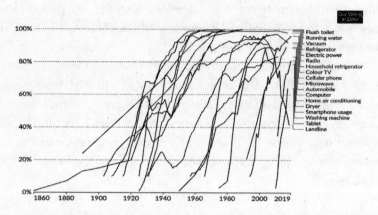

Source: Hannah Ritchie and Max Roser, 'Technology Adoption', OurWorldInData.org (2017), https://ourworldindata.org/technology-adoption, accessed on 29 September 2021.

Flourishing of banking and innovations in finance

As the Industrial Revolution advanced in Britain, America benefited greatly, as it was both the major source of supply of raw materials and the major market for the machine-made textile products. According to Alfred Chandler, a prominent US economic historian, this trade helped US businesses specialize and also professionalize.[11]

Early on in the nineteenth century, British firms, with their greater capital resources, were the financiers of this trade. But the Americans realized that they had to win at the capital game, and not be overly dependent on the British for this core success factor. Over time, US businesses started to pool local capital in state-chartered banks. Early commercial banks also started to provide long- and medium-term capital, more than short-term commercial loans, slowly starting to edge out British financiers and banks.

Unlike the British who had access to global sources of capital, the Americans had to rely largely on domestic sources of capital, in large part by means of corporate banks with limited liability. Much like the Dutch whose financial innovations—raising of capital at the local level and spreading of risk widely to reduce risk—helped catapult them into an economic powerhouse, the American financiers would innovate with financial products and more liberal banking approaches to make capital widely accessible to businesses despite being less wealthy than England.

In fact, according to Richard Sylla, a professor emeritus of economics at NYU and an expert on US financial history, the US underwent a 'Federalist Financial Revolution' starting in the 1790s. This revolution entailed the development of an integrated network of commercial and other banks, a central bank with regional branches, and a proliferation of financial and non-financial corporations in the economy.[12] The fruits of this financial revolution would be reaped by the US economy by the mid nineteenth century: as early as 1825, the United States, with a population approaching similar to that of England and Wales, by certain calculations had 2.4 times the latter's banking capital.[13]

Sylla has argued that the establishment of an innovative financial sector has always predated the emergence of any major economic power, especially in the modern capitalist era[14] and that a strong financial system is 'a nearly universal characteristic of the early stages of modern economic development' of any of the major economic powers of our times.[15] Especially in the case of the US, he has argued that the early development of a modern, nearly world-class financial system was a major, albeit underappreciated, factor behind the rise of the US economy. The US financial system played a critical role in mobilizing savings and allocating capital efficiently,[16] which in turn provided 'a solid underpinning for the country's subsequent growth and development'.[17]

Promotion of competition and rule of law

Just as the US was developing an innovative financial sector, it was also negotiating a relationship between public and private that broke from the British model. At a time in history where trading companies such as the British East India Company were enjoying monopolies on trade, the

US tried to promote competition by breaking up monopolies (though not always successfully). The history of monopolies being broken up in the US goes back a long way, whether it was the Jacksonian-era breakup of the Second Bank, or the US Supreme Court decision in the case of Gibbons v. Ogden in 1824 to end the Fulton-Livingston monopoly on steamships.[18] We will return, later in the book, to this theme of monopolies and anti-trust actions to break them up (and especially how China is rushing to curtail its tech monopolies and might get there faster than the US).

This emphasis in the US on ensuring competition—even if not always realized in practice—would help in boosting economic growth and innovation. While Argentina inherited Spain's top-down controlled imperial system, American business historian John Gordon has posited, 'American politics had the great good fortune to be grounded in English traditions, especially the idea that the law, not the state, is supreme.' Ultimately, inheriting and adopting English concepts such as liberty—the idea that the inherent rights of individuals, including their property rights, may not be arbitrarily revoked—was crucial in shaping America's economic destiny.[19]

The argument that essentially political institutions, rule of law and decentralization of control promote economic competition and shape the economic destiny of nations, has also been made by Daren Acemoglu and James Robinson in their book, *Why Nations Fail*. This view has been seconded by prominent American economists and technology historians such as Nathan Rosenberg as well.[20]

Managerial capitalism and the creation of the largest modern-day corporations

As industrial adoption continued in the United States, it was bolstered by another organizational innovation—a combination of industrial technology with what has been termed as 'managerial capitalism'.[21] Before the 1840s, most businesses in the US were family-owned single-unit firms. But with the coming of new technologies and markets, significant institutional changes would help the US transition to multi-unit, professionally managed firms. These firms would have separate divisions and professionals for various functions such as sales, marketing, accounting and finance, unlike the family-owned single units of yore. According to renowned business historian Alfred Chandler, 'those institutional changes which helped to create the managerial capitalism of the twentieth century were as significant and as revolutionary as those that accompanied the rise of commercial capitalism a half a millennium earlier'.[22] Today, as HBS Professor Shoshana Zuboff has argued, Big Tech firms are combining internet technology with a new form of capitalism—data capitalism.

Chandler has explained that starting in the 1880s, the Industrial Age in the US was characterized by large corporations that 'commercialized, produced, and marketed goods on an unprecedented scale for national and international markets'.[23] Chart 3.2 illustrates how almost half of the top 500 corporate leaders of the US (as of the year 1994) had been founded between the 1880s and 1920s.[24]

Chart 3.2 Breakdown of the 1994 Fortune 500 US Companies by Decade Started

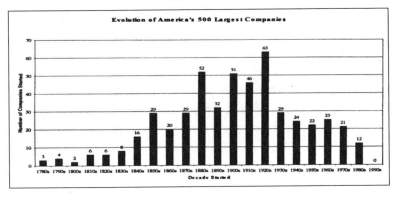

Source: Alfred Chandler ed., *A Nation Transformed by Information: How Information Has Shaped the United States from Colonial Times to the Present* (Oxford University Press, 2000), Kindle.

Ultimately, as Alfred McCoy argues, American supremacy was driven by technological and financial innovation, fusion of science and industry, rapid adoption of technology, and telecommunications and intelligence advancement. In fact, McCoy argues that the emphasis on technological innovation was a unique, distinctive dimension of the US's 'New Empire':

> [It was the] restless, relentless quest for technological innovation that lent it a distinctive dimension. Not only did Washington strive for military superiority in the three conventional domains of air, land, and sea, but its fusion of science and industry opened new arenas for the exercise of global dominion.[25]

In addition, factors such as its ability to profit from the industrialization of its erstwhile colonial master, the UK, and its integration into the world markets would all come together to help it rise to be the pre-eminent power of the twentieth century. Or, as Henry Luce would call it, the American century.[26]

So how is the study of the various factors underlying the ascent of the US relevant to us today? The key lesson here is that with each great game, there is a combination of drivers that determine the ultimate winner(s) for that era. Mastering the game of capital, industrialization and technological innovation was at the core of the US's success. And, of course, the actual set of success factors will differ in each Great Game, depending on the dynamics and particularities of that Great Game. The playbook of the previous Great Game cannot be applied *en masse* to win in the current Great Game. This lesson is especially helpful as we study the rise of China today and its attempt to win at the Great Tech Game.

Impact of the US Empire on the World Order

The manifest destiny, search for markets, and the resulting geopolitical competition

By the early 1900s, the US was increasingly viewing itself as destined to be a global power, as was reflected explicitly in statements and beliefs of the US political leaders. In his remarks to the US Senate in January 1900, Senator Albert Beveridge of Indiana claimed that while European colonial powers were secure in their relationship with their colonies as markets for their manufactured goods, the Americans needed to secure China as the 'natural customer' for their manufacturing surplus. He forcefully posited that 'most future wars will be conflicts for commerce' and that America must rule the Pacific.[27] (Notably, today, most geopolitical analysts believe the future wars will be over technology.)

Walter LaFeber, a prominent US historian, also viewed US expansion was being driven by the 'search for markets, not land'.[28] Between 1850 and 1900, the industrial capacity of the US—driven by the advancement of the Industrial Revolution and the Great Inventions— rapidly developed, becoming 'one of the two greatest economic forces in the world'. And therefore, between 1850 and 1900, the US business community, or what LaFeber also called the Industrial Complex, would focus on extending US interests further afield, ranging from Mexico in the 1870s to as far as China in the 1890s. This expansionism was intended 'not to fulfill a colonial policy, but to use these holdings as a means to acquire markets for the glut of goods pouring out of highly mechanized factories and farms'.[29]

During the second half of the nineteenth century, as a result, the US would find itself at odds with other industrial nations and the large colonial empires for control of the markets not only in neighbouring Latin America, but also in Africa and far-away Asia. This is not unlike a resource- and market-hungry China is clashing with the incumbent empire, the US, around the world.

However, like it is doing today for China, this expansion back then had a major implication for the US and eventually for global geopolitics—a build-up of US military power. LaFeber points out, the military build up also emanated from the 'growing belief that, however great its industrial prowess, the United States needed strategic bases if it hoped to compete successfully with government-supported European enterprises in Asia and Latin America'.[30]

The US expansionism would also come to entail the claiming of dozens of uninhabited islands in the Caribbean and the Pacific, followed by Alaska (1867), Spanish territories such as the Philippines, Puerto Rico and Guam (1898–1900), and later Hawai'i and American Samoa. By World War II, these overseas territories made up nearly a fifth of the land area of the United States.[31] This, the US believed, was its 'Manifest Destiny'[32] and was intended to give the US the strategic bases that it lacked vis-à-vis its European competitors.

However, with every expansionary step and additional military base, the lesson was clear that this was a vicious cycle: 'The growth of economic interests led to political entanglements and to increased military responsibilities.'[33] For example, for US President McKinley at that time, 'the real prize was the fabled China market, which Japan and the European powers had been carving into exclusive areas for investment'.[34] Fearing that the US would be excluded completely from the Chinese market, over 5000 US troops would end up joining those from Europe and Japan in the suppression of the Boxer Rebellion at the turn of the century. Within another few decades, by the end of World War II, in addition to its Pacific empire, it had established thousands of military bases around the world, including in parts of Korea, Germany, Austria and Japan. By some estimates, by the end of 1945, some 135 million people living outside the continental United States were now under US jurisdiction.[35]

The Americans, like others who had come before them, had set out to secure market access but had become entangled in the global geopolitical game, driven by the compulsions of trade and industrialization.

A new emperor, in different clothes

The Americans were intent on building an empire that would differ fundamentally from the European colonial empires.[36] Historian Alfred McCoy argues that if we look back to history, we realize that the Americans *had* to find a different model to follow. After all, America had had to free itself from the shackles of colonialism, and could not just follow the British example of empire. A strong wave of resistance from the colonies of the European empires was forcing 'empire into retreat'. Many of the colonies such as British India, in fact, had contributed to the WWII efforts with the expectation that independence would be forthcoming post the war. It was clear to the United States that these anti-imperialist movements would serve to prevent any further colonial conquests.[37]

By the end of World War II, the US had built an extraordinary range of technologies that provided many of the benefits of a global empire without having to actually formally control colonies.[38] These technologies, such as aeroplanes, radio and other telecommunication networks, in turn, enabled the US to spread its goods, ideas, and people across various countries easily without having to annex them.[39] In addition, the United States built a powerful secret service that also enabled it to exert control in less visible ways.[40]

The dependence on certain raw materials—which had often driven annexation of certain territories by earlier empires—was also getting reduced. Synthetic materials such as plastics had been developed to substitute products that would otherwise have to be sourced from other, faraway countries. In a short period in the 1940s, the US military not only developed many such technologies and materials, it also built a global logistical network with the goal of giving the United States 'a new relationship to territory' and reducing the risks associated with traditional trade choke points.

Of course, the Americans were not the first to face inherent contradictions between their desires and actions, and the values and beliefs they sought to stand for. The British, for example, themselves did not view their colonial empire as the victims of colonialism did. The British also experienced the tension between the illiberal nature of their capitalist relations with the colonies and the theoretical, often philosophical attempts to frame these capitalist relations in liberal terms. To many, the colonial land expropriation, slavery and resource extraction were completely in opposition to the liberal political economic principles that were increasingly popular in Britain.[41]

To solve these inherent contradictions, the British would rely upon the ideological frameworks put forth so eloquently by liberal intellectuals, such as Locke, Burke, and Edward Wakefield. These intellectuals would, through their theoretical frameworks, help 'mediate between the illiberality of British colonial capitalism and the liberal British self-image'.[42]

Similarly, the US has shied away from the familiar strategy of colonization to a new strategy revolving around the spread of globalization, freedom, democracy and capitalism.[43] As Daniel Immerwahr terms it, the US empire was clothed in globalization, or even 'noble rhetoric about prosperity, liberty, and security', much like the British empire had been clothed in self-justifying imperialist ideologies.[44] And much like the intellectual frameworks of John Locke and Edmund Burke, ideologies such as globalization have helped the US citizens to 'comfort themselves with consoling fables of US benevolence while real historical knowledge steadily declined'.[45]

In reality, the US exercises its power and functions like an empire even as it 'does not take on the traditional trappings of one'. Even though it has not followed the path of the European colonial empires, it has been primarily focused on control of markets, and economic access and domination, not necessarily subjecting populations and territory to actual full-fledged control. Accordingly, the United States has repeatedly resorted to the use of military force, and even engaged in short- and long-term occupations to counter any perceived threats to its economic interests and private investments.[46]

The fact remains that the United States still continues to hold on to a territorial empire, just in the form of bases, instead of colonies. In addition to the well-known ones such as Guam and American Samoa, the US still maintains roughly 800 overseas military bases around the world.[47] These bases serve as the foundations for the projection of US world power by housing launchpads, staging grounds, storage, beacons, labs and increasing surveillance capabilities. Much like the British empire of colonies, the American 'empire of bases', as American historian Chalmers Johnson termed it, extends all over the planet.[48] Further, in addition to maintaining a global presence for the US military, the United States 'retains the world's most potent nuclear arsenal, capable of ending life on the planet several times over'.[49]

According to McCoy, the US has developed 'a distinct form of global governance' incorporating 'aspects of antecedent empires, ancient and modern' to form their own version of a new, unique American empire:

> This unique US imperium was Athenian in its ability to forge coalitions among allies; Roman in its reliance on legions that occupied military bases across most of the known world; and British in its aspiration to merge culture, commerce, and alliances into a comprehensive system that covered the globe. [50]

Of course, even the idea of American exceptionalism, therefore, has been termed as a self-serving pretension by some, such as historian Niall Ferguson. Ferguson has wryly observed, 'To those who would still insist on American "exceptionalism," the historian of empires can only retort: as exceptional as all the other sixty-nine empires.'[51]

The unipolar moment

The Soviet Union's demise allowed the US to exert unfettered control over the international system and expand both its ideological and geographic reach. It not only embarked on an effort to wrest control of Eastern Europe and Central Asia, it also tried to redefine the political landscape of the Middle East. The United States, in its unipolar moment, also 'declared that free-market democracy is the world's only viable model for political and economic development'. In fact, after the end of the Cold War, the geostrategic goals of each successive US administration have been to maintain the 'unipolar moment'.

The global developments in recent years have led many to argue that the unipolar moment is already over, with new poles emerging in the form of Europe, Russia and China. The idea of a unipolar world is a relatively recent one. As we saw in previous chapters, the pre-industrial era had seen the existence of several regional civilizations co-existing without any one becoming the globally dominant power. The introduction of modern communications technology has allowed for global wars and even the possibility of a single, globally dominant power.

Moreover, the perspective of many nations is that a unipolar world is an aberration and not a steady equilibrium state for the world order. China, and several other nations, do not want a unipolar world. And as S. Jaishankar, the current minister of external affairs for India, has argued, 'we have been conditioned to think of the post-1945 world as the norm and departures from it as deviations'. He points out, for example, that India's 'pluralistic and complex history underlines that the natural state of the world is multipolarity'.[52] You may recall from previous chapters that the Indian Ocean trade was, for instance, never structured as a monopoly by any of the nations on the rim, until the European colonial powers emerged on the scene. This historical perspective often informs the foreign policy objectives of many Eurasian powers.

Military implications

European colonialism has been attributed, at least partly, to the supremacy of European military capabilities. Similarly, part of the US strategy for complete dominance has been to ensure that it would exercise 'full-spectrum dominance' in all domains of warfare, which could help the US maintain its global standing even if its economic dominance was to recede. It has done this by ensuring that it doesn't become vulnerable in any domain of warfare, old or new. This has meant that space and cyber, and in the previous century, air and nuclear, have been big focus and investment areas for the US military.

This has, to a large extent, ensured that 'at the dawn of the twenty-first century, Washington's bid for what it termed "full-spectrum dominance" across all six domains of warfare—both conventional (air, land, sea) and clandestine (aerospace, cyberspace, covert nether-world)—gave it a national security state of exceptional strength with which to maintain its global power, despite fading economic influence, for decades to come'.[53]

But, of course, as we all know, the military interventions conducted by the US in the last several decades have not been completely successful, whether it has been in Vietnam, Iraq or Afghanistan. Since 1945, US armed forces have been deployed abroad for conflicts or potential conflicts over 200 times across over sixty-five countries.[54] This military interventionism has often bordered on 'imperial overreach', a cause for the decline of many empires, as identified by Paul Kennedy in his famous book, *The Rise and Fall of the Great Powers*.

In fact, the overwhelming dominance in conventional military terms of the US has led to another major trend: guerilla warfare, which has also taken the form of terrorism and increasingly cyberwarfare. And on that front, the US's conventional military superiority has not translated into successful military interventions or wars for the US.[55]

Capitalism and the US—Its Primary Torchbearer—Shaped the Economic Destiny of Nations

US domination of world trade and global financial institutions

The economic implications of the capitalism-led domination of the US of the global economy have been immense. The US-dominated capitalist, free-trade-driven global economic system has become widely adopted. The economic domination of the world's economy and international financial institutions by the US has further reinforced its economic strength.

The US, in the post-World War II era, embarked on a strategy of global governance through a web of global institutions such as the UN, the World Bank and the International Monetary Fund (IMF), as part of what has been called the Bretton Woods regime. Over the subsequent years and decades, this web of institutions has become more intricate, with the formation of specialized institutions such as the World Trade Organization (WTO) and specific arms of the UN for various global issues.

The US has used its dominance of these institutions, built and deepened over decades, to continue to maintain and preserve its power and influence, and also spread the values and systems it espouses. The political implications of the rise of capitalism, and the dominance of the United States, have been intricately linked with democratic political systems. The leader of this era of capitalism has also pushed the concept of liberal democracy. And therefore, much of the global discourse around democracy being the only possible political system has also echoed in the halls of the world's global institutions.

The US government, as well as US companies, have exerted their economic influence globally in multiple ways. One, control of a large share of world trade has historically rested with US companies, though obviously, in recent days, the Chinese have begun to challenge US dominance of world trade. Two, in the post-WWII era, America has also controlled the international financial institutions like the IMF and the World Bank, and the US dollar has now been the primary global currency for several decades. This has ensured that, for the larger part of the twentieth century, the US could also get favourable terms for trade with most countries. The US, by virtue of its predominance, has also been able to push capitalism as the primary mode of economic production around the world during this period. Mass consumerism—to the extent it can be seen as an American ideology or at least a Eurocentric one—has also been spread greatly on the back of this global influence.[56]

Dollar hegemony

Carla Norrlöf, professor of political science at the University of Toronto, argues that the American economic hegemony has three pillars: currency, trade and security. She has argued that all three pillars—the dollar's primacy, the commercial and trading prowess of the United States and its military predominance—support and reinforce each other. The dollar's status as the chief global currency actually grants 'material gains as well as policy flexibility' to the US. While its dominance is today under threat, for several decades, the US dollar has been the primary currency for settling trade and other financial transactions around the world, even when the trade does not actually involve the US. In fact, the US dollar's dominance has also been framed as the 'soft underbelly of empire'.[57]

In addition to enhancing the effectiveness of US financial sanctions, the dollar's centrality also gives the US government and its clearing houses and banks privileged access to global transactions information. Further, the dollar's dominance has insulated it from the effects of long-term trade deficits and allowed the US to more easily fund massive public and private borrowing, an ability that former French finance minister Valéry Giscard d'Estaing famously called America's 'exorbitant privilege'.[58] As you'll see, the dollar hegemony is being challenged, not just by other rival currencies, but even more fundamentally by crypto-currencies and central bank digital currencies (CBDCs).

Capital as a factor of production

Given that countries are differently endowed with the various factors of production, changes in the relative importance of the factors of production also shape the economic destiny of nations. As we saw in Chapter 1, for example, labour and land were the main factors of production driving economic growth in the agricultural era. However, capital became more important as a factor of production, especially in the industrial era, as it was required to scale up trading and manufacturing operations. Capital also made the existing factors of production (such as labour) more productive.

In fact, capital-intensive industrialization has been the major driver of economic growth in the American era. Marx had argued that under the system of industrial capitalism, the labourer was no longer working for himself but for the capitalist who owned the means of production.[59] Fundamentally, the Cold War was a battle between two factors of production: labour and capital. As the labour-rich individuals and countries realized that their importance had dipped during the industrialization era, they began to realize that they had to fight the capital-rich individuals and countries. The collapse of the Soviet Union in the Cold War meant that capital as a factor of production had proven its pre-eminence.

For a large part of the last century, accumulation of capital has been a key driver of economic growth for countries. Those who have managed to attract and accumulate capital have grown faster than those who were not able to, both within and across countries. As a result, income inequality has continued to increase since the 1970s in the rich countries, especially in the United States, at least in part due to the fact that a capitalist system disproportionately rewards those who have capital to deploy.[60]

Economists such as Adam Smith and John Keynes have pointed out, however, that an over-accumulation of capital often leads to a decline in the rate of return to capital. But modern financial engineers have leveraged financial innovation and securitization, along with other ways of accumulation of fictitious value, to get around this potential problem of declining returns to capital. The misleading financial packaging that was on display during the 2008–09 financial crisis, or even the unreasonably high valuations of start-ups funded by firms sitting on massive amounts of capital looking for high returns, could very well serve as examples of fictitious value being created by financial engineers.[61]

Many economists, including Robert Solow, Philippe Aghion and Thomas Piketty believe that technology can help sustain or increase the returns to capital. Like Aghion, Piketty has pointed out technology-enabled productivity increases can serve as a counterbalance to the process of declining returns to this over-accumulation and concentration of capital.[62] Indeed, the rapid transition of the US economy towards a preponderance of large technology firms suggests that an increased allocation of capital towards productivity-enhancing technology could actually increase the returns to capital. Could it be that technology could provide the much-needed boosted returns to capital the same way industrialization did? We consider this in detail in the next chapter, but in brief, when seen from this perspective, the fact that capital is chasing companies in the technology sector today is not that surprising.

China provides an interesting case study on how different factors of production can drive rapid economic growth, and the trade-offs involved. Abundant in cheap labour, China had initially adopted a hybrid style of development or what is known as labour-intensive industrialization. In light of the relative absence of industrial capital, China's industrialization drew upon abundant raw materials and skilled labour.[63]

The development of labour-intensive (as opposed to capital-intensive) technologies and machines has meant that though improvements in living standards have been relatively smaller, employment has continued to be more broad-based than in the West. As a result, the labour-intensive form of industrialization has helped diffuse industrialization and its productivity gains to a much broader swathe of the population in the East than would have otherwise been possible. Over time, this form of hybrid development merged with Western-style capital-intensive and energy-hungry forms of industrialization and development, first in Japan, then subsequently in the capitalist archipelago, and most recently, China.

Historian Henry Heller has argued that 'this synthesis has great importance in terms of the future of the world economy'. Many governments and leaders end up on the extreme end of the spectrum when they reject technology completely for fear of it replacing labour, causing unemployment and losing them elections. Later in the book, this case study will be relevant in our discussion of labour-enhancing technologies (rather than labour-replacing technologies) as a way to avoid structural or mass unemployment.

The East Asian Miracle

Capitalism has not shaped the economic destiny of the US alone. While it has undoubtedly been the main torchbearer of capitalism in the twentieth century, the latter part of the century saw the emergence of what has been termed by Bruce Cumings as the 'capitalist archipelago of East Asia'.[64] This refers to countries and city-states such as Japan, Taiwan, South Korea, Singapore and Hong Kong, which adopted and greatly benefited from capitalism.

Some have argued that instead of capitalism being the defining theme of the twentieth century, 'when history is eventually written from a longer rearview mirror, [it] will be the rise of East Asia'.[65] The West, through its diehard emphasis on globalization and capitalism, created the political and economic conditions that paved the way for the East Asian economic renaissance. This East Asian renaissance has driven the economic miracles in various East Asian countries, starting in Japan in the 1950s and 1960s, South Korea, Taiwan, Hong Kong, Singapore, Malaysia and Thailand in the 1970s and 1980s, and culminating with the rise of China in the 1990s and early 2000s.

These countries demonstrated that laggards in the industrial era could actually catch up by integrating themselves in the global industrial supply chains. The question we consider in later chapters is whether a similar catch up will be possible for laggards in the technology era.

Cultural implications of capitalism

Not unlike the colonial period, the American era has seen the creation of hierarchies of cultures, or as others have termed it, 'civilizational hierarchies'. American culture has seen widespread diffusion around the world, which has further propagated American influence. This has also been termed as its 'soft power' by HKS Professor Joseph Nye. However, it has also been termed as cultural imperialism.[66]

During this era, the cultures of less economically successful nations have often been subsumed by American culture, much like the cultures of the colonies had been by the cultures of their colonial masters.

American cultural imperialism is often thought of as the promotion of Hollywood, Disney and McDonald's,[67] but it is so much more. American culture—mixed with the culture of capitalism—has had several implications for the world, impacting societies and individuals greatly. The concept of the Great American Dream helps explain the impact of American culture and values on the world. At its core, it is about the aspiration for acquiring wealth in a short amount of time, no matter what your background. Implicitly, the message is simple: that money is everything, and that fast growth and upward mobility are what matters.

Indeed, global magazines such as *Forbes*, *Fortune* and *Time* celebrate wealth, power and influence through lists such as the Forbes Richest, Fortune 500 and Times 100 Most Influential, all of which implicitly endorse the values that are associated with 'becoming rich quick'. This has shaped the aspirations—and the values and priorities—of the world.

Anthropologist Richard Robbins, drawing upon writer-philosopher Jacob Needleman's book, *Money and the Meaning of Life*,[68] explains that today money is all that people seem to want, but that was not always true:

> Jacob Needleman wrote that, in another time and place, not everyone has wanted money above all else. People, he said, have desired salvation, beauty, power, strength, pleasure, prosperity, explanations, food, adventure, conquest, comfort. But now and here, money—not necessarily even the things money can buy, but money—is what everyone wants ... Therefore, if one wished to understand life, one must understand money in this present phase of history and civilization.[69]

At the same time, American aspiration has been easy to buy into, unlike the British dream that largely seemed inaccessible for the vast majority. Under the British empire, the colonial subjects of the British empire could rise up the ranks of local administrative structures, but could never become 'British' themselves. In the American capitalist worldview, however, you can become American; in fact, you are effectively required to become American (whether by citizenship or just in behaviour and values) to succeed and be accepted fully in the United States.

Not to say that the glass ceilings have disappeared completely and for everyone. Far from it. But America has brought many groups of people closer to that glass ceiling than earlier imaginable, and that has stoked the aspirations of many groups. And entrepreneurship and innovation—as ways to achieve those aspirations—have been emphasized as the means to that end.

Where the British empire would often judge you by your class (members of the royal or aristocratic class would be treated a certain way), American culture has been about breaking those class boundaries, or the glass ceilings if you will, with an implied irreverence for the traditional and for inherited legacies. A self-made millionaire is much more admired in this era than a billionaire who essentially just inherited the wealth. And while traditional class relations have been de-emphasized to some extent, a new hierarchy of relations have arisen: the capitalists, the financers and the business leaders are the new aristocrats, while everyone else has become either a worker (the blue-collar worker of the industrial era), or a consumer.

Consumerism has been the other big impact of American and capitalist culture. The desire to consume and accumulate have become commonplace in society. Consumption has become the new source of well-being. One can argue that consumerism began with colonization and industrialization when the mass production of goods necessitated that more people become consumers. The emphasis on more and more production has inevitably led to an emphasis on unlimited consumption and perpetual growth. America, probably more than any other country in history, has mastered the art of promotion of consumerism through its global consumer brands and advertising prowess. Brands formed in the 1800s have boomed in the 1900s.

Household, national and world consumption has expanded at an unprecedented pace during the American era. In 2010, it stood at $37 trillion, up three times since 1975 and six times since 1950. This does not seem like it will be slowing down anytime soon, as emerging economies such as China and India add over half a billion middle-class consumers demanding all that consumers in the West have desired and acquired.[70]

This had major implications for our entire society. Robbins wryly observes that the 'genius of capitalism' lies in 'a constant conversion of things that have no monetary value into things that do'.[71] He considers this constant commodification is at the heart of the Faustian bargain that we have struck in the age of capitalism:

> Thus, trees, lakes, and mountains must be converted into things that can be sold in the marketplace; activities once associated with family life and given freely, such as child care, food preparation, and education, must be converted into monetary activities; and freedom itself can be exchanged for money as powerful corporations use their money to gain political access and power.[72]

In the technology era, many argue that seemingly we are striking a similar Faustian bargain, where data and our personal information is converted into a tradeable commodity or converted into a source of wealth. More on this later in the book.

The cultural impact of capitalism and America, then, has also obviously had a dark side. Many have argued that many of the global problems we face today—environmental degradation, loss of biodiversity, unsustainable growth no matter what the cost to the commons, recklessness, short-term mindsets, selfishness, hyper-competitiveness, wastage, mindless consumption and accumulation, rapid and often unsustainable urbanization, an excessive emphasis on fossil fuels, sustained and growing inequality—can all trace their origins to industrialization and capitalism.

Capitalism, much like industrialization and colonialization, has also shaped the individual, specifically the well-being of the individual. As Stephen Butler points out, there are capitalism-specific stresses that arise from the instability and insecurity that has come to characterize family life, employment and intimate relations. The psychological security and stability that the familiar structures of family life and employment traditionally provided have reduced significantly over the past fifty to sixty years. Further, the 'individualistic and materialistic' values fostered by capitalism are believed to affect the prevalent socialization processes and also make it harder for people to form strong, stable bonds in these societies. This, in turn, Butler argues, might contribute to other social developments such as a higher incidence of divorces.[73]

The conclusions of the impact capitalism and industrialization have had on culture are hotly debated, and perspectives vary. Defenders of capitalism argue that the relationship between capitalism and culture is complex and multifaceted, but that capitalism becomes an easy scapegoat for the ills ailing modern society.[74] There is also a debate around whether economic systems shape culture, or cultural values and norms shape our economic structures.

What is less debatable, however, is the conclusion that the trend-shapers of any era or Great Game do shape the culture, values and well-being of individuals, families, nations, societies and the world in myriad, often hard-to-comprehend ways. The pre-existing cultural values and societal norms themselves also shape the Great Game. It is a two-way street, as we will see in the case of the Great Tech Game as well.

Key Lessons

The American era of capitalism provides a gamut of insights and lessons for the Great Tech Game that we delve into subsequently in the book.

As we saw in previous chapters, each era builds upon the trend-shapers of the previous eras. Understanding the previous Great Game is as important as understanding the current one. The winners during the colonial-industrial era sought to excel at agriculture and trade, but adopted a different strategy that would outflank the incumbent powers. Similarly, as exemplified by the US, the winners in the capitalist era sought to excel at industrialization and colonization, albeit using a different approach. If the British had invented the steam engine, the US would first adopt that technology widely, but then invent electricity and lead its industrialization effort with widespread applications of electricity and eventually the internal combustion engine.

The US also adapted and added its own set of rules and strategies to the game. It set up the financial, political and legal institutions, and built up the managerial capabilities that were needed to succeed in the new game, much like Malacca and Venice had done many centuries ago. This lesson will re-emerge as we look at what is needed to win in the Great Tech Game.

Each new empire tends to incorporate the learnings and elements of empires that came before it. America, for example, incorporated the learnings of the British, the Romans and the Mongols. The new emerging powerful actors—whether it be China or Big Tech firms—are likely to also incorporate many of the elements of the American 'New Empire' into their approach, even as they adopt some of the outflanking strategies used by challengers.

A few key strategies adopted by America are likely to be adopted by the challengers. For example, the idea of using global institutions to govern the behaviour of other actors and gain legitimacy for your actions is likely to be leveraged in the future. The idea of an 'empire in hiding' or an 'empire of bases' is also likely to be a more useful analogue for countries and corporations looking to establish global reach rather than an 'empire of colonies'.

On the economic front, the discussion around the factors of production—and their relative importance vis-à-vis each other—is a pertinent one even for the tech era. As we have seen, each era has emphasized a different, sometimes new, factor of production. This is not to say that the other factors of production become irrelevant or unimportant; just that their relative importance changes. Technology had already established itself as a key factor of production and growth even in the capitalist era, but was not necessarily the primary factor. In the next era, we can expect technology, supported by capital, to become the most important factor of production.

The American capitalism era, much like earlier eras, had a massive impact on the culture and values of societies and individuals. As we enter the technology era, its impact on the values, culture and well-being of societies, families, nations and individuals will be equally, if not more, transformative. Much like the Faustian bargains inherent in capitalism and industrialization, the technology era is also likely to entail its own set of Faustian bargains that we would do well to recognize earlier than later.

In Part 1 of the book, we have looked at some of the major forces of history that have shaped us indelibly: agriculture, trade, industrialization, colonization, and capitalism. Each of these great games has created new sets of winners and losers, new rules and dynamics of the game, and ultimately the choices that have been made (by both the winners and losers) have shaped the nature and evolution of the game itself. And I hope it has become clear how each of these 'great games' has had significant economic, political and social ramifications for the world.

Next, we move on to the core theme of the book: the era of technology as the new shaper of our destinies, the new major force of history. Or, as I frame it, the Great Tech Game.

Notes

1. Alfred Chandler ed., *A Nation Transformed by Information: How Information Has Shaped the United States from Colonial Times to the Present* (Oxford University Press, 2000), Kindle.

2. Robert J. Gordon, *The Rise and Fall of American Growth*, The Princeton Economic History of the Western World, (Princeton University Press, 2017), Kindle.

3. Ibid.

4. Ibid.

5. Jeremy Rifkin, *The End of Work: The Decline of the Global Labor Force and the Dawn of the Post-Market Era* (Tarcher, 2004).

6. Chandler, Jr, ed., *A Nation Transformed*, loc. 42–44.

7. Ibid.

8. Philippe Aghion, Céline Antonin and Simon Bunel, *The Power of Creative Destruction: Economic Upheaval and the Wealth of Nations* (The Belknap Press of Harvard University Press, 2021), Kindle.

9. Gordon, *The Rise and Fall of American Growth*.

10. Ibid.

11. Alfred D. Chandler, Jr, *The Visible Hand* (Harvard University Press, 1992), Kindle.

12. Richard Sylla, 'Financial Systems and Economic Modernization', *Journal of Economic History* (2002), 62(2): 277–292.

13. Richard Sylla, 'US Securities Markets and the Banking System, 1790–1840', *Review* (Federal Reserve Bank of St. Louis, May/June 1998), https://files.stlouisfed.org/files/htdocs/publications/review/98/05/9805rs.pdf, accessed on 1 October 2021.

14. Sylla, 'Financial Systems and Economic Modernization'.

15. Howard Bodenhorn, 'Two Centuries of Finance And Growth in the United States, 1790–1980', Working Paper 22652, National Bureau of Economic Research (September 2016), https://www.nber.org/system/files/working_papers/w22652/w22652.pdf, accessed on 1 October 2021.

16. Ibid.

17. Sylla, 'US Securities Markets'.

18. Chandler, Jr, *The Visible Hand*.

19. Gordon, *An Empire of Wealth*.

20. Nathan Rosenberg and L.E. Birdzell, Jr, *How the West Grew Rich: Economic Transformation of the Industrial World* (Bloomsbury, 2020).

21. Chandler, Jr, *The Visible Hand*.

22. Ibid.

23. Chandler, Jr, ed., *A Nation Transformed*.

24. Ibid.

25. Alfred W. McCoy, *In the Shadows of the American Century: The Rise and Decline of US Global Power*, Dispatch Books (Haymarket Books, 2017), Kindle.

26. Henry Luce, 'The American Century', *Life Magazine* (February 1941), https://link.springer.com/article/10.1007%2FBF02693255, accessed on 1 October 2021.

27. Oliver Stone and Peter Kuznick, *The Untold History of the United States* (Ebury Publishing, 2012), Kindle.

28. Walter LaFeber, *The New Empire* (1998).

29. Ibid.

30. Ibid.

31. Daniel Immerwahr, *How to Hide an Empire* (Random House, 2019), Kindle.

32. David Heidler, *Manifest Destiny*, https://www.britannica.com/event/Manifest-Destiny/The-end-of-Manifest-Destiny, accessed on 1 October 2021.

33. LaFeber, *The New Empire*.

34. Stone and Kuznick, *The Untold History*.

35. Immerwahr, *How to Hide an Empire*.

36. LaFeber, *The New Empire*.

37. Immerwahr, *How to Hide an Empire*.

38. Ibid.

39. Ibid.

40. Nick Turse, 'The Future of the American Empire', *The Nation* (February 2017), https://www.thenation.com/article/archive/alfred-mccoy-the-future-of-the-american-empire/, accessed on 1 October 2021.

41. Onur U. Ince, *Colonial Capitalism and the Dilemmas of Liberalism* (Oxford University Press), https://www.umass.edu/economics/sites/default/files/Ince %282018%29 Colonial Capitalism Intro Ch1.pdf, accessed on 1 October 2021.

42. Ibid.

43. Immerwahr, *How to Hide an Empire*.

44. Ibid.

45. Stone and Kuznick, *The Untold History*.

46. Ibid.

47. Immerwahr, *How to Hide an Empire*.

48. Chalmers Johnson, 'Empire of Bases', *The New York Times* (July 2009), https://www.nytimes.com/2009/07/14/opinion/14iht-edjohnson.html, accessed on 1 October 2021.

49. Stone and Kuznick, *The Untold History.*

50. McCoy, *In the Shadows.*

51. Stone and Kuznick, *The Untold History*.

52. S. Jaishankar, *The India Way* (HarperCollins Publishers, 2020), p. 12

53. McCoy, *In the Shadows.*

54. Immerwahr, *How to Hide an Empire.*

55. Stone and Kuznick, *The Untold History.*

56. Heller, *The Birth of Capitalism.*

57. Rohini Hensman and Marinella Correggia, 'US Dollar Hegemony: The Soft Underbelly of Empire', *Economic and Political Weekly*, Money, Banking and Finance (19-25 March 2005), 40(12): 1091, 1093–1095, https://www.jstor.org/stable/4416354, accessed on 1 October 2021.

58. Kenneth Rogoff, 'The US Dollar's Hegemony Is Looking Fragile', *The Guardian* (April 2021), https://www.theguardian.com/business/2021/apr/02/the-us-dollars-hegemony-is-looking-fragile, accessed on 1 October 2021.

59. Karl Marx, *Das Kapital*, vol. 1, https://www.marxists.org/archive/marx/works/download/pdf/Capital-Volume-I.pdf, accessed on 1 October 2021.

60. Piketty, *Capital in the Twenty-First Century*.

61. Marx, *Das Kapital*.

62. Piketty, *Capital in the Twenty-First Century*.

63. Heller, *The Birth of Capitalism*.

64. Bruce Cumings, 'The Political Economy of the Pacific Rim', in *Pacific-Asia and the Future of the World System*, R.A. Palat ed. (Westport, CT: Greenwood Press, 1993), 25–6.

65. Arrighi, *Adam Smith in Beijing*.

66. Tobin, 'Cultural Imperialism'.

67. Elin A. Drysén, 'A Critical Examination of Cultural Imperialism and its Impact on Global Communication Today', LinkedIn (January 2016), https://www.linkedin.com/pulse/critical-examination-cultural-imperialism-its-impact-global-drysén/, accessed on 1 October 2021.

68. Jacob Needleman, *Money and the Meaning of Life* (Currency Doubleday, 1991).

69. Richard H. Robbins, *Global Problems and the Culture of Capitalism* (Pearson Education, 2013), Kindle.

70. Ibid.

71. Ibid.

72. Ibid.

73. Stephen Butler, 'The Impact of Advanced Capitalism on Well-being: an Evidence-Informed Model', *Human Arenas* 2 (2019): 200–227, https://link.springer.com/article/10.1007/s42087-018-0034-6, accessed on 1 October 2021.

74. Michael Matheson Miller, 'Does Capitalism Destroy Culture?', Intercollegiate Studies Institute (February 2021), https://isi.org/intercollegiate-review/does-capitalism-destroy-culture/, accessed on 1 October 2021.

PART TWO

~

TECHNOLOGY: THE NEW ECONOMIC DESTINY OF NATIONS

'The process of technological innovation—invention, commercialization, widespread adoption and use—has been the most powerful driver of wealth and increased well-being since the beginning of history.'

—Klaus Schwab

'As amazing as the changes of the past twenty years have been, they are only the first stages of a multi-decade transition to a digital economy that will rival the industrial revolution in terms of transformative power.'

—Rana Foroohar, *Don't Be Evil*

4

Technology Is the New Wealth
of Nations

'When the wind changes direction, there are those who build walls
and those who build windmills.'

—Chinese proverb

Travelling around India today, you find vestiges of all the previous
Great Games.

Driving for less than an hour outside of Delhi, you find yourself in
the midst of the great Indo-Gangetic plains. The Yamuna River flows
through Delhi, and just a short distance away, the Ganga River makes
its way towards the Bay of Bengal. Fields growing wheat, rice, mustard,
sugarcane and various other crops line the banks of these rivers. The
area between the Ganga and Yamuna is known as the Ganga–Yamuna
Doab and is part of the great Indo-Gangetic plains that extends from
the Himalayas in the north to the Deccan Plateau in the south. This
fertile agricultural belt along with the Indus River plains formed the
cradle of the ancient north Indian civilization. These river-based
civilizations, as we discussed in Chapter 1, were quite successful at the
Great Agri Game.

Amidst the fields of wheat and sugarcane lies Khurja, a small town known for its pottery. Legends of the town's origins differ, but it is one of the oldest centres for glazed pottery in India. Originally all handcrafted, Khurja pottery is now mostly manufactured in small factories. Walking through these shops, you can hear instructions being shouted out for trucks to be loaded for export. Close one's eyes, and you could be transported to the fifteenth century, when a town like Khurja would be an integral trade link in the Silk Roads spanning the Eurasian landmass. India's handicrafts and artisanal products made it a valuable link in the Great Trading Game.

Interspersed with the farms and artisanal centres are the signs of India's attempt at the next Great Game, industrialization. The same Ganga–Yamuna Doab is dotted with factories manufacturing refined sugar and various forms of machinery and equipment. Ghaziabad and Noida, both suburbs east of Delhi, are major hubs for small- and mid-sized factories, as is Okhla, an industrial township in the south east of Delhi.

The signs of the transition to the digital economy are now equally evident. Noida is the hub for PayTM, one of India's largest fintech companies. Many of Okhla's mills and mini-factories have been vacated and converted into start-up offices, accelerators and more recently, co-working spaces. Just a half-hour south of Delhi, the suburb of Gurgaon, is lined with the offices of companies such as Airtel, Times Internet, Google, Facebook, MakeMyTrip, Grofers, Zomato, Uber and many other representatives of the fast-growing digital economy of India. Gurgaon is the face of the new, dynamic Indian economy.

All of these signs of history—and all the Great Games we have seen over the last few millennia—co-exist within an hour's radius of central Delhi, the seat of the Indian government.

~

No matter what country you live in today, you can observe this co-existence of the various economies—agricultural, the trade, the industrial and the digital. By no means does the emergence of a new economy, or a new great game, make the previous one completely irrelevant. Rather, as in the picture I painted of Delhi above, the new economy represents an additional layer of economic activity—the Great Tech Game—that a nation must understand, integrate and master.

Much as trade, industrialization and capitalism did in the previous eras, technology will now increasingly shape the economic destiny of nations. Technology is no longer just one sector among many, but a force permeating and changing all sectors of the economy. In fact, the digital economy, buoyed by its rapid growth, is fast replacing the industrial economy. Technology firms—not the industrial-era firms—are capturing a large part of the value chain or share of wallet of consumers and businesses. And unlike industrial era value chains, value is much less widely distributed across the technology value chains. Technology is enabling the creation of new markets, creating new demand and new supply where none existed before. Tech-enabled marketplaces and platforms are enabling more efficient matching of supply and demand.

Technology is not limited to the offices of Google, Facebook, MakeMyTrip, Zomato and other technology firms in Gurgaon. Rather, technology—albeit to a limited extent—has reached the small-time manufacturers and traders of pottery in Khurja. They are busy sending photos of their latest wares to not just customers in Delhi, Mumbai and Bangalore, but also to buyers in New York, Paris and London. In the process, intermediaries are being replaced, and wastages, inefficiencies or suboptimal transactions are being reduced. All of this is yielding significant economic gains and unprecedented levels of convenience.

Technology often is already driving economic growth across all sectors through great increases in productivity and efficiency. In most sectors, workforces are becoming more productive, as technology allows them to focus on higher value-adding parts of their jobs. Countries are benefiting from the creation of large technology ecosystems as well as the adoption of technology across traditional sectors. The newly emerging technology ecosystems are often becoming the catalysts for economic growth and disruption across multiple sectors of the economy.

But this integration is still incomplete. Unfortunately, however, many still see technology as something that is the exclusive domain of technology firms. Farmers, pottery makers, large industries and small factories and offices need to adopt technology in various aspects of their productive activities, and not just for distribution, communication and marketing. Technology has to be viewed as a factor of production, much like land, labour and capital have been for centuries. Any productive activity requires an optimal combination of these factors. Enterprises which do not fully integrate today's technologies will struggle as certainly as if they had omitted the integration of capital (or finance), mechanization and skilled labour.

However, the changing structure of the economy has also raised many important questions about the implications. The digital economy is growing rapidly, yet the market dominance of a few technology platforms is leading to an unprecedented concentration of wealth amongst a few firms and individuals. The tech sector has become the preferred path for upward economic and social mobility, yet the increasing economic disparity has raised questions about whether the wealth of Big Tech firms will translate to wealth for nations and societies. Technology is leading to the creation of new types of jobs and a transformed vision of the future of work. Yet, as it has done historically, technology is also leading to structural unemployment.

These structural changes—and the accompanying questions—are fundamental, complex ones. Understanding the core drivers of these complexities will be critical for identifying the answers and succeeding in the digital economy. In this chapter, therefore, I first explain some of the core new concepts underlying the structure of the digital economy and the changes in economic thinking it is necessitating. I then proceed to discuss the key drivers of the digital economy, and show how measuring the trends within the digital economy can also enhance our understanding—and embrace—of it.

I. New Concepts and Structures of the Digital Economy

A key aspect of the digital economy is the emergence of digital platforms and online marketplaces, which differ from traditional marketplaces in some key ways. While the traditional market in Delhi, New York or Beijing might traditionally have many shops that consumers could choose between, online marketplaces have sought to become the sole, dominant intermediaries between the consumer and the seller. In the new models, a few intermediaries subsume the intermediary role earlier played by hundreds, if not thousands, of shops.

Network effects are propagating these winner-take-all models in the digital economy, compared to the traditional economy. Platforms such as Facebook and Twitter, for example, are like the telephone industry. The more people have a telephone, the more valuable having a telephone becomes. Similarly, the more the number of your friends or colleagues that are on Facebook or Twitter, the more valuable the platform becomes for you and for them. This is, in technology parlance, called the 'network effect'.

As Prof. Bart Hobijn, an economist and former researcher with the Federal Reserve Banks of San Francisco and New York, explained to me, the operating models in the digital economy often have increasing returns to scale. Given the incremental or marginal cost of serving the additional consumer tends towards zero, there are increasing returns to scale in certain digital goods and services. Structurally, this also leads to the creation of more winner-take-all models in the digital economy compared to the previous era.

The winner-take-all models of the digital economy, however, are largely concentrated on the Business-to-Consumer (B2C) side. The Business-to-Business (B2B) part of the digital economy does not lend itself to the oligopolistic or even monopolistic models that can sometimes dominate the B2C digital economy. The B2B sector is much more fragmented and competitive, and hence still much more open to constant disruption.

Other concepts, such as the gig economy, data economy and the sharing economy, have gained prominence in the context of the digital economy. While some of these ideas are just the digital equivalents of concepts prevalent in the traditional economies, others are absolutely new. For example, the gig economy—freelancers like Uber and Ola cab drivers or Swiggy and Deliveroo delivery executives—is not necessarily a new concept. Similarly, the sharing economy is not quite new—riders would share bus rides or train rides earlier. But the digital economy is indeed making gigs easier to get, through large platforms such as Uber, Ola and Dunzo, and sharing easier through platforms such as Airbnb and Ola.

As William Maloney, chief economist at the World Bank, pointed out to me, several new industries are being created as well in the digital economy. For example, the data economy is a new ecosystem altogether. Between online marketplaces, social media platforms, browsers and the like, the amount of data being generated by users and businesses every day has seen tremendous growth. Data itself has started to become the fuel of the digital economy, with many Big Tech firms ultimately deriving their business models and revenues from the data they are collecting daily. Google and Facebook's ad-driven revenue models, for example, rely on the data they collect about your browsing and search behaviour, your demographics, your connections, your locations, your interests, and any other data they can collect on you through their labyrinth of apps. Many firms have emerged that specialize in data analytics, data infrastructure, data security and related fields. This idea—of tracking as much data as you can and monetizing that data—is new, and not often part of traditional industrial-era business models.

The global data (and intangible assets) economy

The new data economy promises to be a central element of future economic development. During the trade era, connectivity and centrality in trade had been important for a nation's competitiveness. Being at the trading crossroads of the East and the West allowed

Egypt, for example, to prosper greatly from high levels of trade flows. However, as alternative trade routes expanded, non-Mediterranean powers emerged on the global trade scene. Egypt's centrality to global trade flows decreased, as did its prosperity.

Over time, participation in the inflows and outflows of goods, services, finance and people has continued to drive economic prosperity for nations around the world. Historical analogies abound. If states like Egypt, India and Italy were the hubs for global trade of goods, more recently, cities such as London, New York and Hong Kong have been the hubs for financial flows. Today, growth in global data flows is fast outpacing growth in global goods trade and financial flows.[2] Over the last decade and a half, data flows have grown by over 150 times.[3] As per UNCTAD estimates, monthly global data traffic is further expected to surge from 230 exabytes in 2020 to 780 exabytes per month in 2026. To put this into perspective, all global internet traffic in 2022 alone will exceed the cumulative internet traffic up to 2016.[4]

Countries and regions that gain access (or restrict others' access) to data could become the modern-day Egypts. Why does access to data matter for economic prosperity? The data economy is increasingly important as a driver for the digital economy. Having access to both inflows and outflows of data enables greater circulation of ideas, research, technologies, talent, insights and best practices from around the world.[5] As Nobel Laureate Paul Romer has argued, these flows will in turn spur innovation and productivity-led economic growth.

The hubs (whether of goods, finance, or now, technology and data) also historically become centres for economic dynamism. They attract the best talent with the right skills, they develop more sophisticated economies and become the hubs for innovation and enterprise. The benefits then steadily trickle down to the rest of the economy. When London controlled global capital flows, its banks and finance professionals did not just grow richer than their counterparts in Delhi, Moscow or Beijing, they also fuelled growth in other parts of the British economy.

Similarly, today's tech and innovation hubs such as San Francisco, Seattle, Bangalore and Shenzhen are much more intricately linked into the global digital economy than their peers in Cairo, Istanbul or Rome. Therefore, technology professionals and firms in these hubs are more likely to be updated about the latest technologies and ideas and leverage the data they can access to extract more insights and build better products. Eventually, this allows them to capture more value as successful participants of the digital economy. Do the retail professionals at Amazon know more about the trends in retail than the CEO of the largest retail chain in India? Yes, definitely. Will the next retail innovation likely come from those professionals who have the data to identify new opportunities, or from those who don't?

An UNCTAD report has argued that the digital economy's expansion is driven by digital data and by the rise of platforms that exercise dominance over that data.[6] In the global data value chain, countries and companies that actually are better placed to extract the value from the data will gain prominence. The others risk becoming 'mere providers of raw data to those digital platforms while having to pay for the digital intelligence produced with those data by the platform owners'.[7]

Even the stock market is starting to assign greater value to intangible assets vis-à-vis tangible assets. As Chart 4.1 demonstrates, capital is getting reallocated to technology-based business models that are light on tangible assets (land, building and machinery) but heavy on intangible assets (such as data, software, and patents).

Countries must therefore develop clear strategies and build capabilities to enhance their ability to capture and control data, and then use the data to make more intelligent production decisions and also drive innovation efforts. Commercial monetization of large amounts of relevant data, mastery over processing that data into digital intelligence, and finally, the application to productive processes, will drive prosperity in the digital economy.[8]

Chart 4.1 Investors reallocated capital technology-based models

Selected composition of S&P 500 market

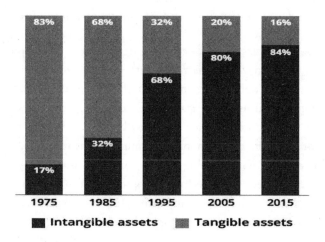

Source: Omar Hoda, Joseph Vitale, Jr, and Craig A. Giffi, 'The Revenue Multiplier Effect', *Deloitte Insights* (2018), https://www2.deloitte.com/content/dam/Deloitte/us/Documents/manufacturing/us-mfg-the-revenue-multiplier-effect.pdf, accessed on 4 October 2021.

The European Commission (EC) seems to have understood this phenomenon better than most. The EC has started studying the state and evolution of what they called the European Data Market. The data economy measures such factors as the number of data professionals and firms, the revenues of data supplier and data user companies, and the size of the digital products and services market.[9] In 2019, the European Data Economy already exceeded €400 billion, and grew 7.6 per cent over the previous year. Much like the overall digital economy, the European data economy is growing many times faster than the overall European economy. This is an effort that other countries and regions would do well to replicate so that they can track the value and growth of their respective 'data economies'.

A case study: 5G technology and its impact on economic growth

Many books, articles and reports have argued about the importance of data or technology in economic growth, or how data is the new oil. For those who are not directly engaged in the field of technology, these claims might seem just that, claims. 5G technology serves as a good case study to illustrate how data can actually drive economic growth.

5G, or fifth-generation mobile communications technology, is set to take over from 4G technology in the coming months and years. In history, we have seen that even a 10x improvement in functionality— speed, capacity, efficiency—can often lead to major economic revolutions. Therefore, a technology such as 5G that will be 100 times faster, and offer 1000 times more capacity than 4G networks is nothing short of revolutionary.[10] Countries such as the US have, in fact, acknowledged that 5G could become the 'primary driver of our Nation's prosperity and security in the 21st century'.[11]

How will 5G networks actually impact our economies and drive economic growth? Let us examine a few examples. 5G networks will enable the faster expansion of services that require higher bandwidths, so we can expect the growth of sectors such as telemedicine and remote education. Already, we are seeing venture capital investments grow in these sectors.

We can also expect an exponential increase in the number of connected Internet of Things (IoT) devices in personal, commercial, industrial and public spaces. Home automation systems, better crop management systems and air pollution sensors will become much more common. Rolled up, these connected devices will facilitate the penetration of autonomous vehicles and make our cities into smart cities.

Many of these developments have hitherto been hampered by the lack of adequate computing or processing power.[12] The rollout of 5G infrastructure is likely to remove these bottlenecks and usher in a much more interconnected and data-driven economy and society than we have seen thus far.

Consider an example used by Michael Porter in a *Harvard Business Review* article about connected products and systems and the economic opportunities it generates.

Chart 4.2: Internet of Things (IoT): The smart tractor example

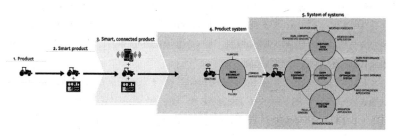

Source: Michael E. Porter and James E. Heppelmann, 'How Smart, Connected Products Are Transforming Competition', *Harvard Business Review* (November 2014), https://hbr.org/2014/11/how-smart-connected-products-are-transforming-competition, accessed on 4 October 2021.

As Chart 4.2 shows, in Stage 1, the tractor is a single, standalone product. 3G and 4G technology—such as Bluetooth, Wi-Fi, smart electronics, and smartphones—enabled the tractor to transition from stage 1 to stages 2 and 3. Today, the tractor can be a smart, connected product, which can send performance data to a computer and even enable access to that data from a mobile device.

However, with 5G, the tractor will transition from a smart, connected product to a product system (stage 4), where it can communicate with other equipment in the farm such as planters, tillers and combine harvesters (which would have gone through a similar evolution to stage 4). Stage 5, enabled by the speeds and capacities offered by 5G technology, will next help the farm equipment system itself to become part of a system of systems. The farm equipment system (containing the smart, connected tractor) will be linked with other smart, connected systems, such as the weather data system, seed optimization system and the irrigation system.

Now, also imagine how the data that was being generated in stage 1 of a product will differ from the data being generated in stages 4 and 5. The data associated with stage 1 was limited to the one-time date of sale and purchase of the tractor, the manufacturer, location of the buyer, etc., recorded on paper records in a completely decentralized manner. By stage 5, however, via the IoT-enabled sensors, we are likely to be centrally tracking hundreds, if not thousands, of data points on a daily basis about the tractor (how many hours it was operated for, its location, its fuel efficiency, its performance level, etc.) and all the connected systems it is part of.

This data now will be transferred to a central data management software, with its servers located in any of the data centres around the world. Companies, and countries, with control and access to data at this level can now start to make extremely informed, data-driven decisions on marketing, sales and strategy that will be much smarter than the decisions taken by companies and countries that do not have access to such data. Information, as they say, will be economic power.

5G rollout is expected to bring significant economic benefits across the world. A Congressional Research Service report suggests that in the United States itself, the adoption of 5G could lead to the creation of three million new jobs, and add an incremental $500 billion to its GDP. The world numbers are even bigger—22 million new jobs by 2035 and over $12 trillion in incremental output. To put that into perspective, the entire US GDP annually is close to US$ 20 trillion, so 5G could help create another economy half the size of the US economy.[13]

And we're not quite done yet. Technology futurists like Peter Diamandis and Steven Kotler have pointed to the coming convergence of technologies as a key trend that could shape economic growth. So far, technologies such as the internet, robotics or quantum computing have mostly operated independently to remove growth constraints. But what is most exciting, from the perspective of the future, is the innovation that these technologies acting together—or in convergence—are likely to unleash.[14] During our conversation, Philippe Aghion, a French economist and a professor at INSEAD, similarly expressed his optimism that the convergence of technologies will create a lot of 'creative destruction' and hence unleash a new wave of growth.

A clear example of the coming convergence of technologies is the Hyperloop, a new form of mass transportation system made up of tubes through which pods can travel without much air resistance and therefore achieve airline speeds. As Diamandis and Kotler point out, the Hyperloop has been made possible 'because of the rapid acceleration of power electronics, computational modelling, material sciences, and 3-D printing'.[15] Rapid increases in computational power have enabled simulations that were earlier not possible, while manufacturing breakthroughs in 3-D printing have made it much cheaper and faster to manufacture large concrete structures required for the Hyperloop.

The convergence of technologies, Kotler and Diamandis argue, will help the human brain move from operating in a local, linear environment to a global and exponential environment now. This—as futuristic and dreamlike as it sounds—could lead to 'paradigm-shifting, game-changing, nothing-is-ever-the-same-again breakthroughs'.[16] As American inventor and futurist Ray Kurzweil has argued in his book, *The Law of Accelerating Returns*, we're going to experience 20,000 years of technological change over the next 100 years. Essentially, we're going from the birth of agriculture to the birth of the internet twice in the next century.[17]

Technology (and data) should be viewed a factor of production for economic growth, not just a sector

Many view technology today as a sector. But really, technology is much more than that. It is a factor of production, just like land or labour or capital (defined as investment or money). The field of economics has lagged in its focus on exploring the complex linkages between technology and economic growth. Technology has remained within the larger bucket of Total Factor Productivity (TFP) in economic growth accounting studies. But increasingly, the case is being made for technology to be measured separately.

In fact, economists are beginning to argue that data is also becoming a factor of production. As Jessica Nicholson at the US Bureau of Economic Analysis (BEA) pointed out to me, given the heavy reliance of digital business models on data ownership and access, data will soon need to be incorporated into national (and company) accounts as capital formation or capital stock.

What does this mean for nations, businesses and individuals? Simply, technology (and specifically, even data) must be viewed the way businesses have viewed capital, for example. Accumulation of technology and data will become an asset for companies and nations, just as accumulation of capital on the balance sheet.

The deployment of technology will also help boost productivity of the other factors of production—land, labour and capital—deployed across all sectors of the economy. Put differently, technology should no longer be seen as just a standalone sector or a standalone factor of production. Rather, its contagion effect on the productivity of various sectors and the other factors of production must be better appreciated. For example, the use of IoT sensors in car manufacturing would lead to greater productivity within the auto sector, and also improve the returns to capital deployed in the auto industry.

Technology must therefore be leveraged widely in productive economic activity across all sectors of the economy, whether it be the production of goods or services, or even trade. This ripple down, waterfall effect can boost the nation's economy greatly.

The Duopoly of Technology and Capital

Economists led by Joseph Schumpeter and Robert Solow have long pointed to technology and innovation as key drivers of economic growth. As Solow found, productivity in the twentieth century came not from working more hours (more labour), or deploying more capital, but from increased productivity (that is, gaining more output per unit of input). And that increased productivity, in turn, came from new technology that enabled new, more productive techniques of production and distribution.[18]

In fact, the Solow–Swan model demonstrated that 'only technological progress, and not capital deepening, can sustain the growth of output per worker over the long run, offsetting diminishing returns on capital'.[19] Simply put, by the twentieth century, technological advancement had become the most important factor driving economic growth, at least for the developed economies.[20] In fact, capital growth and technical progress were found to account for over 75 per cent of economic growth in countries like the United States. This contribution is almost 95 per cent of growth in other industrial economies which do not see as high a growth in labour force as the US.[21.]

Capital and technical progress mutually reinforce each other. The benefits of technical progress are greater the bigger the capital stock of a country, all other things being equal.[22] And the greater the technological progress, the higher the returns to capital. Put simply, the more capital you have, the greater the benefits of incremental technological progress. On the one hand, this implies that countries that want technological progress will need to attract capital. On the other hand, countries that have excess capital, in their quest for higher returns, will look to deploy it in countries that are experiencing technological innovation.

The overwhelming significance of this duo of technology and capital is nowhere more evident than in the vibrant, fast-growing world of technology-focused venture capital (VC), which I've been part of for the last decade. In the tech VC world, large amounts of venture capital are financing technological innovation and yielding extraordinary returns. Technology and capitalism are the new tag team in the Great Tech Game.

All of this is not to say that investments and improvements in labour or human capital are not important or significant. On the contrary, in many ways, human capital investments and improvement are a prerequisite for technology and capital to grow, as we will see throughout this book. Ultimately, technology is being developed by humans, after all. Human capital also happens to be the only factor of production that is not subject to diminishing returns.[23]

Nobel Laureate Paul Romer's theory of endogenous technological change states that the search for new ideas by profit-maximizing entrepreneurs and researchers is at the heart of economic growth.[24] Furthermore, Romers has argued that since ideas are non-rival (that is, ideas can be used by more than one person), and not limited or depleted by use, they give rise to increasing returns to scale, and growth follows. To the extent that technology and capital can facilitate the generation and diffusion of new ideas, it will also lead to greater economic growth.

Again, I have seen evidence of this in the last decade. The more capital that has entered the tech ecosystem in India, the more innovative ideas have gotten generated and improved upon by entrepreneurs. As a result, the quality of ideas has also improved, as has the quality of the human capital engaged in the start-up space. This, in turn, has attracted further capital. This virtuous cycle can also partly explain the boom in funding that Indian technology start-ups have attracted in recent years.

Technology is helping remove constraints to growth

Erik Brynjolfsson and Andrew McAfee present a very simple yet powerful example of how technology is removing constraints to growth. The Industrial Revolution, leveraging the power of steam, allowed us to overcome the constraints of muscle power—whether of humans or animals—and leverage the energy of steam.[25] This, in turn, led to bigger factories, railways and the consequent mass production and transportation. At that point, this was 'the most profound time of transformation our world [had] ever seen'.

Now, in the second machine age, computers and digital technologies are doing for mental power what the steam engine did for our muscle power. Computers and other technologies such as Artificial Intelligence are pushing our mental limits outwards. Removing these mental constraints is deceptively transformative. The ideas, the insights and patterns our brains could not detect earlier might be within reach with the help of these technologies (again, think back to Romer's theory of ideas leading to increasing returns and economic growth). This could be a great boost for humanity.[26]

Technology actually must be used by each country smartly to remove the particular constraints it is facing in its growth journey. The set of growth constraints facing an African nation will be very different from a European nation, and therefore, it follows that the kinds of technologies that need to be developed, adopted or leveraged by an African nation will be very different.

Where costs have been constraints to growth, technological innovation is also lowering the cost of doing business, in the process increasing productivity gains and driving economic growth. Fewer technicians controlling robotic systems can operate entire manufacturing plants at much lower costs than earlier. Small businesses can now much more cheaply and quickly reach potential customers from across the world. As Microsoft CEO Satya Nadella has explained, technology is not just a factor of production but also a factor of distribution.[27] Physical barriers and distances have been largely overcome through the internet and other emerging technologies, making supply chains much more connected, transparent and efficient. Transactional costs—such as payments, transfers, logistics—have also been rapidly reduced. The spread of e-commerce and the rise of e-commerce giants like Amazon and Alibaba are prime examples of this.

But as Prof. Karthik Muralidharan summed it aptly, policymakers must identify the specific constraints of growth in each sector (or the overall economy) and leverage technology to solve that. If the immediate constraint to growth is, let's say, education access, then technology must be leveraged to remove the specific constraints that are preventing broader or better education access in a nation. Technology could, for example, solve for specific constraints, such as lack of good quality teachers in remote or rural areas, or heavy teacher absenteeism, the unsuitability of the curriculum, or the lack of personalized teaching.

This approach of mindfully and purposefully identifying ways to leverage technology to remove nation-specific constraints is a key lesson for all policymakers.

Rapid diffusion, adoption and commercialization of technology is critical

As we had seen in the American era, technologies are not useful in and of themselves. Rather, the rapid diffusion, adoption and commercialization of technology and its new applications are important for the full benefits of technology to be reaped. America did that very successfully with electricity, for example, and reaped immense benefits. As a result, it has become critical for nations to understand the drivers of diffusion, adoption and commercialization of technology.[28]

The lesson from the Industrial Revolution was quite clear: 'The extent to which society embraces technological innovation is a major determinant of progress.'[29] It is critical to develop new technologies rapidly *and* become effective adopters. Developing new technologies creates wealth for the inventors or the companies that develop them, while effective adoption allows you to extract value from its widespread use. But if the former is harder to do, countries must at the very least do the latter.

Many non-US firms and countries have internalized this lesson in recent decades. While the US scientific research establishment still retains its pre-eminence on invention of new technologies, firms and countries elsewhere have improved their ability to commercialize and adopt new technologies, thus shrinking the lead time that US firms have enjoyed vis-à-vis their non-US competitors.[30] China, for example, would be a prime example for having skillfully executed this '*diffuse, adopt and commercialize*' strategy.

In general, studies have found a trickle-down pattern in the adoption of technologies. Technologies originating in the developed world, for example, get adopted there first. Subsequently, they'll trickle down to the developing countries. But the pace of diffusion of technology has also sped up across the world. Global telecommunication networks, along with capital and entrepreneurs, are helping new technologies and ideas diffuse much faster than ever before. Yet, adoption rates still remain much lower in developing countries due to various factors related to their human capital endowment, institutional frameworks and openness to trade, and technology adoption.[31]

We are still far from truly broad-based adoption of technologies, whether emerging or established. For example, nearly 1.3 billion people still lack access to electricity, while over 3 billion people still lack internet access. But the encouraging sign here, as chart 4.3 shows clearly, the technology adoption lags are falling rapidly. The internet is permeating the globe—if the last decade is any indication—multiple times faster than technologies such as electricity that were the hallmarks of the earlier Industrial Revolution.[32]

But technology adoption is not the same as technology penetration. A country might have adopted, let's say, the internet, but the actual penetration or widespread use of internet might still be low. In fact, as Diego Comin and Marti Mestieri have argued, there has indeed been convergence in technology adoption lags between developed and developing countries, but the divergence in penetration rates still remains high.

This differentiation (between adoption and penetration) is important because they have also shown that divergence in adoption and penetration of technology accounts for almost 80 per cent of the Great Income Divergence between the rich and poor countries since 1820. Let that sink in for a second. Eighty per cent of the disparity in income levels between the rich and poor countries can be explained by differences in penetration rates of technology across these countries.[33,34]

The New Digital Global Value Chains or Ecosystems

As the global digital economy grows, the global value chains (GVCs) are being transformed in ways that will have significant implications for

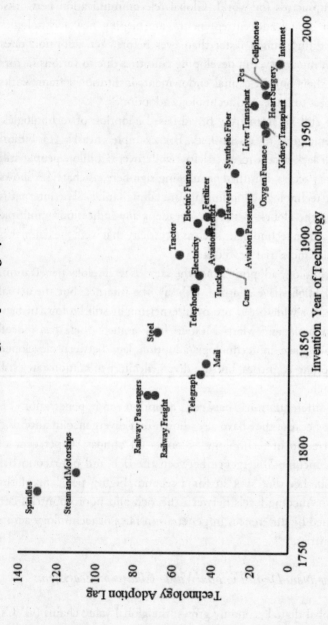

Chart 4.3: Technology adoption lags (years), 1750–2000

Source: Indermit Gill, 'Whoever Leads in Artificial Intelligence in 2030 Will Rule the World until 2100', Brookings (January 2020). https://www.brookings.edu/blog/future-development/2020/01/17/whoever-leads-in-artificial-intelligence-in-2030-will-rule-the-world-until-2100/, accessed on 4 October, 2021.

economic development across the world. The digitization of the existing global industrial-era value chains is underway. Digital technologies such as the internet, cloud computing and artificial intelligence are reshaping GVCs by enabling greater efficiencies across different aspects of the value chains, such as production, product development, sales and logistics.[35]

With the rapid spread of IoT, sensors, 5G technologies and AI, software-enabled manufacturing is being considered as the future of industrial manufacturing in the twenty-first century. Adoption of technology at each step of the value chain is changing the connectivity, transparency, traceability and verifiability of these value chains as well. This digitization of the value chains is part of the digital transformation efforts of most large traditional firms and industrial giants across the world.

At the same time, digital communication technologies such as WhatsApp are creating greater opportunities for smaller firms to integrate more deeply into the GVCs by removing the earlier barriers to exporting. Recall the example of the Khurja pottery firms I mentioned earlier and the ease with which they are able to now connect directly with buyers and customers across the world. Over time, this will have an incredible impact on the nature of the global economy and trade patterns, as countries with a predominance of smaller firms might be able to gain share vis-à-vis nations with predominantly larger exporting firms.

But most importantly, technology is creating completely new global digital value chains (GDVCs). Alongside, it is enabling opportunities for a wide range of absolutely new services in these GDVCs. For example, as the UNCTAD Digital Economy report has pointed out, 'an entirely new "data value chain" has evolved', made up of specialized data-focused firms that support the generation and collection of data, the creation of insights from data, data storage, data flows, complex modelling and big data analysis.[36] Each of these firms add value to the data as it gets transformed from raw data to digital intelligence of great value to firms and countries.

The large Big Tech firms, and digital platforms, are also spawning new global value chains, and in fact, new ecosystems altogether. As a former colleague at McKinsey & Co. explained, these ecosystems are distinct from the industrial-era supply chains in two key ways. One, these ecosystems are no longer industry-specific. Rather they cut across multiple industries usually. Two, these ecosystems are not linear, unlike many earlier value chains. Actors within the value chain are often playing the role of consumer and supplier at the same time.

As Chart 4.4 shows, the ecosystem spawned by Facebook looks extremely different from the supply chain or the value chain of an industrial-era giant like General Motors (GM), for example.

Let us also briefly examine what the traditional value chain looked like. According to David Tulauskas, director of sustainability at General Motors (GM), GM's value chain—which I assume is representative of the global auto value chain—consists of 20,000 suppliers that provide them with the various parts and components that go onto GM's vehicles. From these 20,000 suppliers, they buy roughly 200,000 individual items, which in 2017–18 translated into spending of about $100 billion.[37] In comparison, while exact numbers are not available publicly, Facebook probably has a lot fewer suppliers and is likely buying much less (in percentage and value terms) from external vendors.

Sharad Sharma, founder of the iSPIRT Foundation based in Bangalore, shared a few other examples of how today's technology value chains compare with industrial value chains. In the car industry, for example, the dealer, the ancillary parts manufacturers, and others in the value chain typically retained about 40–50 per cent of the profit, while the manufacturer kept the remainder. This meant that in a large automobile market like India, rising sales of cars meant more value added for Indian dealers and ancillary parts manufacturers. But in the EV industry, a much larger share (almost 70–75 per cent) of the profit

Chart 4.4: The Ecosystem of Facebook (or the Global Digital Value Chain of Facebook)

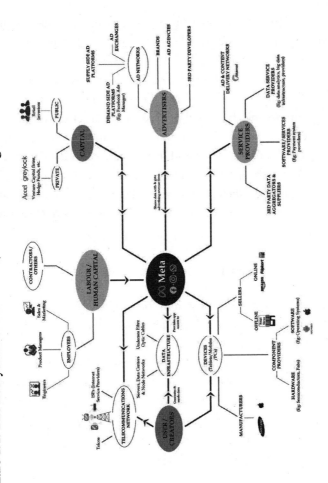

Source: Author compilation.

pool is expected to be retained by the manufacturers of the EV batteries and smart electronics such as the navigation systems, leaving very little for Indian players in the ecosystem. Similar stories, Sharma pointed out, are playing out in consumer electronics, solar panels, and other industries.

This, in turn, offers some clues about what the new digital ecosystems mean for the world. First, greater concentration of functions and technological capabilities within the Big Tech firms will imply much less of the economic benefits their expansions will accrue to other parts of the world. Just being a consumption economy will not be enough. Second, firms will need to work harder to become part of the global digital value chains as the club of suppliers will be much more exclusive. Third, countries and firms will need to dig deeper and better understand the various components of these ecosystems. That will help them identify their niches, where they have a right to play and can retain decent margins. We discuss this last point in further detail in the next chapter.

II. Measuring the Digital Economy

The economy of a nation must now be understood, analysed and measured through two lenses: the digital economy and the traditional industrial-era economy. This divide has parallels to the divide that industrialization likely brought to the world: the industrialized economy and the traditional agricultural and single-unit economy. Understanding trends in the digital economy is a must for any nation or firm that hopes to succeed in this new economic paradigm.

Though understanding the digital economy is critical, it has proven to be difficult to measure accurately and comprehensively. Many existing tools for measuring economic output are calibrated to industrial rather than digital activity—and there is as yet no uniformly accepted definition of the digital economy. For many, the digital economy equates to e-commerce or the start-up ecosystem. But it is much more.

The US Bureau for Economic Analysis (BEA) has highlighted the key components: infrastructure, e-commerce and digital services. Infrastructure, for example, includes hardware (e.g., semiconductors or IoT devices), software (e.g., operating systems) and building structures that house digital infrastructure (e.g., data centres). E-commerce includes Business-to-Business (B2B), Business-to-Consumer (B2C) and Peer-to-Peer (P2P) e-commerce of goods and services.

Finally, digital services currently consist of only priced digital services, as many digital services today are provided for free (e.g., Google searches). Digital services refer to a broad set of services such as cloud services (e.g., cloud hosting and storage of data), telecom services (e.g., telephony and cable TV), internet and data services (e.g., internet service providers), digital intermediary services (e.g., fees charged by digital platforms such as Netflix or food ordering platforms or even education platforms), among others.

The US is not alone in attempting to standardize the measurement and definition of the digital economy. There have been several attempts to define the digital economy by various countries and organizations. For example, the Organisation for Economic Co-operation and Development (OECD) has defined the digital economy as 'all economic activity reliant on, or significantly enhanced by the use of digital inputs, including digital technologies, digital infrastructure, digital services and data'.[38] The digital economy can have a tiered definition: core sectors of the digital economy being the ones that have the highest reliance on digital technologies, and the broad sectors the least reliance, with narrow being in the middle. Certain countries such as Canada, Australia and New Zealand have also produced estimates of their digital economies using a methodology similar to the US BEA and OECD.

The definition and measurement techniques employed by countries like China and the US also differ on what to include. China has often erred on the side of including more than less, to showcase a large digital economy.[39] The US BEA had been more circumspect earlier but is also now converging to a broad, instead of narrow, definition of the digital economy.[40] Many experts as well as international economic organizations such as OECD, IMF, World Bank and UNCTAD have acknowledged the challenge of standard definition and measurement.[41] For example, many of the digital products tend to be free and do not get measured even within the traditional construct of the GDP of a country.[42]

New concepts have also been put forth, given the concept of GDP is also fundamentally challenged by some as being imperfect to begin with. Erik Brynjolfsson and others have, for example, developed the concept of GDP-B. GDP-B is a new metric that takes into account the 'welfare contributions of the digital economy, characterized by the proliferation of new and free goods' that are currently not measurable in the national accounts of countries.[43]

For all of these reasons and more, reliable statistics are often lacking, not to mention that it is difficult to measure precisely the extent of digital technologies being used in certain activities.[44] The statisticians also need to distinguish between fully digitally delivered products and services and partially delivered ones. Another challenge, Jessica Nicholson of the US BEA informed me, lies in the measurement and accounting of the intangible assets being generated in the digital economy, such as data assets and cryptocurrencies. National accounts departments are currently debating whether and how to incorporate data in measures of capital formation or capital stock. This becomes especially critical in light of the emergence of new business models that rely on the accumulation of data and other such intangible assets through R&D and other activities.

Data definitely drives future benefit, but is not reflected on balance sheets. As the technology industry leader at global valuation firm Duff & Phelps, Glen Kernick, sums it up, 'the US GAAP accounting model, developed during the industrial age, is not equipped to evaluate technology companies and the digital economy'.[45]

Nicholson says, 'The biggest challenge is the rate of technological change relative to the speed with which official statistics can adapt to collect data on the digital economy.' The world has faced such definition and measurement challenges before. Various national and international organizations have in the past, and now must again, come together to find widely accepted methodologies. A standardized definition would help with more accurate global comparison and analysis of digital economies around the world. The sooner this is done across the world, the better.

As a result of such challenges and inconsistencies, estimates about the digital economy vary. Researchers estimated that in 2016, the digital economy, broadly defined, was worth $11.5 trillion globally, equivalent to 15.5 per cent of global GDP. With a narrower, core definition, the digital economy estimates are closer to 4.5 per cent of global GDP.[46] Regardless of the definition, there is broad consensus that it has grown almost two-and-a-half to three times faster than global GDP over the past fifteen years.[47] This pace will likely increase further in the coming years. The digital economy is estimated to double to $23 trillion by 2025, representing 25 per cent of global GDP in 2025.[48]

Understanding both the present and future trajectories of the digital economy—which will determine not only tech outcomes but, increasingly, the fates of other industries as well—is crucial. There is already great variation in the size and share of digital economies across nations and regions. Table 4.1 shows a cross-section of countries, comparing the size and growth rates of their digital economies. The US has the largest digital economy, followed by China. China's growth rates exceed those of the US and therefore a convergence is likely. India has a fast-growing digital economy, but obviously a smaller base. Taiwan, Ireland and Malaysia have the largest digital economies in the world if measured as a share of GDP.[49]

Table 4.1: Digital economies around the world, 2020

US$

Country	Size of digital economy		Average growth rate	
	Value	**As a percentage of GDP**	**Digital economy**	**GDP**
United States	$2 trillion[50]	9.6%[51]	6.5% (2005–2019)	-3.5% (1.5% average over 2005–2019)
China	$6 trillion[52] (broad definition) $1.1 trillion (narrow definition)	38.6%[53] (broad definition) 7%[54] (narrow definition)	9.7%[55]	2.3%[56]
UK	$206 billion[57] (GVA, 2018)	7.7%[58]	7.9%[59]	1.4%[60]
India	$413 billion[61] (2018)	7.5%[62]	n/a	-7.9%[63]

Source: Author's estimates, various sources

The digital economy is not growing in importance to nations simply because of its size. Rather, it has been a bright spot for many countries due to its rapid growth rate compared to the rest of the economy. The digital economy of the US grew at a 5.6 per cent average annual growth rate from 2006 to 2016, compared to just 1.5 per cent growth in the overall economy during that period. The US digital economy accounted for 6.5 per cent ($1.2 trillion) of current-dollar GDP ($18.6 trillion) in 2016, but by 2019, the digital economy had rapidly grown to 9.6 per cent of the economy. These differences became particularly pronounced during the COVID-pandemic-related economic changes.

The digital economy, if considered as a sector, is becoming amongst the largest sectors for most countries. For example, by 2016, the digital economy was already the US's seventh-largest, China's sixth-largest, India's eighth-largest and South Korea's fifth-largest sector.[64] By 2019, as Chart 4.5 shows, it had climbed up three spots to become the fourth-largest industry in the US, only behind real estate, government and manufacturing (data for other countries is not readily available). At this pace, it could become the largest sector in the US economy within the next few years.

Similarly, in China, the technology-driven new age economy has actually helped China's economy avoid a downturn in the last few years. As Ruchir Sharma, author of *Breakout Nations*, has pointed out, China's digital economy, led by its largely debt-free internet giants, has helped offset the decline faced in often debt-ridden older industries such as steel.[65]

Employment in the digital economy

The digital economy is also fast emerging as a significant employer across the world, though its share of total global employment is disproportionately low compared with its share of total global GDP. Estimates in 2015 showed that over 39 million people were employed in the digital economy—up from 34 million in 2010. This constitutes about 2 per cent of total global employment, whereas the digital economy constitutes at least 5 per cent of global GDP.

There is significant variation among countries. In the G-20 nations, the digital economy contributes anywhere from 1 per cent to over 5 per cent of total employment. Countries such as Saudi Arabia and Turkey, for example, are at the lower end of the spectrum (around 1 per cent employment in digital economy jobs), while countries such as South Korea, the UK, US and Japan are at the higher end of the spectrum.

Why is the digital economy's contribution to employment disproportionately low? The US example is instructive. Though

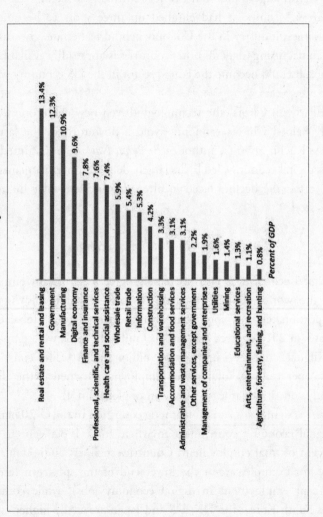

Chart 4.5 Digital Economy and Industry Share of Total Gross Domestic Product, 2019

Per cent of GDP

Industry	Percent of GDP
Real estate and rental and leasing	13.4%
Government	12.3%
Manufacturing	10.9%
Digital economy	9.6%
Finance and insurance	7.8%
Professional, scientific, and technical services	7.6%
Health care and social assistance	7.4%
Wholesale trade	5.9%
Retail trade	5.4%
Information	5.3%
Construction	4.2%
Transportation and warehousing	3.3%
Accommodation and food services	3.1%
Administrative and waste management services	3.1%
Other services, except government	2.2%
Management of companies and enterprises	1.9%
Utilities	1.6%
Mining	1.4%
Educational services	1.3%
Arts, entertainment, and recreation	1.1%
Agriculture, forestry, fishing, and hunting	0.8%

Source: 'Updated Digital Economy Estimates', US Bureau of Economic Analysis. https://www.bea.gov/system/files/2021-06/DE June 2021 update for web v3.pdf, accessed on 4 October, 2021.

Chart 4.6 Digital Economy and Industry Share of Total Employment, 2018

% Share of Total Employment

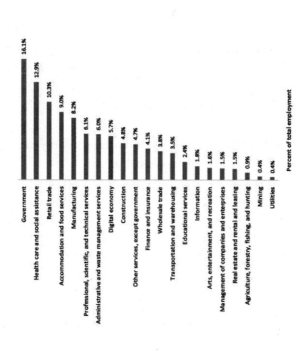

Source: Jessica Nicholson, 'New Digital Economy Estimates', US Bureau of Economic Analysis (August 2020), https://www. bea.gov/system/files/2020-08/New-Digital-Economy-Estimates-August-2020.pdf, accessed on 4 October 2021.

the digital economy was the seventh-largest sector, in terms of employment share, Chart 4.6 shows that the digital economy in the US was lagging as the eighth-largest employer in 2018. As per the US Bureau of Economic Analysis (BEA), by 2019, the digital economy was supporting 7.7 million jobs or roughly 5 per cent of the total employment in the US.

As Chart 4.7 shows, the answer lies partly in the fact that the average annual compensation of employees in the digital economy ($114,275) was almost twice as much as the average US worker ($66,498). This is not surprising, as the productivity of the average ICT worker also tends to be higher than the traditional economy worker. So you can expect a smaller share in employment, but a higher share of GDP for sectors that are more productive than the others.

Chart 4.7: Digital economy and total economy average compensation

US$

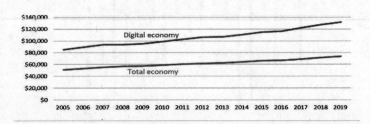

Source: 'Updated Digital Economy Estimates', US Bureau of Economic Analysis. https://www.bea.gov/system/files/2021-06/DE June 2021 update for web v3.pdf, accessed on 4 October 2021.

The Chinese tech companies have performed well on the job-creation front, though detailed data for it is not readily available. Estimates suggest that up to half of the job growth in China is coming from tech. As Ruchir Sharma points out, small enterprises selling on Alibaba have created over 30 million jobs in the last decade.[66] More studies are, however, needed to study what the nature of the new jobs are, the skills required to succeed at the new jobs, and the net employment effect of the technology sector in each country, a theme I return to in the last section of the book.

What drives the digital economy?

Once the components of the digital economy are clear, the drivers also become evident. Nations must consider elements that act as the drivers of the key elements: digital infrastructure (hardware and software), digital and cloud services, and digital trade and e-commerce. As Chart 4.8 shows in the case of the US, priced digital services (including ad services provided by Big Tech firms, for example) constitutes almost half of the US digital economy, but B2B e-commerce is now growing twice as fast as the priced digital services (Chart 4.9). Tracking the share and growth rates of each in the digital economy is the starting point. It can help countries understand their relative strengths and weaknesses, and identify areas that it needs to focus on.

Chart 4.8 Component Share of the Digital Economy, Current-Dollar Value Added, 2018

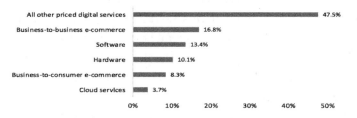

Source: Jessica Nicholson, 'New Digital Economy Estimates', US Bureau of Economic Analysis (August 2020), https://www.bea.gov/system/files/2020-08/New-Digital-Economy-Estimates-August-2020.pdf, accessed on 4 October, 2021.

Chart 4.9 Components of the Digital Economy: Real Value-Added Average Annual Growth, 2006-18

Annual Growth Rate, % Change

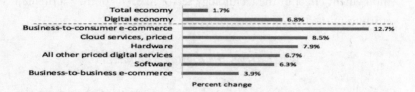

Source: Jessica Nicholson, 'New Digital Economy Estimates', US Bureau of Economic Analysis (August 2020), https://www.bea.gov/system/files/2020-08/New-Digital-Economy-Estimates-August-2020.pdf, accessed on 4 October, 2021.

For most countries, however, access remains the most fundamental driver. A World Bank study has concluded that 'access to broadband internet is as clear a booster of economic development as anything'. As per the World Bank estimates, an increase in fixed broadband penetration of 10 percentage points results in a 1.35 per cent increase in per capita GDP for developing countries and a 1.19 per cent increase for developed countries.[67]

Further, investments in technology or the digital economy can yield significantly better results from a GDP growth perspective. Another report on the digital economy has found that, over the past thirty years, every US $1 investment in digital technologies has led to an average US $20 increase in GDP, compared to a US $3 return per US $1 of non-digital technology investments over the same period.[68]

Every policymaker around the world should take note of these two metrics:

i. For every 10-percentage-point increase in internet access penetration, countries can see a 1.2–1.35 per cent increase in per capita GDP.

ii. A US $1 investment in technology or digital investments could yield up to seven times higher return than the same investment in the traditional economy.

Investment in various aspects of technology (from infrastructure to services) to drive growth of the digital economy is becoming a core strategy for some countries, especially those who wish to substantially increase their productivity and innovation levels. The choice of which levers to prioritize will often be country-specific depending on the existing sectoral strengths, comparative strengths, and endowments of other factors of production in the country.

For example, a World Bank report concluded that China could achieve a high-income country status through a strategy of high levels of investment driving rapid advancements in technology, comparable to the efforts made by Japan and Korea in the twentieth century. The productivity gains from such technology advancement, adoption and adaptation could become a significant source of economic growth and comparative advantage in China.[69]

Even as countries like China play technological catch-up, innovations combining different existing technologies or tailoring existing technologies for specific markets could serve as the stepping stone for original innovations. As the World Bank report concludes, China does not even need to deliver original and large technological breakthroughs to achieve economic growth, but instead can continue to be a 'successful second-generation innovator' since the range of innovation potential with existing technologies itself is quite large.[70]

Many economists, having done growth accounting studies for China, have concluded that in the past, capital has played a leading role, followed by technology. But this will likely reverse, with technology playing the leading role and capital the supporting one. This view is reflected in the industrial strategy plans of China (such as China 2025 and China 2035), where technological leadership is portrayed as the key lever for achieving global economic leadership.

This lesson could similarly apply to other large economies that are relative tech laggards, such as India, Indonesia, Vietnam and others. Yet, as the World Economic Forum (WEF) Global Competitiveness Report 2018 argued, technology cannot be seen as the cure-all for driving greater productivity, economic competitiveness and growth.[71] Many academics have highlighted the foundations and constraints for economic growth and competitiveness, such as the lack of proper institutions, regulations and rule of law. These pillars need to be built for the success of the digital economy as well.

~

Ultimately, understanding the new structure and drivers of the digital economy—and ensuring that there is a widespread understanding of it—will be the foundational step for success in the economic aspects of the Great Tech Game. What hopefully has also come across is that the structural changes are fundamental—whether it be the evolution of new global digital value chains and ecosystems or the power of the duopoly of technology and capital, or the growing importance of intangible assets.

Secondly, we must measure what matters. One of the books that has greatly influenced me has been *Measure What Matters: OKRs,* by legendary venture capitalist John Doerr (and backer of firms such as Google and Amazon). In it, Doerr has made an emphatic appeal to managers to embrace OKRs (Objectives and Key Results) as a process to 'guide you to the mountain top'.[72] Essentially, my fundamental argument in this section—to measure the digital economy as a way to understand it and hopefully grow it—echoes his appeal. To me, it is a sign that only certain countries are systematically measuring the digital economy. They are likely to also, as a result, be able to focus on the most important drivers for growth of the digital economy.

The Phenomenon of Big Tech firms

One cannot understand the digital economy fully without understanding the phenomenon of Big Tech firms. The last telecommunications revolution, using electricity and the telegraph, created the likes of GE, AT&T and Reuters. These companies spawned multi-billion-dollar industries around them and their leadership lasted for several decades. Today, the Facebooks and Googles of the world are the new GEs and AT&Ts.

Big Tech firms have become quite large, by any metric. A peek into America's top companies over the last 100 years provides an interesting perspective (see chart 4.10). The tech sector has climbed up steadily from being completely absent in 1917 to the second largest sector in 1967. By 2017, however, the market cap of technology companies is almost three times that of the financial services and healthcare companies.

Just in the last decade, technology companies have more than tripled their share of the world's top twenty companies by market cap (see chart 4.11). The five largest tech stocks constitute a quarter of the value of the Standard & Poor's index (or S&P) in the US. The market capitalizations (or market caps) of these five tech firms exceed the economy of France.[73] Companies like Apple, with their high market caps, command a large share of indices such as the Dow Jones Industrial Average (DJIA) that any unexpected variations in their earnings or results can significantly move the entire index. Until a few decades ago, such impact would be attributed to large industrial-era corporations such as GM or the oil and gas companies.[74]

Chart 4.10: America's top companies, 1917, 1967 and 2017

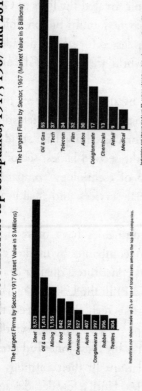

The Largest Firms by Sector, 1917 (Asset Value in $ Millions)

Sector	Value
Steel	3,573
Oil & Gas	1,418
Mining	1,155
Food	842
Telecom	762
Chemicals	527
Autos	407
Conglomerate	397
Rubber	396
Textiles	304

Industries not shown made up 2% or less of total assets among the top 50 companies.

The Largest Firms by Sector, 1967 (Market Value in $ Billions)

Sector	Value
Oil & Gas	55
Tech	37
Telecom	34
Film	32
Autos	30
Conglomerate	17
Chemicals	13
Retail	9
Medical	8

Industries not shown made up 2% or less of total market value among the top 50 companies.

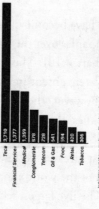

The Largest Firms by Sector, 2017 (Market Value in $ Billions)

Sector	Value
Tech	3,710
Financial Services	1,377
Medical	1,359
Conglomerate	978
Telecom	728
Oil & Gas	541
Food	994
Retail	420
Tobacco	306

Industries not shown made up 2% or less of total market value among the top 50 companies. Market values are as of July 31, 2017.

Source: Jeff Kauflin, 'America's Top 50 Companies 1917-2017', *Forbes* (September 2017). https://www.forbes.com/sites/jeffkauflin/2017/09/19/americas-top-50-companies-1917-2017/?sh=6bb829751629, accessed on 1 October 2021.

Chart 4.11: World's top 20 companies by market cap, by sector, 2009 vs 2018

Per cent, %

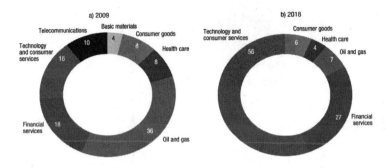

Source: UNCTAD, Digital Economy Report 2019, https://unctad.org/system/files/official-document/der2019_overview_en.pdf, accessed on 1 October 2021.

Examining the market capitalization of the top ten global corporate giants now, we find that most of the positions globally are taken up by Big Tech firms, including two of China's, Alibaba and Tencent.[75] The US and Asia (mostly China) account for over 90 per cent of the market capitalization value of the world's seventy largest digital platforms, while Europe's share is 4 per cent and Africa and Latin America have a combined share of 1 per cent (See chart 4.12). Evaluated by market value, out of the seventy largest digital platforms, seven super platforms—Microsoft, Apple, Amazon, Google, Facebook, Tencent and Alibaba—account for almost two-thirds of the total market value.[76]

In fact, the number of unicorns by country shows a similarly heavy-at-the-top picture, with the US (396) and China (277) leaving behind the rest by a big margin (see chart 4.13). India (51), UK (32) and Germany (18) make up the remaining positions in the top five. The pace of start-ups becoming unicorns has picked up: just in 2021, India

Chart 4.12: Geographical distribution of the main global platforms of the world, 2018

Market capitalization in billions of dollars

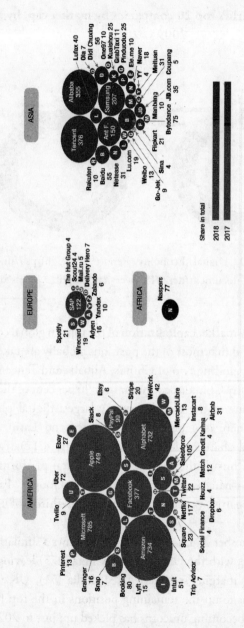

Source: UNCTAD, Digital Economy Report 2019, https://unctad.org/system/files/official-document/der2019_overview_en.pdf, accessed on 1 October 2021.

added three unicorns each month, driven by greater adoption of digital platforms by consumers and favourable capital inflow conditions.

Chart 4.13: Top 5 Countries, by number of unicorns, September 2021

	USA	China	India	UK	Germany
No. of Unicorns	396	277	51	32	18
Avg. Years to Unicorn	7	6	7.3	6.5	6
Avg. Valuation (US$ bn)	3.1	4.7	3.3	2.7	2.5
No. of Unicorn added	217	98	31	14	10

Source: Hurun India Future Unicorn List 2021, https://www.hurunindia.net/hurun-india-future-unicorn-list-2021, accessed on 4 October 2021.

Big Tech firms have become systematically crucial in financial systems. Of the $1 trillion in off-shore savings held by US corporates, 80 per cent are controlled by the largest 10 per cent of firms, including Big Tech giants such as Apple, Microsoft, Cisco, Oracle and Alphabet. The investment portfolios of the Big Tech firms are bigger than the bond or credit portfolios of the largest US banks. For example, Microsoft's portfolio of US treasuries is twice the size of the Bank of America's or JP Morgan's. Similarly, Google and CISCO both hold more US treasuries than the Bank of New York. The result is that the top ten have become some of America's largest debt collectors along with foreign governments and central banks. It is clear that Big Tech firms, not the big banks, have become the 'new too-big-to-fail industry'.[77]

However, the emphasis on unicorns is often misplaced. As University of California, San Diego economist Prof. Karthik Muralidharan explained to me, not all countries will need to aim for unicorns (or, for that matter, decacorns, or companies valued at over $10 billion). Focusing too much on country-wide distribution of unicorns leads to presumptions that, one, building unicorns should be the objective of start-up ecosystems, and, two, that the country's digital economy is doing well if it can boast the presence of unicorns. Both presumptions, as you might guess, could be mistaken.

Questions have also been raised about whether this list of top technology giants will sustain. History suggests that, especially in the technology sector, leaders continue to be disrupted by challengers, and that as technology evolves, new companies will constantly rise to the top. Proponents of this view point out that the only company in this list that is three decades old is Microsoft. Looking at historical data and trends, chief global strategist at Morgan Stanley Investment Management, Ruchir Sharma, has concluded that today's top performers are equally unlikely to stay there.[78]

But the past is not always the best predictor of the future. The question is whether the nature of the technology today is structurally different than the past? If the structures today are inherently more winner-take-all, then are today's winners likely to remain winners for much longer, as industrial era winners used to? Success in today's technologies breeds further success. These new tech giants could, therefore, likely rule the roost for several decades because of network effects. The barriers to entry for new players in the oil, steel or sugar industries used to high upfront capital expenditure or exclusive access to raw materials. Today, technology know-how, data, large locked-in customer bases, and access to incredible amounts of capital serve as moats for the Big Tech firms to defend their economic positions. Regulation, as we will see in later chapters, could be the critical determining piece here.

Is the wealth of Big Tech translating into the wealth of nations?

In the industrial era, the interests of large firms and their home nations were often aligned—successful firms drove local economic growth, and friendly governments worked to create positive business environments.

In the Great Tech Game, it is an open question whether the same arrangements will prevail—whether, in particular, the astonishing success of the leading tech firms will create wealth and power for their nations, or simply for the firms themselves. To examine this issue, we can look at a few different aspects: is Big Tech contributing to GDP enhancement, government's taxation receipts, shareholder wealth and returns, employment and investment in the country.

Big Tech firms undoubtedly increase the GDP of the country that hosts their economic activity. But the bigger question is whether the success of Big Tech firms is actually translating into the wealth of nations. Are the nations that host these Big Tech firms benefiting economically, and if so, to what extent? That largely depends on how many supporting firms—that is, firms that provide core goods and services to them—benefit from these Big Tech firms' presence.

Big Tech firms—much like hosting large factories—has a multiplier effect on the domestic economy, as economist Enrico Moretti and others have found. Apple, for example, Moretti found, employs 13,000 people directly in Cupertino, but indirectly led to the spurring of 70,000 non-tech jobs in the region. These jobs were both skilled (lawyers, teachers, nurses) and unskilled ones (waiters and carpenters).[79] Real estate prices go up in areas with large offices of Big Tech firms. Deloitte has estimated that the revenue multiplier effect of tech firms ranges from 4x (for biotech and software companies) to 8x (for social networks, marketplaces and other network orchestrators). The equivalent revenue multipliers for traditional industries such as industrials, hospitals or even financial services is between 1x to 2x.[80]

But Moretti's research also found evidence that a 'Great Divergence' is emerging between innovation hubs such as San Francisco, Seattle, Boston and Austin that are 'poised to become the new engines of prosperity'—and other 'technologically sluggish cities'. [81] Moreover, unlike industrial corporates that created a high level of employment in the US, technology firms like Apple or Netflix do not. For example, despite their high share of total market capitalizations, only one of the

Big Tech firm—Amazon—makes it to the top fifty largest companies globally based on number of employees in 2019.[82] Only one.

Big Tech firms have used loopholes to avoid paying taxes in the US, China, Europe and elsewhere, often helped by their intangible assets and the fact that taxmen do not yet fully understand their business models and ways of value creation. The Big Tech firms have also set up their regional headquarters in low-tax jurisdictions such as Ireland. According to a report, the 'Silicon Six'—Amazon, Apple, Facebook, Google, Microsoft and Netflix—have paid over $100 billion less in taxes across all global territories than what the actual tax rates would suggest.[83]

The developing countries that are home to these firms have been even worse off than countries like the US. Developing countries have often not been able to tax global platforms such as Facebook and Google, as their revenues have traditionally not been reported in the jurisdictions from where they have been earned. As chart 4.14 shows, Facebook earned 56 per cent of its revenues and 66 per cent of its profit outside the US but paid 92 per cent of its taxes in the US and the remaining 8 per cent primarily in other developed nations.

Chart 4.14: Facebook and Alphabet (Google) revenues, profits and taxes, 2017

$ million and per cent

Facebook	Foreign	United States	Total	Foreign share (per cent)	United States share (per cent)
Revenue ($ million)	22 919	17 734	40 653	56	44
Profits ($ million)	13 515	7 079	20 594	66	34
Share of revenue (per cent)	59	40	51		
Taxes (current) ($ million)	389	4 645	5 034	8	92
Share of profits (per cent)	2.9	65.6	24.4		
Alphabet (Google)					
Revenue ($ million)	58 406	52 449	110 855	53	47
Profits ($ million)	16 500	10 700	27 193	61	39
Share of revenue (per cent)	28.2	20.4	24.5		
Taxes (current) ($ million)	1 746	12 608	14 354	12	88
Share of profits (per cent)	10.1	>100	53.8		

Source: UNCTAD, Digital Economy Report 2019, https://unctad.org/system/files/official-document/der2019_overview_en.pdf, accessed on 1 October 2021.

In India, for example, the top tech companies currently pay taxes only on 8–10 per cent of their total revenue in India, and not their entire income, as they claim to not have a permanent establishment in India. India's new IT rules, which require these firms to have nodal officers physically located in India, might lead to substantially higher tax bills for the Big Tech firms.[84] Globally, similar efforts to tax Big Tech firms in the countries where the revenues are actually being generated are underway.

For now, lower taxes paid in certain jurisdictions means higher retained earnings elsewhere, which implies higher share values and increased shareholder wealth for the company's investors. The top shareholders of these firms tend to be large investment firms and the founders of the firms. As of June 2021, almost 80 per cent of Facebook's shareholding, for example, was with institutional investors, and the top five shareholders in Facebook were Mark Zuckerberg (~400 million shares), Vanguard Group (~172 million), Fidelity Management and Research (~119 million), T. Rowe Price (~105 million), and BlackRock (~103 million).[85]

The various large institutional shareholders of the stock of these companies have definitely witnessed wealth creation. But have others, including retail investors? The latest data from the Federal Reserve suggests that only 14 per cent of American families are directly invested in individual stocks. Indirectly through retirement accounts, about 52 per cent of the population has some investments in stocks. That is also highly lopsided, with 90 per cent of families in the top income tiers, but only a third of the families in the low-income tiers, having stock ownership.[86] The question then becomes, how will non-shareholder Americans—especially those in the lower-income tiers—benefit, if at all, from the success of Big Tech firms?

Big Tech firms are not the first companies to adopt such off-shoring and low-tax jurisdiction strategies. Many analysts believe that the US citizens and taxpayers are not receiving their fair share of returns from the Big Tech firms, despite the fact that the success of the internet industry is in no small measure attributable to the government's funding of research efforts in technology in Silicon Valley many decades ago.

Yet, the same Big Tech companies—usually only considered 'off-shore hoarders'—are also the largest spenders and investors. In the US, for example, they account for 31 per cent of the investment of the S&P 500 companies today, and a disproportionately high portion (47 per cent) of the absolute rise in those investment levels. Just ten years ago, the biggest investors were old-economy incumbents like AT&T, Chevron, ExxonMobil, General Electric and Verizon.[87]

The tech companies re-invest over 50 per cent of their gross cash flow, with half of this amount going into plant, property and equipment, that is, hard physical assets such as data centres, e-commerce fulfilment centres, redevelopment of real estate, and building cloud computing capacity. Furthermore, if one was to capture venture capital activity, off-balance sheet capital investments, and expenditure and expense items such as content IP, estimates suggest that 20 per cent of the absolute business investment in the US economy is being done by tech companies, and 83 per cent of the growth is attributable to tech companies.[88]

Overall, after considering contribution to GDP, taxation, shareholder returns, employment and investment, Big Tech firms contribute substantially to their home economies and their shareholders, but less so directly to governments and the average taxpayer. The benefits also accrue least to those in the lower economic income tier of the host nations. Further, the non-host nations experience significantly less economic benefits than the host nations. Not surprisingly, many nations, including most visibly, China, the US and Europe, are rethinking the role that Big Tech firms can—and should—play in broad-based economic development, and the values and principles that should guide this.

Key Conclusions

Today, in the age of technology, connectivity to global data flows, access to data surpluses, rapid adoption and penetration of new technologies, and innovation capabilities are the key drivers of the new 'virtuous cycle of technology'. Entering and staying in that virtuous cycle is today critical in shaping the economic wealth of nations.

Many countries are not grasping the gravity of the change underway as we transition from an industrial economy to a digital economy. As an UNCTAD report concluded, developing countries can ill-afford missing this new wave of technological change. [89] Promoting the use, adoption and adaptation of these technologies is a pre-requisite for success in the twenty-first century'.[90]

Yet, it is not sufficient. Harnessing the power of the new tech revolution will require countries to understand the structure and concepts underlying the new digital economy. I have presented a few different frameworks and concepts to understand the digital economy more rigorously and systematically. Breaking down the digital economy into its constituent elements—tech manufacturing, digital infrastructure, digital services and digital trade and commerce—allows countries to think about the drivers for each, and its strengths and weaknesses in each.

The concept of global digital value chains or ecosystems provides another way to look at the digital economy. As new ecosystems and new data value chains emerge, countries must think about what parts of that ecosystem they can play in. Not all countries can expect to build hundreds of unicorns or Big Tech firms such as Apple and Google, but there exist several other alternative strategies to compete in the digital economy. As old industrial-era supply or value chains get replaced by digital value chains and ecosystems, countries will need to identify strategies to become part of these new emerging global digital value chains (GDVCs) or ecosystems. This, in essence, is the theme of our next chapter.

Notes

1. Daniel Susskind, *A World without Work* (Penguin Books Ltd, 2020), Kindle.

2. 'Digital Globalization: The New Era of Global Flows', McKinsey Global Institute (March 2016), https://www.mckinsey.com/~/media/McKinsey/Business Functions/McKinsey Digital/Our Insights/Digital globalization The new era of global flows/MGI-Digital-globalization-Full-report.ashx, accessed on 1 October 2021.

3. UNCTAD, Digital Economy Report 2019, https://unctad.org/system/files/official-document/der2019_overview_en.pdf, accessed on 1 October 2021.

4. UNCTAD, Digital Economy Report 2021, https://unctad.org/system/files/official-document/der2021_overview_en_0.pdf, accessed on 1 October 2021.

5. UNCTAD, Digital Economy Report 2019.

6. Ibid.

7. Ibid.

8. Ibid.

9. 'Final Study Report The European Data Market Monitoring Tool Key Facts & Figures, First Policy Conclusions, Data Landscape And Quantified Stories', European Commission, D2.9 (June 2020), https://digital-strategy.ec.europa.eu/en/library/european-data-market-study-update, accessed on 1 October 2021.

10. 'Fifth-Generation (5G) Telecommunications Technologies: Issues for Congress', Congressional Research Services CRS Report No. R45485 (January 2019), https://fas.org/sgp/crs/misc/R45485.pdf, accessed on 1 October 2021.

11. 'National Strategy to Secure 5G Implementation Plan', US Department of Commerce (January 2021), https://www.ntia.gov/files/ntia/publications/2021-1-12_115445_national_strategy_to_secure_5g_implementation_plan_and_annexes_a_f_final.pdf, accessed on 1 October 2021.

12. 'Fifth-Generation (5G) Telecommunications Technologies', CRS Report.

13. Ibid.

14. Peter H. Diamandis and Steven Kotler, *The Future Is Faster Than You Think: How Converging Technologies Are Transforming Business, Industries, and Our Lives*, Exponential Technology Series (Simon & Schuster, 2020), Kindle.

15. Ibid.

16. Ibid.

17. Ibid.

18. National Academies of Sciences, Engineering, and Medicine, 'Information Technology and the US Workforce: Where Are We and Where Do We Go from Here?' (Washington, DC: The National Academies Press, 2017), https://doi.org/10.17226/24649, accessed on 1 October 2021.

19. Enrique Martínez-García, 'Technological Progress Is Key to Improving World Living Standards', Federal Reserve Bank of Dallas 8, no. 4 (June 2013), https://www.dallasfed.org/research/eclett/2013/el1304.cfm, accessed on 1 October 2021.

20. In fact, the rate of growth of capital (physical and human) and technical progress have been found to account for a significant proportion of economic growth by a long line of distinguished economists: Abramovitz (1956), Denison (1962 a, b; 1967), Griliches and Jorgenson, Kendrick (1961, 1973), Kuznets (1965, 1966, 1971, 1973) and Solow (1957), to name only a few.

21. Michael J. Boskin and Lawrence J. Lau, 'Capital Formation and Economic Growth', *Technology and Economics*, National Academy of Engineering (Washington, DC: The National Academies Press, 1991), https://www.nap.edu/read/1767/chapter/4, accessed on 4 October 2021.

22. Ibid.

23. Isaac Ehrlich and Yun Pei, 'Human Capital as Engine of Growth: The Role of Knowledge Transfers in Promoting Balanced Growth within

and across Countries', *Asian Development Review* 37, no. 2, (September 2020), https://direct.mit.edu/adev/article/37/2/225/93307/Human-Capital-as-Engine-of-Growth-The-Role-of, accessed on 1 October 2021.

24. Charles I. Jones, 'Paul Romer: Ideas, Nonrivalry, and Endogenous Growth', *The Scandinavian Journal of Economics* 121, no.3 (2019): 859–883, https://web.stanford.edu/~chadj/RomerNobel.pdf, accessed on 1 October 2021.

25. Erik Brynjolfsson and Andrew McAfee, *The Second Machine Age: Work, Progress, and Prosperity in a Time of Brilliant Technologies* (W.W. Norton & Company, 2014), Kindle.

26. Ibid.

27. Satya Nadella, Interview with Kara Swisher at Code 2021, October 2021, https://www.youtube.com/watch?v=-Osca2Zax4Y, accessed on 4 October 2021.

28. Robert U. Ayres, 'Technology: The Wealth of Nations', *Technological Forecasting and Social Change* 33, no. 3 (1988): 189–201, ISSN 0040-1625, https://doi.org/10.1016/0040-1625(88)90013-3.

29. Professor Dr. Klaus Schwab, *The Fourth Industrial Revolution* (Penguin Books Ltd., 2017), Kindle.

30. Nathan Rosenberg, Ralph Landau and David C. Mowery, *Technology and the Wealth of Nations* (Stanford University Press, 1992).

31. Diego Comin and Bart Hobijn, 'Cross-Country Technology Adoption: Making the Theories Face the Facts', Federal Reserve Bank of New York Staff Reports, no. 169 (June 2003), https://www.econstor.eu/bitstream/10419/60558/1/368504972.pdf, accessed on 1 October 2021.

32. Schwab, *The Fourth Industrial Revolution*.

33. Diego Comin, 'Technology Adoption and Growth Dynamics' (2014), https://www.semanticscholar.org/paper/Technology-Adoption-and-Growth-Dynamics-Comin/1f76728473ee4fb154fe1655a4645c4b4 3b29358#citing-papers, accessed on 1 October 2021.

34. Diego Comin, 'The Evolution of Technology Diffusion and The Great Divergence', Brookings (August 2016), https://www.brookings.edu/wp-content/uploads/2016/08/session-3-leapfrogging-comin_post-final.pdf, accessed on 1 October 2021.

35. Karishma Banga, 'Digital technologies and 'value' capture in global value chains', United Nations University WIDER Working Paper 2019/43 (2019), https://www.wider.unu.edu/sites/default/files/Publications/Working-paper/PDF/wp-2019-43.pdf, accessed on 1 October 2021.

36. UNCTAD, Digital Economy Report 2019. https://unctad.org/system/files/official-document/der2019_overview_en.pdf, accessed on 1 October 2021.

37. Alyssa Danigelis, 'General Motors Delves Deep Into Its Value Chain: Q&A with David Tulauskas', *Environment Leader* (June 2018), https://www.environmentalleader.com/2018/06/general-motors-value-chain-qa/, accessed on 29 September 2021.

38. OECD, 'Going Digital: Measurements', https://www.oecd.org/going-digital/topics/measurement/, accessed on 1 October 2021.

39. Longmei Zhang and Sally Chen, 'China's Digital Economy: Opportunities and Risks', VoxChina (August 2019), http://voxchina.org/show-52-139.html, accessed on 4 October 2021.

40. 'Digital Economy', US Bureau of Economic Analysis, https://www.bea.gov/data/special-topics/digital-economy, accessed on 4 October 2021.

41. 'Trends in the Information Technology Sector', Brookings Report (March 2019), https://www.brookings.edu/research/trends-in-the-information-technology-sector/, accessed on 4 October 2021.

42. Maëlle Gavet, *Trampled by Unicorns* (Wiley, 2020), Kindle.

43. Erik Brynjolfsson, et al., 'GDP-B: Accounting for the Value of New and Free Goods in the Digital Economy', working paper, National Bureau of Economic Research (March 2019), https://www.nber.org/system/files/working_papers/w25695/w25695.pdf, accessed on 1 October 2021.

44. UNCTAD, Digital Economy Report 2019.

45. Sherree DeCovny, 'Assessing Value in the Digital Economy', CFA Institute Blog (April 2018), https://blogs.cfainstitute.org/ investor/2018/04/18/assessing-value-in-the-digital-economy/, accessed on 4 October 2021.

46. UNCTAD, Digital Economy Report 2019.

47. Huawei and Oxford Economics, *Digital Spillover: Measuring the True Impact of the Digital Economy* (2017), https://www.huawei. com/minisite/gci/en/digital-spillover/files/gci_digital_spillover.pdf, accessed on 1 October 2021.

48. Inter-American Development Bank, *Exponential Disruption in the Digital Economy* (2018), https://publications.iadb.org/publications/ english/document/Exponential-Disruption-in-the-Digital-Economy. pdf, accessed on 1 October 2021.

49. UNCTAD, Digital Economy Report 2019.

50. US Bureau of Economic Analysis (June 2021), https://www.bea.gov/ data/special-topics/digital-economy, accessed on 1 October 2021.

51. Ibid.

52. 'China's Digital Economy Sees Robust Growth amid Pandemic', China. org.cn (April 2021), http://www.china.org.cn/business/2021-04/27/ content_77444263.htm, accessed on 1 October 2021.

53. Ibid.

54. Longmei Zhang and Sally Chen, 'China's Digital Economy: Opportunities and Risks', IMF Working Paper No. WP/19/16 (January 2019), https://www.imf.org/~/media/Files/Publications/ WP/2019/wp1916.ashx, accessed on 1 October 2021.

55. 'China's Digital Economy', China.org.cn.

56. Jonathan Cheng, 'China Is the Only Major Economy to Report Economic Growth for 2020', *Wall Street Journal* (January 2021), https://www.wsj.com/articles/china-is-the-only-major-economy- to-report-economic-growth-for-2020-11610936187, accessed on 1 October 2021.

57. UK Department for Digital, Culture, Media and Sport, *DCMS Sectors Economic Estimates 2018 (Provisional): Gross Value Added, (2018)*, https://assets.publishing.service.gov.uk/government/uploads/system/ uploads/attachment_data/file/959053/DCMS_Sectors_Economic_ Estimates_GVA_2018_V2.pdf, accessed on 1 October 2021.

58. Ibid.

59. Ibid.

60. Ibid.

61. Bhaskar Chakravorti, 'Competing in the Huge Digital Economies of China and India', *Harvard Business Review* (November 2018), https://hbr.org/2018/11/competing-in-the-huge-digital-economies- of-china-and-india, accessed on 1 October 2021.

62. 'Government Working to Increase Digital economy's Contribution to 20% of GDP in 5 Years', *The Times of India* (September 2020), https://timesofindia.indiatimes.com/business/india-business/ government-working-to-increase-digital-economys-contribution- to-20-of-gdp-in-5-years/articleshow/78133670.cms, accessed on 1 October 2021.

63. 'GDP Growth of India', *Statistics Times* (June 2021), https:// statisticstimes.com/economy/country/india-gdp-growth.php, accessed on 1 October 2021.

64. *The Internet Economy in the G-20*, Boston Consulting Group (2012), https://image-src.bcg.com/Images/The_Internet_Economy_G-20_ tcm9-106842.pdf, accessed on 1 October 2021.

65. Ruchir Sharma, 'How Technology Saved China's Economy', *The Economic Times* (January 2020), https://economictimes.indiatimes. com/news/international/business/how-technology-saved-chinas- economy/articleshow/73542691.cms, accessed on 1 October 2021.

66. Ruchir Sharma, 'How Technology Saved China's Economy', *The New York Times* (January 2020), https://www.nytimes.com/2020/01/20/ opinion/china-technology-economy.html, accessed on 1 October 2021.

67. Maëlle Gavet, *Trampled by Unicorns* (Wiley, 2020), Kindle.

68. Huawei and Oxford Economics, *Digital Spillover*.

69. *China's Growth through Technological Convergence and Innovation*, World Bank, https://www.worldbank.org/content/dam/Worldbank/document/SR2--161-228.pdf, accessed on 1 October 2021.

70. Dan Breznitz and Michael Murphree, *Run of the Red Queen: Government, Innovation, Globalization and Economic Growth in China* (Yale University Press, 2011).

71. Klaus Schwab, 'The Global Competitiveness Report 2018', World Economic Forum (2018), https://www3.weforum.org/docs/GCR2018/05FullReport/TheGlobalCompetitivenessReport2018.pdf, accessed on 1 October 2021.

72. John Doerr, *Measure What Matters: How Google, Bono, and the Gates Foundation Rock the World with OKRs* (Portfolio, 2018), Kindle.

73. Rana Foroohar, *Don't Be Evil*, (Penguin Books Ltd, 2019), Kindle.

74. Marco Antonio Cavallo, 'The Growing Importance of the Technology Economy', *CIO* (December 2016), https://www.cio.com/article/3152568/the-growing-importance-of-the-technology-economy.html, accessed on 1 October 2021.

75. 'New Kind of Conglomerate: Bigtech in China', International Institute of Finance (November 2018), https://www.iif.com/Portals/0/Files/chinese_digital_nov_1.pdf, accessed on 1 October 2021.

76. UNCTAD, Digital Economy Report 2019.

77. Zoltan Pozsar, 'Global Money Notes #11: Repatriation, the Echo-Taper and the €/$ Basis', Credit Suisse Global Strategy (January 2018), https://research-doc.credit-suisse.com/docView?language=ENG&format=PDF&sourceid=emcsplus&document_id=1080159501&serialid=aTLhvGKTNzOcCGepV3GdfaqUCIwiKgNs7b1cnj30b%2B0%3D, accessed on 1 October 2021.

78. Ruchir Sharma, 'How the US Tech Giants Could Fall', *Financial Times* (August 2021), https://www.ft.com/content/40ca92da-d3ef-47bb-b421-7d446d67bc52, accessed on 1 October 2021.

79. Enrico Moretti, 'The Multiplier Effect of Innovation Jobs', *MIT Sloan Management Review* (2012), https://sloanreview.mit.edu/article/the-multiplier-effect-of-innovation-jobs/, accessed on 1 October 2021.

80. Omar Hoda, Joseph Vitale, Jr, and Craig A. Giffi, 'The Revenue Multiplier Effect', *Deloitte Insights* (2018), https://www2.deloitte.com/content/dam/Deloitte/us/Documents/manufacturing/us-mfg-the-revenue-multiplier-effect.pdf, accessed on 4 October 2021.

81. Enrico Moretti, 'The Multiplier Effect of Innovation Jobs', *MIT Sloan Management Review* (2012), https://sloanreview.mit.edu/article/the-multiplier-effect-of-innovation-jobs/, accessed on 1 October 2021.

82. 'Leading 500 Fortune Companies Based on Number of Employees in 2019', Statista, https://www.statista.com/statistics/264671/top-50-companies-based-on-number-of-employees/, accessed on 1 October 2021.

83. Erik Sherman, 'A New Report Claims Big Tech Companies Used Legal Loopholes to Avoid Over $100 Billion in Taxes. What Does That Mean for the Industry's Future?', *Fortune* (December 2019), https://fortune.com/2019/12/06/big-tech-taxes-google-facebook-amazon-apple-netflix-microsoft/, accessed on 1 October 2021.

84. 'Taxing Times for Big Tech', ET Tech Morning Dispatch (June 2021), https://m.economictimes.com/tech/newsletters/morning-dispatch/taxing-times-for-big-tech/articleshow/83704494.cms, accessed on 4 October 2021.

85. CNN Business (30 June 2021), https://money.cnn.com/quote/shareholders/shareholders.html?symb=FB&subView=institutional, accessed on 30 June 2021.

86. Teresa Ghilarducci, 'Most Americans Don't Have a Real Stake in the Stock Market', *Forbes* (August 2020), https://www.forbes.com/sites/teresaghilarducci/2020/08/31/most-americans-dont-have-a-real-stake-in-the-stock-market/?sh=3f172ed01154, accessed on 4 October 2021.

87. James Pethokoukis, 'The Growing Investment Impact of Big Tech on the US Economy', AEI Blog (May 2018), https://www.aei.org/

economics/the-growing-investment-impact-of-big-tech-on-the-us-economy/, accessed on 1 October 2021.

88. Ibid.

89. UNCTAD, Technology and Innovation Report 2021, https://unctad.org/system/files/official-document/tir2020_en.pdf, accessed on 1 October 2021.

90. Ibid.

5

New Winners and Losers

'Economic leadership among nations is clearly a mantle that passes from place to place over time. The last thousand years have seen global primacy pass from China to the Italian city-states, to Portugal and Spain, to the Low Countries [the Netherlands], to Britain, and then to the United States. Which will be next in the van?'[1]

—David Landes, *The Wealth and Poverty of Nations*

During the nineteenth century, the economic competition amongst the newly industrialized nations led to an explosion of economic growth. Led by Britain, nations competed to build factories, maximize the output of coal, iron, steel and textiles, develop extensive railway and telegraph networks, secure the cheapest raw materials, and build larger industrial towns and cities. At each stage, crucially, these competitors sought to take full advantage of emerging technologies in each phase of industrialization. Rapid and enthusiastic embrace of technology by emerging leaders manifested in the higher revenues and profits of their industrial firms, and grew the size of the industrial economy as a share of the overall economy.

If I was writing in the early to mid nineteenth century, the UK, Belgium, Austria–Hungary, Germany, Sweden, the US and Japan would have been the new emerging winners of the industrial era. Success in this past series of economic changes explains why many of these nations are so well-positioned in the current world economic order. Unlike them, the likely losers—the colonies of the European empires, for example—would have been lagging on many of the industrial-era success metrics.

The nature of economic competition amongst nations—or the Great Economic Tech Game—has changed. Though the economic aspects of the Great Tech Game are still unfolding, the world is already seeing a new set of winners and losers emerge. Nations, especially those that have lagged behind in productivity because they did not industrialize as fast as others in the last few centuries, have a unique opportunity now to leverage the new technologies to increase their productivity to global best-in-class levels. But, at the same time, there are again signs of a widening gap between the nations who are the technology haves and those who are the technology have-nots. In fact, this widening gap might be the beginning of the second Great Divergence, reversing the gains from the Great Convergence that we witnessed in the second half of the twentieth century.

The rich or developed nations seem to have an inherent advantage, as their existing wealth has ensured better adoption and penetration of technology, skills, training and infrastructure. More importantly, certain nations and leaders have understood the significance of our once-in-a-multiple-century structural economic transition. Those nations are transforming their economies to digital economies and finding their competitive edge in the new digital value chains. Others are missing the boat and will end up being digital laggards. The consequences of both courses will be as significant and long-lasting as in the previous eras.

Inequality amongst Nations: The Second Great Divergence?

The industrialization era led to the first Great Divergence that the world economy had ever seen. Chart 5.1 below maps out Asia's loss of share in world output between 1800 and 1950. Post that, however, a period of convergence began. This period saw Asia starting to catch up with its European and American counterparts. At the peak, European and American GDP constituted between 70 and 80 per cent of global GDP, but by 2010, this dropped to roughly 50 per cent (approximately the same level as 1860).

Chart 5.1: The distribution of world output, 1700–2012

Per cent, %

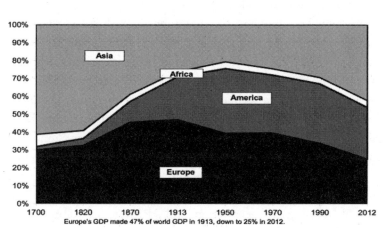

Europe's GDP made 47% of world GDP in 1913, down to 25% in 2012.

Sources: Thomas Piketty, http://piketty.pse.ens.fr/files/capital21c/en/pdf/F1.1.pdf, accessed on 1 October 2021.

This Great Convergence, much like the Divergence that preceded it, was driven by diffusion and adoption of technology, especially manufacturing-related technology, during the post-World War II era. The East Asian countries that adopted technology most intensely, widely and deeply during this era saw a rapid increase in their economic growth.[2] For the East Asian nations, this has been an incredible achievement, and has been termed the 'East Asian miracle'.

Diego Comin argues, however, that this kind of technological leapfrogging is actually both uncommon and difficult. Countries that were earlier to adopt new during the Industrial Revolution also developed the capacity to use new technologies faster. Moreover, there are always predecessor technologies that serve as foundations or prerequisites for finding an innovative and profitable application of new technologies. And therefore, 'jumping ahead of this curve is way too difficult for most companies and individuals in most countries'[3]—the 'East Asian miracle' was a miracle not only because it was so impressive but because it was so unlikely.

Worryingly, there are now increasing signs that a second Great Divergence might be on the cards. This will constitute both a threat and opportunity for countries—a second chance to be on the right side of economic history. Powerful incumbents will have an advantage— those who have been technological leaders in the past are typically the ones who are adopting the new, emerging technologies the fastest as well. Moreover, they are also most likely to invent innovative applications of these new technologies, and identify convergences of these technologies that push outward their economic frontier curves. Today's technologically developed nations already have higher rates of both internet penetration, and adoption and roll out of 5G networks. Ultimately, the command and control over disruptive technologies are often likely to go to countries with existing robust innovation ecosystems, advanced manufacturing and access to large pools of capital.

Can laggards catch up or will richer countries win this game?

High GDP per capita currently correlates with success in digital evolution—countries like Singapore or the Netherlands have been able to move faster on building digital infrastructure for their populations. The richer, more educated populations have adopted digital technologies much faster as well. According to Thomas Piketty, the forces of divergence seem to be more powerful than the forces for convergence in the twenty-first century. Nations and companies that are leveraging the fruits of the new technology revolution are spawning multi-billion-dollar empires and massive ecosystems around themselves. Lower- and middle-income countries do not have these advantages, and therefore are often ill-placed to seize the opportunities presented by the move towards digital economies.[4]

At the same time, though, technology has given nations the possibility to catapult their economies into unprecedented growth. China, whose rapid embrace of digital technology has supercharged the national economy, is an example of an industrial-era laggard that has thrived in the digital economy. But they have done so by mounting concerted, single-minded (and generously funded!) campaigns to push tech adoption and penetration—options that may be challenging for other nations to implement.

Several indicators do suggest a certain slow level of convergence. Overall, digitalization is offering the opportunity for many countries to start catching up in the years ahead with the early leaders.[5] The Digital 2020 Global Overview Report offers some interesting insights. It highlights that internet penetration rates are much higher in the developed nations, while poorer regions like Africa still have low internet penetration rates. At the same time, indicators suggest there is growing convergence between regions when it comes to internet penetration. The growth rates of internet users of laggard regions are among the highest, with 20–40 per cent growth compared to low single-digit growth rates in Europe.[6]

Similarly, the Boston Consulting Group's BCG E-Intensity Index—an index that measures digital infrastructure, internet and technology adoption, and expenditure on online platforms across eighty-five internet economies globally—also suggests that convergence, however slow, is indeed possible. The index, when compared between 2011 and 2015, for example, demonstrates 'The rich are getting richer, but the not-as-rich are slowly catching up.'[7]

A McKinsey report in 2020 argued that Asia has been rapidly building up its technological capabilities and infrastructure. Sample this. During the last decade, Asia accounted for over 50 per cent of global growth in technology company revenues, over 40 per cent of global start-up funding, over 50 per cent of global R&D spend and a whopping 87 per cent of patents filed.[8] The 2020 PREDICT project report also highlights that the technology sectors of India and China have shown the fastest growth rate over the 2006–2017 period.[9]

Furthermore, in terms of tech-driven employment, India, followed by countries such as Australia, Brazil and China, have shown the largest growth in recent years. Similarly, labour productivity growth is also highest in countries such as China, followed by India, Taiwan and South Korea. Compared with these Asian countries, the technology sectors of the EU and the US have shown only modest growth rates in all the dimensions of growth.[10]

These indicators—and the strength and fast-paced growth of the digital economies of several Asian countries—suggest that while the first Great Divergence had left Asia behind, this time, Asia might be better prepared to be on the right side of history. Not only could Asia succeed at technological leapfrogging, but as a Singapore-based technology investor argued, in addition to China, India and Southeast Asia could also emerge as independent technology power centres in the world.

But, are internet users sufficient to become a major digital power?

While having internet users is a necessary prerequisite to participating in the digital economy, it is definitely not sufficient for becoming a major digital power. As a World Economic Forum (WEF) report suggested, success (and prosperity) in the digital economy will not be determined by the number of mobile phones and internet connections, but rather by the ownership of infrastructure, technologies, code and data. Over 90 per cent of the world's data centres are housed in select wealthy countries of Europe, North America and East Asia, while Latin American and African states have less than 2 per cent of the world's data centres. Similarly, the US and China account for over 90 per cent of the world's largest tech firms and 75 per cent of cloud computing capacity. The vast majority of blockchain patents, IoT and AI investments are also dominated by the same regions, indicating that the core control of the digital economy is likely to remain within these regions for decades to come.[11]

Many emerging digital economies are unfortunately focused on patting themselves on the back for their fast-growing number of internet or smartphone users. When India touts itself as the second- or third-largest smartphone internet market, it is important not to forget that India was also the largest colony controlled by the colonial powers a couple of hundred years ago. It was 'the jewel in the crown' of the British empire, much like today it might be the 'jewel in the crown' of the tech empires.

Instead, the real conversation and analysis have to be around questions such as: Who is building and benefiting from the digital infrastructure? Who has the ability to cut off the digital access to certain regions? Who owns the technology underlying most of today's technological advancements? Who owns the immense amount of data being generated every second and the insights that can be derived from that? Who derives or extracts the most value from the new digital value chains? When these questions are asked, then the conclusion around the potential digital convergence between the leaders and laggards also starts to be very different.

The fate of the laggards?

Given the stark differences amongst different regions, what is likely to happen to nations in Latin America, Africa, Central Asia, South Asia, and South and Eastern Europe that are getting left behind? Has the boat already sailed? Or can they catch up? Is convergence possible? If so, how? How should policymakers think about this vast chasm that may develop?

According to Indermit Gill of the World Bank, in technology, genuine leapfrogging in the technology world is 'practically impossible'. While a country may leapfrog in its adoption of a specific technology (India, for example, largely skipped landline telephones and went straight to mobile phones), it is hard to leapfrog in more general-purpose technologies. Gill argues that technological advancement is a 'cumulative process'. Those who did not utilize the innovations around steam engines were not able to take advantage of electric power. Similarly, those countries that do not have widespread access to electricity cannot have widespread access to the internet. Those who do not have access to the internet today are unlikely to be the shapers or early adopters of emerging technologies such as 5G or AI.[12]

Moreover, Diego Comin of the Brookings Institution has pointed out that new technologies disseminate and penetrate much more rapidly in rich countries. The poorer countries also 'struggle to employ these technologies with the same degree of intensity and versatility'. Like Gill, Comin has concluded that 'the potential for technological leap-frogging is over-hyped'.[13]

Yet, as the taxonomy of strategies presented later in this chapter suggest, I argue there are many strategies that countries can adopt to succeed. Fortunately for today's laggards, their current positions are not terminal. The East Asian Tigers were able to catch up with the developed and industrialized nations in the second half of the twentieth century, despite being clear laggards. Their success is testament to the fact that laggards historically have stood a chance. When I started writing this book, I believed that the digital laggards might not have a chance to catch up. But as I dug in deeper, and spoke to economists, policymakers, entrepreneurs, venture capitalists, management consultants and economic thinkers, my view evolved. I now believe that the laggards in the digital era can also catch up, but it will not be easy. As difficult and uphill the road might seem to the digitally laggard nations, the importance of trying to catch up through a clear, differentiated and often niche strategy cannot be overemphasized. This is one of the core goals of this book.

Framework for Assessing Comprehensive Digital Competitiveness

The starting point for any strategy has to be a deep, comprehensive understanding of the problem at hand. Nations are now seeking to become digital powers. The leading candidates to become digital superpowers are obviously the US and China. As we saw in the previous chapter, their digital economies, their technology firms and their innovation systems are the biggest in the world. They have the lion's share of unicorns across the world. And as other nations get some unicorns, nations often feel they have arrived. But do those metrics offer us a complete view of the digital competitiveness of nations? Are there countries other than the US and China that are likely to become major digital powers? Are there more comprehensive frameworks that can be used to assess which nations are best positioned to succeed in the digital era?

Various international organizations have historically created indices or scorecards, like the UN Human Development Index, to track countries' progress toward certain political, economic, social and developmental goals. Similarly, the European Commission and a few others have come up with systematically created indices and scorecards that help us track progress of countries on various aspects of digital readiness and competitiveness. The European Commission's Digital Economy and Society Index (DESI), the Digital Intelligence Index (DII) developed by Tufts University, and the IMD World Digital Competitiveness Rankings are some of the scorecards I have found to be particularly helpful.

Given that these frameworks have all been developed recently and the fact that international consensus on key capabilities of the digital economy is still evolving, these indices will likely undergo further revisions and adaptations. Today, though, they provide us with a multidimensional framework that is helpful in identifying emerging digital winners and losers. They offer insights about gaps in capabilities for individual countries and regions, and can also help track progress over time.

The Tufts–Digital Intelligence Index (DII) scorecard, for example, covers ninety economies and segments them into four groups—Stand Outs, Stall Outs, Break Outs and Watch Outs—by combining both their absolute scores or performance on the abovementioned metrics and also the momentum or pace of growth (see chart 5.2). Such frameworks also serve as useful diagnostic tools to identify the key levers that need to be pulled for a nation to move to the next step in its digital journey—with the Break Outs looking to become Stand Outs, and Watch Outs looking to become Break Outs, for example.

The Standout Nations include Singapore, the US, Hong Kong, South Korea, Taiwan, Germany and Israel, among others. Other smaller nations such as New Zealand, Estonia and the United Arab Emirates are also consistent top performers. These nations, according to the report, have demonstrated an ability to adapt and build institutional support for digital innovation.

The Breakout Nations are those that might be starting from a lower base but are growing their digital competitiveness rapidly. Prominent in this group are China, India, Indonesia, Vietnam and Russia, with China being a 'noteworthy outlier' within this group. As the report highlights, China is not only a large player in the global digital economy—it is also moving faster than all other economies in the world. Other large, populous developing economies such as Indonesia and India are also growing fast, though not as fast as China.

The Stall Out group is made up largely of developed and advanced economies of Western and Northern Europe such as the UK, Denmark, the Netherlands and Finland. While these countries have achieved great advances in their digital journeys, their pace or momentum is slowing, which does not necessarily bode well for their long-term continued digital competitiveness. The parallels that come to mind here are the early colonial powers such as Portugal, Spain and the Netherlands, who ultimately had to make way for the later but more aggressive entrants such as the UK.

A final note about an interesting subgroup: the Middle Nations or the 'Potential Leapfroggers'. The framework identifies a group of mid-sized nations in Africa, Latin America and South and South-East Asia, such as Kenya, Vietnam, Bangladesh, Rwanda and Argentina, which are uniquely placed to 'leapfrog and transform their economies'. These nations could serve as role models and benchmarks, especially for their neighbours, on how to use the digital economy as a lever for change.[14]

Ultimately, the different scorecards developed by various organizations and universities by and large point towards a combination of the following factors:

- Digital access, fulfilment and transaction infrastructure
  (*internet penetration, smartphone usage, data speeds, data costs, number of internet users, payments and logistics infrastructure, etc.*)
- Size and growth rates of the digital economy
  (*revenues and profitability of tech firms, size of the market, average online spends, etc.*)
- Sufficient availability of capital
  (*both risk capital and later-stage growth capital*)
- Quality and quantity of entrepreneurs
  (*founders and entrepreneurs with tenacity and ambition*)

Chart 5.2: How countries scored across four drivers on the Digital Evolution Index (out of 100)

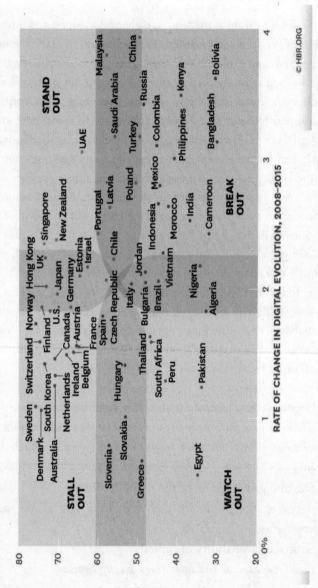

© HBR.ORG

Source: '60 Countries' Digital Competitiveness, Indexed', Harvard Business Review (July 2017), https://hbr.org/2017/07/60-countries-digital-competitiveness-indexed, accessed on 1 October 2021.

- Skilled talent
  (engineers, data analysts, founders, product managers, digital marketing experts, infrastructure experts, etc.)
- Digital skills training and education
  (level of digital literacy and skills amongst the population)
- Attitudes towards digital adoption
  (willingness of people and businesses and government to adopt and use digital technologies)
- Spending on (and quality of) research and development
  (R&D spends, university research spends, number of patents)
- Level of digital transformation of traditional industries
  (how much traditional industries are leveraging technology to transform their operations and businesses)
- Business environment
  (rule of law, predictability, peace and stability, overall business friendliness)
- Regulatory frameworks and government policy
  (policies around foreign investment, data, privacy, competition, etc.)

This list is illustrative, and by no means exhaustive or definitive. The more these metrics for success in the digital economy can be standardized into one or two universally accepted and respected scorecards, the better it will be. Using the UN Human Development Index (HDI) as a benchmark, international organizations must attempt to create a similar scorecard for the state of the world's digital economy (let's say, the State of the Global Digital Economy Report). The United Nations Conference on Trade and Development (UNCTAD), which publishes the Digital Economy report currently, or other such global organizations might be well-positioned to take this on.

Strategies to Compete in the Global Technology Ecosystems

We now turn to the main goal of this chapter. The ongoing structural economic transition offers some new, unique opportunities for nations to carve out their roles in new, emerging value chains and ecosystems. We have already seen that although the US and China have the world's largest digital economies in absolute terms, a large economy is not a prerequisite for digital maturity and competitiveness. Rather, countries that build the necessary digital infrastructure, the institutions, the business and regulatory environments and other capabilities as outlined in the various scorecards will be best positioned to enable their companies and citizens to participate in the value chain fully and creatively.[15]

However, these foundational blocks will be necessary but not sufficient for success in the digital era. Most importantly, countries will need to evaluate their existing strengths, capabilities, endowments (in terms of the factors of production), and comparative advantages to develop their own strategies. As the nature of economic activity is transformed, the value chains are shifting and changing constantly, and new hubs are emerging to take advantage of the new opportunities. The strategies adopted to capture value in the global technology sector and its value chain or new ecosystems will therefore determine the winners.

Already, countries are taking different paths towards digital prosperity. Countries like the US and the UK have adopted a generalist approach to succeed. Others have followed a more niche strategy. Trading hubs are attempting to reorient themselves to become digital entrepots. Singapore, for example, had positioned itself decades ago as the Malacca of the capitalist and technology era. It first became South-East Asia's pre-eminent shipping hub, and then worked towards becoming the regional hub for financial services as well. It is now trying to again be a regional hub for technology, capital, data, and talent in the South-East Asia region. Still, others might seek to become the most attractive destinations (from a tax or regulation perspective) for large tech firms. In Europe, Ireland, for example, has positioned itself as a low-tax jurisdiction for Big Tech firms today.[16]

In the section below, I propose a taxonomy or categorization of strategies for countries to consider, depending on their existing size, capabilities, strengths and endowments. As part of this exercise, I also examine a few select strategies that countries have deployed thus far. This is by no means a comprehensive list of strategies. Rather, the main point is to show that there will not be a one-size-fits-all approach to winning in this era.

Strategy 1: The Digital Blitz strategy (US and China)

There are certain digital powers such as the US and China that are aiming for complete technological dominance. And they are adopting what I call the Digital Blitz strategy. They are attempting to excel at all aspects of digital power—whether it be digital services, tech manufacturing, or digital trade—and achieve excellence across all of them. Already they are host to 90 per cent of the top technology platforms of the world, the largest internet user bases in the world, half of the world's hyperscale data centres, over 90 per cent of all AI start-up funding, and 70 per cent of the world's AI researchers. They also have access to the deepest pockets of private venture capital funds, as well as government funds as and when required. And their Big Tech firms are the biggest investors in, and beneficiaries of, the various parts of the global data value chain—from data collection, transmission through cables and satellites owned by them, storage in data centres and global node networks, to data analysis and processing for intelligence through their AI capabilities. As the UNCTAD 2021 report argues, these companies now possess a significant 'competitive data advantage'.[17]

Both the US and China have come up with comprehensive strategies to become the technological superpowers of this era. China, facing the difficult task of catching up to various incumbency advantages held by the US and Europe, has chosen to invest in a comprehensive Digital Blitz strategy, and build up all the necessary elements together. China has displayed its strength in tech manufacturing, B2C and B2B e-commerce, fintech and other sectors. Its China-2035 plan focuses on achieving excellence in emerging technologies such as 5G, IoT, AI and biotech. The US, on the other hand, has also come up with a comprehensive strategy to constrain China's attempts on the technology front, as I discuss in detail later.

Very few countries can succeed at such a comprehensive strategy. Mastery of all the pieces of the digital economy such as digital infrastructure, digital manufacturing, e-commerce and services is not easy. From a research expenditure standpoint, for example, the US leads with ICT research expenditure of US $100 billion in 2017, followed by China (US $56 billion) and Europe (US $38 billion) as measured by purchasing power standards. All these factors combined demonstrate that while the US continues to be the digital or technological leader, China is threatening to catch up.[18]

Europe and India are the only other contenders currently for this strategy, though both have significant constraints to overcome before a Digital Blitz strategy would make sense. For example, European experts such as Eric Hazan (of McKinsey France) and my former classmate, Manuel Muniz (now the Dean of the IE School in Madrid and former secretary of state for Global Spain) have emphasized the obstacles posed by Europe's fragmented digital market. A Digital Single Market for Europe, they argue, would help the continent benefit from its scale rather than being constrained by fragmentation. Similarly, for India, as we will see, the foundations are being built in the various sub-sectors of technology, upon which India could eventually seek to adopt a Digital Blitz strategy. While India benefits from its large market, it currently lags substantially in certain critical dimensions such as fundamental, long-term-oriented research and development (R&D).

Strategy 2: The digital challenger strategy (Europe, and maybe India)

As we just discussed, European nations and India could be the challengers to the US and China's dominance of the digital economy. As Eric Hazan of McKinsey pointed out to me, several European nations have many of the prerequisites for winning in the digital era and re-assert global technological leadership: a well-educated workforce, widespread access to tech infrastructure, R&D and regulatory capacity. But should these 'digital challengers' go head-to-head with the US and China, or have a differentiated strategy?

I argue the latter approach would be more effective. Again, as we discussed in Chapter 2, the principles for disruptive innovation and how disruptors challenge the incumbent—as laid out effectively by my late professor Clay Christensen[19]—are as relevant and applicable here as they were for the Portuguese trying to get past the established incumbents in the Mediterranean during the pre-colonial era.

The European nations today have varying sets of digital market regulations and are all at different stages of digital evolution and maturity. A unified European digital market would definitely help European start-ups tap all the different national markets within Europe much more easily. That ability to scale and greater R&D spend are critical for Europe to emerge as a serious challenger to the dominance of the US and China.

But until then, however, European countries (and other digital challengers such as India) must each identify their comparative advantages and own areas of digital specialization in terms of sectoral and size focus. For example, Germany could capitalize on its industrial technological prowess to establish leadership in the Industrial IoT and software-enabled manufacturing space. Such deep specialization works well for countries, as Israel has illustrated in its quest to become the cyber-security hub for the world.

Besides sectoral specialization, focusing on the mid-market spaces could be a viable option. As Hermann Simon of Simon-

Kucher & Partners pointed out to me, Germany's industrial-era economic leadership was often driven by its 'hidden champions.'[20] Hidden champions, Simon has argued, are companies that are highly successful and enjoy high market shares (upwards of 50 per cent) in their respective markets but are not as well-known or deeply studied as the large conglomerates. They 'operate in the hinterland of the value chain, supplying machinery, components or processes that are no longer discernable in the final product or service.' A similar hidden champions–style approach in IoT and software-enabled manufacturing could work well.

This is not unlike the argument made by Sridhar Vembu of Zoho Corporation for India to dig deeper into the layers of enterprise technology and not just the most visible 'application' layer that is visible to the consumer. In fact, Vembu specifically points to the *Mittelstand* (the small- and medium-sized companies) in industrial Germany as an example for India to emulate in the enterprise software space.[21]

These strategies, focusing on deep specialization and maximizing existing capacities, would be a much more positive digital strategy for Europe than the current focus on regulating Big Tech firms. The current regulatory strategy seems rooted in a concern that Europe will not be able to replicate foreign Big Tech firms and therefore must control them, but this concern is overplayed.

In any case, the dominance of Big Tech firms, as I have pointed out earlier, has been largely in the B2C space thus far. Many other spaces are still open for the digital challengers to capture, especially in the B2B space. As discussed earlier, a deeper analysis of the new data value chains and digital ecosystems could yield some interesting spaces for the digital challengers to capture before they aim for a US and China style Digital Blitz strategy.

Digital challengers, especially India, could also adopt a sectoral focus. Besides commerce, search, and social media, there are several other sectors where globally or even regionally dominant tech leaders are yet to emerge. Specifically, sectors such as education, financial inclusion, healthcare and agriculture where the US, for example, is not best positioned to innovate for the world. By focusing on such sectors where the US and China are not yet entrenched, or are just too far removed from to be the primary innovators, the digital challengers could succeed in climbing up the digital ladder. India, for example, could see the emergence of global education, healthcare and agriculture technology firms that could serve the needs of developing (and maybe even developed nations) in these sectors.

Finally, the digital challengers must also keep an eye on new, emerging technologies. As our historical analysis had suggested, the US had leapfrogged the UK by first adopting the steam engine and other industrial-era technologies that emanated from the UK, and then inventing electricity itself. Similarly, the digital challengers should continue to push adoption of the technologies emanating from the US currently, but keep pushing for inventions in the emerging technologies such as AI, blockchain, IoT and even climate tech and biotech. New winners will emerge in niche, less obvious spaces, not broad, visible-to-all spaces. Moreover, new technological waves—in climate tech, healthcare, or bio-technology, for example—could change up the game again, and the digital challengers should be ready for their moment in the sun.

Strategy 3: The Technology manufacturing strategy (East Asia)

Countries that are seeking to be the winners in this era must keep an eye out on emerging technologies. They must closely examine each new cluster of technologies and identify areas or niches in that technology's value chain where they could exercise leadership. As my former HKS professor and economist Ricardo Hausmann has argued, 'A country's future is more likely to be bright if it focuses on ensuring it can master every new technology and exploit every new opportunity that comes along.'[22]

Economic historians split the industrial era into phases, largely defined by the cluster of technologies invented during each phase. The first phase in the eighteenth century was characterized by the invention of technologies such as spinning frames, the power loom, the steam engine and the railways. The second phase, starting from about 1850, would see the introduction of technologies such as steel furnaces, chemicals, petroleum and electricity.

Similarly, in the current technology era, we are likely to see different phases of change oriented around new clusters of technologies being invented and gaining prominence. Just as the winners in the first phase of industrialization would not necessarily be the main winners of the second phase, different phases of today's technological revolution could have different winners and losers. In fact, digital challengers in the technology manufacturing space are betting on this fact.

Bangalore-based iSPIRT Foundation founder and start-up investor Sharad Sharma pointed out that every country has an airline, mobile operator and a bank, and in today's context, an e-commerce firm, a food delivery platform and a cab company. But according to him, the real question is, how many countries actually manufacture the planes, the telecom equipment or the financial payment platforms? Usually, Sharma says, it's the 'Circle of Five'. There are usually four to five countries that capture that manufacturing edge, whether you look at aeroplanes or telecom equipment. And the goal must be to be in that Circle of Five for the new, emerging technologies.

That Circle of Five for technology manufacturing thus far has typically been comprised of the US and certain European and East Asian nations. Taiwan, for example, has the highest share of the ICT sector as a percentage of the overall economy (over 16 per cent), followed by South Korea, largely driven by its strengths in manufacturing electronic components. This focus on tech manufacturing is also reflected in their high research expenditure in tech manufacturing, compared to tech services or the rest of their economies. Currently, the US leads in labour productivity per hour worked in the tech sector (for tech manufacturing), likely driven by its competitive leadership in hardware (e.g., Apple, Cisco, Intel). But China is actually exhibiting the fastest growth in productivity in tech manufacturing, indicating that China is starting to move up the value chain as well.

At the same time, other conditions are arising for potentially new winners to emerge. One, a whole new set of new general-purpose technologies such as AI, 5G, and IoT could see new winners emerge. These technologies could represent a new phase of the current technology revolution, and hence potentially new winners and losers. 5G technology, as one of these emerging technologies, is a prime example. Given its fundamentally transformative power, countries and companies have been racing to establish dominance in 5G technology, infrastructure and standards, and to establish an early-mover advantage.

As of 2019, South Korea was the leader on both 5G infrastructure development and deployment as well as commercialization. Its telecom operators, such as SK Telecom, had rolled out 5G nationally and were also completing initial commercial deployments of the technology. But countries like the US, Japan and Singapore were close on the heels of South Korea. The Arthur D. Little Global 5G Leadership Index categorizes countries as 5G leaders, followers and laggards (see chart 5.3).[23]

However, the years-long process of rolling out fully mature 5G ecosystems are expected to mean that these metrics reflect an early image of a rapidly evolving ecosystem. From a long-term leadership perspective, besides the rollout, other factors become more important. In addition to the expected R&D and capex investments in 5G, leadership in 5G would depend also on how much of the 5G value chain—technology, infrastructure, standards, commercial applications and deployment—is captured by companies of a particular nation, along with how deeply 5G is integrated into, and applied in, industries and other parts of the economy.

Based on expected R&D and capex investments in 5G from 2020 to 2035, a study conducted by IHS Markit in 2017 concluded that the US and China would likely dominate 5G technology over the next decade. On the value chain, technology leadership in 5G can be split into a few

Chart 5.3: Results of the Arthur D. Little 5G Leadership Index

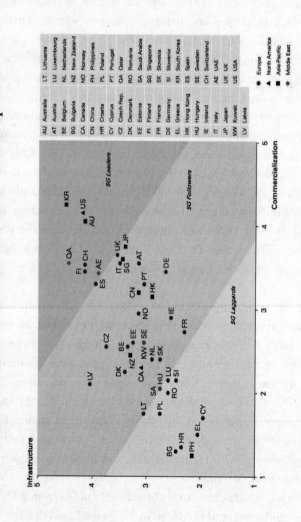

Source: 'The Race to 5G', Arthur D. Little (March 2019),

https://www.adlittle.com/sites/default/files/reports/adl_the_race_to_5g_report_-min.pdf, accessed on 1 October 2021.

key aspects. These include: innovation and standards, manufacturing (of equipment and infrastructure), services, and government policies and regulations.

Using this framework, analysts have argued that US-based Qualcomm, for example, is the current leader in 5G innovation and standard settings, though China-based Huawei has also made some significant contributions in this regard.[24] The leaders in 5G manufacturing include Qualcomm (chipsets), South Korea-based Samsung (5G smartphones and 5G infrastructure), Ericsson, Huawei, Hewlett-Packard, Cisco and Dell (all for 5G infrastructure).

Finally, in terms of conducive government policy and regulation for promotion of 5G, the US and China seem currently best placed, followed by Korea, Japan and Europe, in that order.[25] Given current trends, it appears that leadership in all aspects of 5G technology shall rest with countries in East Asia, the US and certain countries in Europe. Countries across Africa, Latin America, Eastern Europe and South Asia might not be able to crack the 'Circle of Five' for core 5G technologies.

While some current 5G laggards, like India, are stepping up their game in partnership with private technology partners, global leadership and opportunities for significant value capture in the global 5G technology space might well be beyond reach already. Yet, opportunities still remain at the national or regional level. The two largest home-grown telecom players, Reliance Jio and Bharti Airtel, have invested heavily in the 5G spectrum.[26] Moreover, Jio is working closely with companies such as Qualcomm (Qualcomm also invested in Reliance Jio in 2020), Google Cloud, and Dutch chipmaker NXP Semiconductors to fast-track the development of 5G network infrastructure and services in India.[27],[28] While there is no doubt that the Indian telecom players will be the primary carriers for 5G rollout in India, it remains to be seen whether Reliance or India will be able to take up any global leadership position in other aspects of 5G, such as technology innovations, setting of standards, or share of manufacturing.

As further new technologies emerge, countries could utilize such frameworks to analyse both their comparative strengths vis-à-vis other countries and also which aspect of that new technology's value chain they could compete best in.

In addition to the emergence of new (and potentially general purpose) technologies, a second set of events might also cause potentially new winners to emerge in the tech manufacturing space. Due to the growing geopolitical conflict between the US and China, the US and its allies are increasingly moving towards decoupling their supply chains from China, especially for core components such as semiconductor chips and rare earths. This has incidentally led to an increased attempt by other countries such as India to capture some of the space thus vacated.

According to ex-colleagues from the ministry of electronics and information technology (MeitY) in India, the stars are actually aligning for Indian tech manufacturing to become a significant part of India's national digital strategy. The government has plans in place to not just onshore much of the mobile phone manufacturing and increase its individual parts and components. In addition, it is also hoping to prepare itself for the semiconductor wars by setting up its first semiconductor fabrication (fab) facility soon. Even as it aims to grow its tech manufacturing industry by 3x in five years, it will be difficult for India to become amongst the top leaders in tech manufacturing that quickly. But as they say, it's never too late to start.

Yet, there are large macro risks around a strategy that focuses too heavily on tech manufacturing alone. Many reports from the World Bank and other economists have pointed to the fact that 'changing technologies and shifting globalization patterns call the feasibility of manufacturing-led development strategies into question'.[29] A significant global trend towards onshoring and reshoring of manufacturing, along with decreasing labour cost arbitrage and rise in protectionist sentiments, means that nations hoping to serve as low-cost manufacturing centres risk finding fewer and smaller foreign markets than they may assume.

Furthermore, manufacturing is increasingly relying on what are termed Industry 4.0 technologies such as advanced automation, robotics, IoT and additive manufacturing (3-D printing). Since these technologies are often labour-replacing, many lower-income countries that leverage their labour cost arbitrage could stand to lose out. This trend is also evident in the slowing pace of globalization, considerable decline in the trade of parts and components, and a reduction in FDI going to low- and middle-income countries (LMICs). [30]

Countries that possess the technology, the skilled labour and cheap capital could still adopt a tech manufacturing-focused strategy. Existing industrial manufacturing powerhouses like Germany, for example, that could move towards establishing niches in emerging IoT and software-enabled manufacturing processes. Essentially, countries that decide that leadership in emerging technologies is a core part of their strategy for digital competitiveness must closely monitor and study new technologies as they emerge. Instead of waiting for the global landscape for that technology to become clearer, they must think deeply—and early—about where they can find their competitive edge within that technology's emerging ecosystem or value chain.

Strategy 4: The Digital Services strategy (India)

In sharp contrast to the pessimistic outlook on tech manufacturing, digital services offer a significant ray of hope for countries around the world. As Zia Qureshi of the Brookings Institution pointed out, digital platforms and communication technologies are lowering transaction costs to connect to global markets. Consequently, they are increasing opportunities for countries to tap into the burgeoning trade in services facilitated by digitization.

Digital services can broadly be categorized into two buckets: one, the set of tech-enabled services that enable the digital transformation of existing firms, supply chains, manufacturing and other processes; and two, the new set of digital services (such as online advertising, search, social media, communication, sales force management and CRM) being offered by B2C (such as Google, Facebook, Netflix) and B2B technology firms (such as Zoho, Freshdesk and Salesforce).

The US is the leader in the digital services space, courtesy of its massive Big Tech firms that provide digital services (take Google or Facebook's ad services, for example). But amongst the developing countries, India has the largest digital services sector, and serves as an excellent case study for the digital services strategy—and more relevant for nations that are laggards in the digital economy.

One, India already has existing strengths and a comparative advantage in the space. India has for long been known as the IT outsourcing hub for the world, and also has some of the largest tech outsourcing firms such as Infosys, Tata Consultancy Services and Wipro, among others. India has had the highest growth rate in the digital service sector over the period 2006–17.[31] It is well positioned to focus on the digital services sector and emerge as one of the biggest players in that space.

Two, the potential for technology's impact in improving productivity is immense. India's labour productivity in IT services is almost four times higher than its overall labour productivity, suggesting that moving a greater percentage of its labour to digital services would yield significant productivity gains for India. In contrast, the gap between ICT sector productivity and total productivity in Europe and the US is much lower (1.43 for the EU and 1.69 for the US).

S.D. Shibulal, founder of Infosys, described to me how Infosys thought about the services sector when Infosys was founded in the 1980s. During that era, he explained, the global manufacturing supply chains were being disintegrated or unbundled, and various South-East Asian nations were increasingly becoming the beneficiaries of this unbundling of manufacturing processes. The founders of Infosys saw the opportunity to leverage technology (and talent) in unbundling the services processes and capturing some part of the services value chain.

That concept is as relevant today. As the world tends towards onshoring and reshoring manufacturing, countries must double down on digital services as part of their digital strategy. India has the unique opportunity of building both the IT services sector focused on enabling the digital transformation of the world, but also capture parts of the global data and services value chains and ecosystems being spawned by Big Tech firms. India must think of not just building large Big Tech firms and unicorns. Rather, a multi-pronged approach here would be appropriate.

One element of this strategy would involve traditional IT services firms moving up the value chain. Indian IT services firms have been moving up from doing fixed-price projects to solutions, consulting and advisory services and eventually developing platforms. India's competitive edge in services, Shibulal believes, will depend on the ability of India's IT services firms to continually evolve, upskill and reskill and master emerging technologies such as AI, machine learning and blockchain. Others—such as French economist Prof. Philippe Aghion and Arindam Bhattacharya from BCG's Henderson Institute—have emphasized the necessity for India to improve the quality of its education so that its engineers can move to high value-added digital services in AI, data analytics, algorithm design, and platform-based solutions.

But will this strategy be sufficient to help India extract significantly more value from the services value chains? Likely not. India will also need to evaluate how its firms can go from system integrators of existing products such as SAP and Oracle to builders of such enterprise software products. Therefore, a second critical element of India's quest for dominance of global tech services has to necessarily involve focusing on enterprise or B2B tech platforms and (Software-as-a-Service) SaaS platforms. While the conversation has focused on the concentration of unicorns and Big Tech firms in the US and China, another key aspect is often missed: B2B tech. B2B tech and SaaS platforms often do not have the winner-take-all dynamics that currently, many B2C markets seem to have. The B2B market is fragmented, and hence offers much more opportunity for newer firms and competitors to emerge.

Europe, India and other nations could find their competitive advantage in this space, instead of being overly anxious about the dominance of foreign Big Tech firms and the monopolistic nature of some B2C markets. According to a McKinsey–SaaSBOOMi report,

India could be on the cusp of unlocking a $1 trillion opportunity if its SaaS companies are able to scale to their full potential in the global SaaS market.[32] An enormous opportunity, given that India's GDP in 2021 is approximately $3 trillion.

Indian services firms can think of carving out their own niches to support and benefit from the ecosystems that have been built around the likes of Facebook, Google, Amazon and Netflix. This could mean obviously building large brands that could leverage Amazon's marketplace to become global players, or digital media companies that could serve as the production studios for the likes of Netflix. At the same time, there are other opportunities such as becoming a major player in the data analytics industry. As I explained in the previous chapter, the new ecosystems—and the data economy—being spawned by the Big Tech players has to be understood better, so countries can identify which niches to play in.

Ultimately, much like anything, the digital services-focused strategy will require nations like India to build up the talent required to both scale and upgrade its digital services. As Debjani Ghosh, president of India's premier technology industry body, NASSCOM, has argued, India can, and must, become 'the world's talent hub for digital skills'.[33] At the same time, India has to move up and away from a simple labour arbitrage strategy to a tech arbitrage strategy. India cannot simply continue to play on its cheap labour (where you rely on labour as a factor of production) but must also play on unique, innovative technology (where you rely more on technology as a factor of production).

Sridhar Vembu, founder and CEO of Zoho Corporation and a member of India's National Security Advisory Board, has similarly argued that India must solve this structural economic problem and focus on R&D and build deep tech capabilities.[34] Vembu, who has built one of India's most successful India-to-the-world SaaS companies, has further recommended that India needs to play in all the layers of deep tech (such as operating systems, databases, platforms, etc.) and not just the application layer that the consumer sees. This approach is effectively akin to the digital value chain analysis I have alluded to as well.

Strategy 5: The Digital Entrepots strategy (Ireland, Singapore, Estonia)

The idea of 'digital entrepots' refers to nations (typically smaller nations or city-states) that can stand out due to their adaptability to change, and institutional support for innovation.[35] As per the Tufts-DII categorization, the 'Super Stand Outs' included countries such as South Korea, Singapore and Hong Kong. Other smaller nation states such as New Zealand, Estonia and the United Arab Emirates are also consistent top performers.

This idea is a natural evolution from the earlier concepts of trading entrepots of the mercantile and colonialist periods such as Alexandria, Malacca, Amsterdam and Venice. More recently, in the industrial–capitalist era, global financial centres such as London, New York, Singapore and Hong Kong have played the role of financial entrepots. Much like these trading and financial entrepots, the digital entrepots are building the basic blocks to attract the global tech talent, build the best institutions, develop the services and digital infrastructure to become an attractive destination as regional hubs for Big Tech firms and start-ups (think how Malacca had attracted merchants from all over the world during the Great Trade Game).

Sithu Ponraj, a Visiting Senior Fellow at S. Rajaratnam School of International Studies, explained to me, Singapore is looking to attract the best global tech talent, focus on emerging technologies, and build the institutional and physical infrastructure to remain the pre-eminent digital hub in Southeast Asia and even all of Asia. And it seems to be succeeding. As Drew Thompson of the National University of Singapore highlighted to me, Singapore already hosts the cloud infrastructure for Southeast Asia, and the data centres for most of the Big Tech firms are located there.

While mainstream media focuses only on start-up hubs such as Silicon Valley, Bangalore, Shanghai, Shenzhen, London and Tel Aviv, there is more to becoming a digital entrepot than just being home to large tech start-ups. The digital revolution offers opportunities to new cities and nation states to develop themselves as hubs for data flows or innovation by building the necessary infrastructure and institutions. For example, Estonia, with its innovative e-residency programme, has positioned itself as the gateway to Europe for tech entrepreneurs from around the world.

Ireland started their digital journey (and one-upped the UK) by getting Microsoft to set up its first and largest European data centre in Ireland. Microsoft's Brad Smith explains that tax incentives and an English-speaking population had first drawn Microsoft to the Emerald Isle. [36] But the story doesn't end there. Ireland used its membership in the European Union to attract talent from the region and eventually the world to Dublin. Moreover, the Irish Department of Enterprise, Trade and Employment did a 'masterful job' of filling the gaps where needed to suit the needs of firms such as Microsoft. For example, within three months, Ireland negotiated a contract to build exactly the kind of high-speed fibre optic cable to the European mainland—a key demand of Microsoft.

Its mild climate and favourable political climate (including from Smith's perspective pragmatic data protection policies) further added to its attraction as a hub to store users' personal information. Ireland offers an essentially zero-tax base for Big Tech corporations, which have leveraged it extensively. The tax rate is lower by over 10 percentage points than continental Europe, and there is also a 25 per cent tax credit to offset R&D costs. [37] Most of the major tech firms now have their European headquarters in Dublin, including Apple, Google, Facebook, LinkedIn, Salesforce and Dropbox.

Today, by many metrics, such as the EU's DESI 2020 scorecard, Ireland would seem like a digital superpower. Ireland's digital economy accounts for over 13 per cent of its economy now (recall that number is

5–10 per cent for the US, China, UK and India), and has been growing at an average of 12 per cent per annum since 2013.

And there has been significant spillover. Exports in the digital sector account for over a quarter of total Irish exports. From the employment perspective, the digital sector employs at least a quarter of a million people in Ireland (over 10 per cent of total employment), and wages are estimated to be 50 per cent higher than the rest of the economy.[38] Ireland, by all accounts, is positioning itself as the Switzerland for the digital era. As Switzerland had positioned herself during the era of industrialization as an attractive hub for capital and banking, Ireland seems to be doing the same for the tech era. As Smith says, 'Ireland is to data what Switzerland is to money.'[39]

Whether Ireland will be able to sustain this position is often called into question. Sinead O'Sullivan, a professor at MIT, has called Ireland 'the biggest tax haven in the world, used by multinationals to shelter profits'.[40] O'Sullivan believes that this strategy is a double-edged sword. Even as it enables Ireland in its journey to becoming a digital economic power, she argues that it hinders the fair and equitable distribution of taxes to democratic governments globally and therefore threatens democracy itself.

A recent agreement between the US and the EU for a global minimum tax regime also threatens the strategic space Ireland will have to retain to continue to be a tax haven. If Ireland falls in line with the US and EU's plans, other countries might step in to explore an Ireland-like strategy. After all, several tax havens have continued to survive (and thrive) for several decades, if not centuries.

As different nations move differently to regulate Big Tech firms (which I explore in detail in a later chapter), there is also the opportunity (and risk) for Big Tech firms to engage in regulatory arbitrage. Big Tech firms will increasingly look for nations that provide friendlier regulatory frameworks to set up their regional bases. Nations will compete with each other to attract these Big Tech firms by providing a friendlier regulatory framework, or 'regulatory arbitrage.' Whether it was intended as a core economic strategy or not, the case of El Salvador, which recently made Bitcoin an officially recognized currency, comes to mind.

But the key point here is that the digital entrepot strategy is not limited to taxation or regulatory arbitrage. Tax incentives should be—and are often—used as conversation starters by countries with Big Tech firms. It is the subsequent set of elements—on attracting the right pools of talent to serve the firms, build the necessary digital infrastructure, and having the stability of rule of law and other institutional frameworks such as privacy—that transform the conversation into a much deeper partnership.

The successful digital entrepots, often by virtue of their size, work to figure out what the Big Tech firms or start-ups (as in the case of Estonia) need. Such a tailored and targeted strategy, especially for city-states and smaller nations, could help them grow their digital sectors faster than might otherwise be possible. Though this strategy is probably best suited for smaller nations, even larger nations such as India or China can consider developing special digital zones (SDZs, somewhat similar to SEZs or special economic zones), or to use a tech term, Sandbox Zones (SBZs). With the right strategy, institutional vision and support, even larger countries could build digital entrepots along the lines of Singapore, Estonia and Ireland.

Strategy 6: The GovTech (or the Government Kickstarter) strategy (Israel, Rwanda, India)

Historically, governments have often played a key role in the development of new strategic industries. The efforts had varied results, from storied successes to dismal failures. The story of Silicon Valley is often told to showcase the role government-funded research played in its early days. In addition, government or defence procurement is also often cited as a way to kick-start industries in the past. The US aircraft industry or even the internet, for that matter, were largely enabled by government demand. Israel is often cited in this context as well. Full-fledged ecosystems for bio-technology and cyber-security (including surveillance) have arisen from the particular priorities of Israel's military needs.

This strategy, as sceptically as it might be viewed from some quarters, can actually be a great option for countries that need to kick-start their digital economies but do not currently have large start-up ecosystems and venture capital firms present. The most fundamental way could actually be to focus on Government-to-Citizen (G2C) services, which are also often referred to as GovTech. Certain countries, such as Denmark, driven by their citizens' high levels of trust in the government, have also greatly digitized their G2C services. Denmark, Korea and Estonia consistently rank at the top, for example, in the United Nations E-Government Survey that benchmarks countries on their uptake of digital government services.[41]

The process of building the infrastructure for digital G2C services can then hopefully create significant spillover effects for the rest of the digital and overall economy. And this doesn't have to be limited to only smaller or richer nations. Here again, India as a case study offers some interesting insights. The digital public infrastructure and goods being developed in India, also known as the India stack, could be a potential game-changer for India. The India Stack, conceptualized over the last few years as a platform- or operating-system type play, represents a fascinating integration of government, business, start-up and development infrastructure. With the Aadhaar (the unique digital ID), Unified Payments Interface (UPI), DigiLocker and eKYC (digital know your customer process) forming the infrastructure layer, IndiaStack is envisioned to help entities of all kinds access the data made available through data exchanges to build innovative applications in various sectors such as financial inclusion, healthcare, education, logistics and mobility, and agriculture.

The concept of the India Stack is still evolving, and has many different elements in various stages of its evolution and implementation. Post-conceptualization, successful implementation will be the key challenge. The JAM Trinity (Jan Dhan– Aadhaar–Mobile), the most advanced in its implementation, has focused on enabling financial inclusion using this architecture, and by many metrics succeeded. Further sectoral platforms that are in various stages of development include the National Health Stack (NHS), the National Digital Education Architecture (NDEAR) and the Digital Infrastructure for Knowledge Sharing in School Education (DIKSHA), the Bharat Bill Payment System (BBPS) and the Electronic Toll Collection (FASTag) system.

Nandan Nilekani, founder of Infosys and former chairman of India's Unique Identification Authority of India (UIDAI), believes India Stack to be 'India's single most important innovation to formalize India's domestic economy through digital services'.[42] But interestingly, there are several opportunities to export this digital infrastructure to other countries. As Alok Kshirsagar, Senior Partner and contributor-author of McKinsey's reports on India's digital opportunity, suggested to me, this digital infrastructure would be extremely helpful for mid-sized developing countries such as Indonesia and Nigeria, given their scale of population, and other similarities with India.

In fact, there is already evidence of the internationalization of IndiaStack. Many countries such as Nigeria and Singapore have approached India for help with building their own digital ID or payments infrastructure. In 2018, for example, a partnership between the National Payments Corporation of India (which oversees India's Unified Payments Interface) and its Singapore counterpart was announced as part of the effort to extend the UPI to Singapore.[43] And then in September 2021, India and Singapore announced that they would link their respective payment systems, UPI and PayNow, by July 2022 in order to facilitate instant, low-cost fund transfers between the two countries. Could this develop into a template for building an international digital payments system similar to Society for Worldwide Interbank Financial Telecommunication (SWIFT)? Surely.

Many of these digital platforms being built by Indian companies could lead India Stack's global outreach. One way to think about it would be that IndiaStack could be the digital operating system (much like Apple's iOS or Google's Android) upon which a marketplace of applications could be built by Indian and global companies and entrepreneurs. If China is exporting hard digital infrastructure globally, India (and other countries like India) could very well export soft public digital infrastructure globally.

While it might seem far-fetched today, UPI and NPCI, or start-ups that innovate upon these platforms, could be the global Big Tech firms of India tomorrow—and models for how existing digital laggards might find valuable niches in the emerging digital economy. For many countries, implementing such a vast digital public goods infrastructure in their countries could serve as the building block for sparking technological innovation and spillovers, especially in sectors such as education, healthcare, agriculture and logistics—which often tend to be critical sectors for developing nations anyway.

Strategy 7: The Digital Laggards' strategy (Latin American and African nations)

As per the Tufts-DII, some other large, populous nations such as Brazil and Nigeria have unfortunately suffered from very low momentum, which is why they are members of the 'Watch Out' group along with countries such as Mexico and South Africa. This group of what could also be termed as 'digital laggards' is largely made up of countries from Latin America, Africa, and South and Eastern Europe.

The primary focus must obviously be to actually systematically build the foundation: build the digital infrastructure, increase access to the internet, build up digital skills and training, stable business and political environment, appropriate government and regulatory frameworks and other such foundational pieces that are critical for success in the digital era. Beyond that, from a strategy standpoint, conversations with economists, venture capitalists, academics and government officials from Latin American and African nations have suggested a few guiding elements.

One, these laggard nations should focus on local adaptations of globally available technologies, or as Prof. Hausmann put it, 'solving their biggest headaches'. Adaption of globally available technologies has worked well in increasing adoption, diffusion and penetration of technologies, which, as we discussed, is a critical factor for success in the digital economy.

Former vice-minister of commerce and trade strategy for Colombia (and a former classmate), Mariana Sarasti, pointed out to me that Latin American nations are witnessing a lot of technological innovation to solve Latin America-specific problems, whether in commerce, fin-tech or other sectors. While Brazil is ahead of the rest, other nations such as Mexico, Colombia, and Chile are also attempting to use tech for solving uniquely local problems. That is where the unicorns are emerging in Latin America.

Similarly, in Africa, nations such as Kenya, South Africa, Nigeria, and Rwanda are focusing on local innovations for local problems. Fintech, including mobile payments and cross-border payments, have therefore been top of the agenda for many countries. This is not unlike the digital journey of India, which initially focused on solving India-specific problems of logistics, payments, financial inclusion, commerce and mobility. I am reminded of how local Indian e-commerce firms such as Flipkart relied heavily on innovations such as Cash on Delivery in their early days, or even how telecom firms such as Bharti Airtel implemented a strategy revolving around pre-paid SIM cards, and not post-paid plans.

Two, these regions could focus, much like Europe, on becoming single, unified digital markets. With over 50+ nations in Africa, and 30+ nations in Latin America and the Caribbean, these regions would become much more attractive digital markets if they were to reduce barriers for technology companies to operate seamlessly across borders. Currently, different regulations in each country make it almost impossible for start-ups to scale effectively. Instead, the top talent, as in Europe, often moves to other more attractive destinations such as Silicon Valley.

Three, as we discussed earlier, the Government-to-Citizen (G2C) or Business-to-Government (B2G) sectors are always a good starting point for laggard nations. Much as India is attempting, the digital laggards could kick start their digital economies (even in the absence of large venture capital ecosystems) by digitizing government services for citizens, enhancing public procurement of technology products and services, and opening up access to public data to seed country-specific innovation as well. Rwanda, in particular, has stood out in this regard, in the African context. By all accounts, Rwanda has moved rapidly on its digitization journey, with a 'digitize government services first' approach.

For both African and Latin American nations, G2C services infrastructure—built along the lines of the India Stack—could also serve as a stepping stone to adopting a digital services-focused strategy. Given linkages to Europe and North America, and large, young Spanish-, French- and English-speaking populations, niches in the global digital services value chains could be identified and focused upon.

Four, these countries must focus on supplementing their endowments of human capital, financial capital and technology know-how. A digital entrepot strategy could be relevant one way. As the McKinsey Global Digitalization report showed, data flows to all regions are increasing quite rapidly, including laggard regions such as Latin America. This will eventually mean that the likes of Facebook, Netflix, Google and Amazon will need to build data centres or their regional headquarters in these regions. The more forward-looking nations in these regions might position themselves as the new 'Irelands' of their regions, by providing additional incentives for Big Tech firms and consequently reap the economic, infrastructure and employment benefits.

Another way could be through better inward migration policies that might encourage the flow of regional or even global talent to these nations. Much like the diasporas of India and China, the diasporas of various laggard nations must be fully leveraged, for their talent, knowledge, ideas, connections and capital. As Prof. Hausmann pointed out, often countries view foreign talent—especially skilled talent—as potential threats to the domestic talent. Rather, foreign talent is often a complement to, not a substitute for, domestic talent. They're sugar and tea, not coffee and tea, he quipped.

Two more elements are important for laggards to consider. One, especially in mid-income nations, the existing large industrial or other companies must actively focus on diversifying into technology-driven business models. An interesting example is how Tata Sons, the Indian steel-to-retail conglomerate, has managed to build one of the world's largest IT services firm in the world, Tata Consultancy Services (TCS), whose market cap recently surpassed that of IBM.[44] Acquisitions of foreign technology-based firms can also be a great way. Examples of this strategy abound as well: Turkey's Yıldız Holding has bought Belgium-based Godiva Chocolates; India's Tata has bought Jaguar Land Rover; and China's Geely Holdings has bought Volvo.

Laggard nations need to fill another gap: poor R&D capabilities. Many countries often have a big disconnect between industry and academia. These linkages are not hard to build. For example, like the OECD nations often do, governments can offer tax rebates to corporates to channel their R&D expenditure to local universities. Essentially, industry should demand and fund the research it needs, and academia should respond by leveraging its talent to supply answers for those particular problems.

In 1945, an influential and path-breaking report to US President Roosevelt by Vannevar Bush, the then-director of the US Office of Scientific Research and Development, had emphasized the utmost importance of long-range, publicly funded fundamental scientific research to be carried out autonomously in public and private universities and research labs.[45] That model has worked wonderfully as evident in the case of leading research institutions such as MIT. Governments around the world should imbibe that approach, and also figure out innovative ways to kick-start these linkages.

Key Conclusions

As the structure of the economy shifts drastically, countries must reorient themselves to become digitally competitive, just as traditional corporate firms are seeking to do. Countries cannot be thinking only of industrial policies and strategies; they must also be thinking about their technology and digital strategies. Countries must focus on the Great Tech Game, and not just on the previous economic game of industrialization. A 'Make in India' programme, for example, must therefore be supplemented with a 'Digital India' or 'Code in India' programme.

Mainstream media has painted a picture that suggests that the US–China battle for technological leadership is the main economic battle to track. But this is a very myopic and narrow view. A global, long-term perspective here, which this book seeks to provide, is essential. Most countries in the world will not end up fighting with each other for technological supremacy. Rather, they will be concerned with finding their own niches in the digital economy for technological competitiveness.

To better understand their strengths and weaknesses and devise the best strategies, countries must first track and measure the key drivers and metrics for the competitiveness of the digital economy. A survey of all the indices created thus far by various organizations shows that a few core factors matter to digital competitiveness: capital, infrastructure, integration of technology across sectors, attitudes and openness, talent and skills, fundamental research and development capabilities, and regulatory frameworks.

These frameworks also provide a much broader, more comprehensive picture of the emerging winners and losers. The rankings throw up the same countries, by and large, as the leaders: countries such as the United States, Singapore, Denmark, Sweden, Switzerland, the Netherlands, Hong Kong, Norway, Korea, Canada and UAE. Many of these countries have adopted the right set of strategies to boost their digital competitiveness.

Thankfully for developing nations, while existing levels of prosperity do seem to matter, they are not necessarily a prerequisite. Some 'poorer' nations (i.e., with GDP per capita of below $20,000) have also managed to rank highly in the digital competitiveness tables, such as China, Malaysia, Lithuania, Poland and Latvia. Growth rates or momentum in building great digital competitiveness is also important. From this perspective, countries like India, China, Vietnam, Indonesia and Russia seem to be doing well. These are signs that a certain level of convergence, albeit slow, is underway.

Still, regional differences remain quite stark. While North America, Western Europe, Australia and East Asia are leading in most indicators of digital competitiveness, Latin America, Africa and Eastern Europe are mostly lagging behind. It is also important to note that significant intraregional differences exist even within the above regions. But the new divides suggest that the old North–South split might no longer be valid. Notably, the regions or countries left behind during this technology era might be different than those left behind during the industrialization and colonization era.

Writing 250 years ago, it would have seemed that the UK and the US and certain other select states might take and retain the lead, and keep succeeding on the basis of their earlier success. However, while the US and the UK and other early industrialized nations have indeed remained substantially ahead, other nations such as the East Asian Tigers have been able to catch up to a large extent. Notably, they were able to do so despite starting off as quite poor.

The East Asian Tigers learnt and played the game of that era exceptionally well. Often with the help of the leaders of the era (the Americans), they positioned themselves to become critical parts of the global industrial supply chain. As Harvard Professor Dwight Perkins explained, the East Asian nations also played the game differently. While South Korea encouraged its chaebols, or family-run conglomerates like Hyundai, to build industrial capacity, Taiwan set up SEZs such as the Hsinchu Science Park to attract both talent and capital to build up technology giants from scratch. Regardless, most of these nations adopted a 'government-directed but private player-executed' strategy to compete in the game.

As economist Thomas Piketty has argued, knowledge and skill diffusion can help increase productivity, and also, importantly, reduce inequality both between and within countries.[46] Many countries that have risen up the economic ladder have done so by encouraging that knowledge and skill diffusion, and adopting the modes of production of the richer countries. Further, this has often been done with the assistance of the government and not just complete reliance on the market forces.[47] The challenge for the laggard nations will be to invest in the right kinds of knowledge and skills so that technologies—even if imported from other countries—can be more effectively harnessed and productively used.[48] Accelerating widespread adoption and deep penetration of a wide range of technologies, amongst as many workers, companies and sectors as possible, will be critical in raising the productivity growth rates of nations.[49]

Further, barriers to adoption of technology, such as introduction of inappropriate technologies, policy-induced barriers, or misallocations of technology across sectors within the country, need to be watchfully avoided.[50] A deep, collaborative, multi-year exercise must be conducted by nations to identify the path forward that works for them. It will require a lot of hard work, coordination amongst various stakeholders, cross-functional coordination and a real will to succeed. Nations can also learn from the digital transformation journeys being undertaken by legacy firms.

Going forward, it might also be helpful to build globally accepted scorecards or frameworks for technological development, similar to indices such as the UN Human Development Index. The world's countries can be split up under the following categories: Digital Superpowers (large and fast-growing digital economies), Digital Challengers or Emerging Powers (the digital version of groups such as BRICS or traditional emerging powers that have the potential to become Digital Superpowers), Digital Entrepots (small cities or nation states that have positioned themselves centrally in the global digital value chains), and Digital Laggards (that is, the digital version of 'least developed countries', or LDCs, or nations that have small digital economies and low rates of growth).

Nations that are thus aware of their current positions, and their particular set of endowments, strengths and comparative advantages, might develop clearer strategies for enhancing their digital competitiveness. As the taxonomy of strategies suggests, some will need to focus on a specific part of the digital supply chain, whether tech manufacturing or digital services. For others, emphasizing a focus on emerging technologies will help them assume a bigger leadership role. Alternatively, other countries might be well-positioned to pursue a digital entrepot strategy.

The taxonomy of strategies presented here is obviously not a comprehensive one. Many other strategies may exist, but each will depend on nations making clear assessments of their current positions and moving decisively to secure the appropriate position in the new economy. The priority, in some ways, must shift from trying to only integrate into global trade or goods value chains, and instead also prioritize the integration into global digital value chains. Ultimately, capturing and extracting your share of value from the global digital economy will become a core aspect of determining whether you as a nation win or lose in this era.

The stakes in this process are huge, extending to the future destinies of entire nations. Nations that fail to understand that technology is the new shaper of their economic destinies might miss the boat, again.

Notes

1. Review of *The Wealth and Poverty of Nations*, David S. Landes (New York: W.W. Norton & Company, 1998), https://hbr.org/1998/07/what-drives-the-wealth-of-nations, accessed on 1 October 2021.

2. Diego Comin, The Evolution of Technology Diffusion and the Great Divergence, Brookings (August 2016), https://www.brookings.edu/

wp-content/uploads/2016/08/session-3-leapfrogging-comin_post-final.pdf, accessed on 1 October 2021.

3. Ibid.

4. 'New Economy Drivers and Disrupters Report', Bloomberg (October 2019), https://www.bloomberg.com/graphics/2019-new-economy-drivers-and-disrupters/, accessed on 1 October 2021.

5. 'Digital in the Time of Covid'.

6. 'Digital 2020: Global Digital Overview' (January 2020), https://datareportal.com/reports/digital-2020-global-digital-overview, accessed on 1 October 2021.

7. 'The 2015 BCG e-Intensity Index', Boston Consulting Group (November 2015), https://www.bcg.com/publications/interactives/bcg-e-intensity-index, accessed on 1 October 2021.

8. 'The Future of Asia: How Asia Can Boost Growth through Technological Leapfrogging', McKinsey Global Institute, Discussion Paper (December 2020), https://www.mckinsey.com/~/media/mckinsey/featured insights/asia pacific/how asia can boost growth through technological leapfrogging/mgi future of asia-technology_discussion paper_december 2020.pdf?shouldIndex=false, accessed on 1 October 2021.

9. Matilde Mas et al., The 2020 PREDICT Report Key Facts Report, Publications Office of the European Union (2020), doi:10.2760/291872, JRC121153, https://publications.jrc.ec.europa.eu/repository/handle/JRC121153, accessed on 1 October 2021.

10. Ibid.

11. Robert Muggah et al., 'The Dark Side of Digitalization—And How to Fix It', World Economic Forum (September 2020), https://www.weforum.org/agenda/2020/09/dark-side-digitalization/, accessed on 1 October 2021.

12. Indermit Gill, 'Whoever Leads in Artificial Intelligence in 2030 Will Rule the World until 2100', Brookings (January 2020),

https://www.brookings.edu/blog/future-development/2020/01/17/whoever-leads-in-artificial-intelligence-in-2030-will-rule-the-world-until-2100/, accessed on 1 October, 2021.

13. Comin, 'The Evolution of Technology Diffusion'.

14. Digital Intelligence Index, 'Digital in The Time Of Covid', Digital Planet, The Fletcher School at Tufts University (December 2020), https://sites.tufts.edu/digitalplanet/files/2020/12/digital-intelligence-index.pdf, accessed on 1 October 2021.

15. 'Digital Globalization', McKinsey.

16. Ibid.

17. UNCTAD, Digital Economy Report 2021.

18. Matilde Mas et al., The 2020 PREDICT Report.

19. Clayton Christensen, *The Innovator's Dilemma: When New Technologies Cause Great Firms to Fail* (Harvard Business Review Press, 1997), Kindle.

20. Hermann Simon, *Hidden Champions of the Twenty-First Century: Success Strategies of Unknown World Market Leaders* (Springer New York, 2009), Kindle.

21. Sridhar Vembu, 'Interview with Harichandan Arakali', *Forbes* (August 2017), https://www.forbesindia.com/article/bootstrapped-bosses/vcs-can-end-up-using-young-men-and-women-as-cannon-fodder-zohos-sridhar-vembu/47835/1, accessed on 30 September 2021.

22. Ricardo Hausmann, 'What Should Countries Do to Catch Up? The Challenge of Technology Diffusion', *OECD,* https://www.oecd.org/naec/events/understanding-the-economy/the-challenge-of-technology-diffusion.htm, accessed on 4 October 2021.

23. 'The Race to 5G', Arthur D. Little (March 2019), https://www.adlittle.com/sites/default/files/reports/adl_the_race_to_5g_report_-min.pdf, accessed on 1 October 2021.

24. Patrick Moorehead, 'Who Is "Really" Leading in Mobile 5G—Part I', *Forbes* (May 2019), https://www.forbes.com/sites/patrickmoorhead/2019/05/15/who-is-really-leading-in-mobile-5g-

part-1-tech-innovations-and-standards/?sh=5a09bc9aa6a8, accessed on 1 October 2021.

25. Will Townsend, 'Who Is "Really" Leading in Mobile 5G—Part 6', *Forbes* (October 2019), https://www.forbes.com/sites/moorinsights/2019/10/12/who-is-really-leading-in-mobile-5g-part-6-policy-regulation-and-consortia/?sh=71e4e8122755, accessed on 1 October 2021.

26. Campbell Kwan, 'Reliance Jio Spends ₹57,100 Crore at Indian Spectrum Auction', ZDNet (March 2021), https://www.zdnet.com/article/reliance-jio-spends-inr57100-crore-at-indian-spectrum-auction/, accessed on 1 October 2021.

27. Campbell Kwan, 'Reliance Jio Chairman Announces Plans for 5G Rollout in Latter Half of 2021', ZDNet (December 2020), https://www.zdnet.com/article/reliance-jio-chairman-announces-plans-for-5g-rollout-in-latter-half-of-2021/, accessed on 1 October 2021.

28. 'Jio Platforms to Use NXP Multicore Processors in 5G NR O-RAN Small Cell for New Use Cases', *The Economic Times* (June 2021), https://telecom.economictimes.indiatimes.com/news/jio-platforms-to-use-nxp-multicore-processors-in-5g-nr-o-ran-small-cell-for-new-use-cases/83952761, accessed on 1 October 2021.

29. Mary Hallward-Driemeier and Gaurav Nayyar, 'Trouble in the Making?: The Future of Manufacturing-Led Development', The World Bank (2017), https://www.worldbank.org/en/topic/competitiveness/publication/trouble-in-the-making-the-future-of-manufacturing-led-development, accessed on 1 October 2021.

30. Ibid.

31. Ibid.

32. 'Shaping India's SaaS Landscape: Built in India, Built for the World', SaaSBOOMi—McKinsey report, July 2021, https://www.slideshare.net/SocialSaaSBOOMi/saasboomi-saas-landscape-report-2021, accessed on 1 October 2021.

33. Debjani Ghosh, 'The War for Digital Talent: India Can Emerge as a Global Hub for It', *Mint* (September 2021), https://www.livemint.

com/opinion/online-views/the-war-for-digital-talent-india-can-emerge-as-a-global-hub-for-it-11632847335532.html, accessed on 29 September 2021.

34. Sridhar Vembu, 'Importance of Deep Tech Knowhow for India', NASSCOM Emerge 50 Awards 2020 (February 2021), https://www.youtube.com/watch?v=KEnpPBMEYuQ, accessed on 29 September 2021.

35. Bhaskar Chakravorti, et al., 'Digital in the Time of Covid: Digital Intelligence Index', *Digital Planet*, The Fletcher School at Tufts University, https://sites.tufts.edu/digitalplanet/files/2021/03/digital-intelligence-index.pdf, accessed on 29 September 2021.

36. Brad Smith and Carol Ann Browne, *Tools and Weapons: The Promise and the Peril of the Digital Age*, (Hodder & Stoughton, 2021), p. 64.

37. Ari Levy, 'Why Silicon Valley Likes Ireland So Much', CNBC.com, August 2016, https://www.cnbc.com/2016/08/31/why-silicon-valley-followed-apple-to-ireland-eventually.html, accessed on 1 October 2021.

38. 'Brexit and the Irish Technology Sector', Frontier Economics Report, https://www.technology-ireland.ie/Sectors/TI/TI.nsf/vPages/Influence~Working_Groups~data-working-group/$file/TI+Brexit+Impact+Report+WEB.pdf, accessed on 1 October 2021.

39. Brad Smith and Carol Ann Browne, *Tools and Weapons: The Promise and the Peril of the Digital Age* (Hodder & Stoughton, 2021), p. 64

40. Sinead O'Sullivan, 'Is Ireland Using Its Diplomatic Superpower for Good or Evil?', *The Irish Times* (August 2020), https://www.irishtimes.com/opinion/is-ireland-using-its-diplomatic-superpower-for-good-or-evil-1.4332288, accessed on 1 October 2021.

41. '2020 United Nations E-Government Survey', United Nations Department of Economic and Social Affairs (July 2020), https://www.un.org/development/desa/publications/publication/2020-united-nations-e-government-survey, accessed on 4 October 2021.

42. 'India Stack', https://www.indiastack.org/, accessed on 29 September 2021.

43. Joint Statement by the Republic of Singapore and the Republic of India, June 2018, https://www.pmo.gov.sg/Newsroom/joint-statement-republic-singapore-and-republic-india, accessed on 29 September 2021.

44. Harichandan Arakali, 'How TCS Trumped IBM's Market Value', *Forbes* (June 2019), https://www.forbesindia.com/article/leaderboard/how-tcs-trumped-ibms-market-value/53983/1, accessed on 1 October 2021.

45. 'Science: The Endless Frontier', A Report to the President by Vannevar Bush, Director of the Office of Scientific Research and Development (July 1945), https://www.nsf.gov/od/lpa/nsf50/vbush1945.htm#ch6.3, accessed on 1 October 2021.

46. Piketty, *Capital in the Twenty-First Century*.

47. Ibid.

48. Ibid.

49. Comin, *The Evolution of Technology Diffusion*.

50. Gino Gancia and Fabrizio Zilibotti, 'Technological Change and the Wealth of Nations', *Annual Review of Economics* 1, no. 1, (2009): 93–120, https://www.annualreviews.org/doi/pdf/10.1146/annurev.economics.050708.143333, accessed on 1 October 2021.

PART THREE

~

TECHNOLOGY, GEOPOLITICS AND THE NEW WORLD ORDER

'If we have learned anything in the past century, it is that technology confers power, but that the consequences of that power are anything but predictable.'

—Daniel R. Headrick, *The Invisible Weapon* (2012)

'A revolution cannot be mastered until it is understood.'

—Henry Kissinger, *Nuclear Weapons and Foreign Policy* (1957)

'These are the stakes in play: working out how to shape and control the internet means working out how to shape and, to an extent, control the world.'

—James Ball, *The System* (2020)

The Geopolitics of Technology

Geopolitics has historically been linked with territory, international politics and strategic objectives of nation states. Typically, geopolitical objectives would revolve around acquisition, protection and expansion of territorial borders, trading routes or strategically important militarily bases. That would constitute their strategic advantage.

In essence, geopolitics has been about the intersection of geography, politics, strategy and foreign policy. Starting from the Mediterranean powers such as the Minoans and the Phoenicians, Greek city-states, the colonial empires all the way to the American empire, geopolitics has retained these characteristics. The Greek city-states and Romans were fighting for grain, and access to fertile, irrigated land. The Mediterranean trading powers were fighting for trading routes and trading rights. The Islamic empires similarly fought to maintain control of the markets and trading points connecting the East and the West.

The European empires of Britain and France were fighting for colonies, natural resources, and trading rights across the Indian, Atlantic and Pacific Oceans. For the British colonial empire, geopolitics was about acquiring control of more colonial territories, strategic trade routes and choke points such as the Straits of Malacca and the Suez Canal from strategic rivals such as Russia and France. And that is how the academics and practitioners of geopolitics—the likes of Emil Reich,

Alfred Mahan, Halford Mackinder, Henry Kissinger and Zbigniew Brzezinski—have understood it.

But there is a tectonic shift underway as the arena of geopolitical rivalry shifts to technological competition. Even as most of the traditional dimensions of geopolitics continue to remain relevant, a new significant layer has been added to geopolitics: technology. States are increasingly realizing that 'technology will give them a strategic advantage in the twenty-first century'.[1] Today, the major powers in the world believe that 'if you can get ahead in the technology race now, you'll stay ahead for a very long time'.[2] The strategic advantage is not just economic; rather, it spans the geopolitical and security spheres as well. While battles between Big Tech and governments continue to dominate mainstream media, behind the closed doors of government offices, many nations and governments are actually figuring out how they can leverage technological advancement to further their role in the world order.

This is a big change. Until a couple of decades ago, the internet was left largely to fend for itself. But governments across the world are now realizing that they need to think strategically about controlling the technologies that are shaping our world today. Increasingly, countries are realizing that their strategic objectives in the technology era are sowing the seeds for conflict with other nations.

The key question is, what is that new valuable resource or strategic advantage that countries would go to war over? I believe that resource today is information or data, and more broadly, technology. And the major powers of the world are engaged in an era-defining competition for technological dominance.

First, along with the strategically important shipping routes, we now have strategically critical information infrastructure such as undersea fibre optic cables and data centres. These are essentially 'information highways'—the 'technology silk routes'—and their security has become strategically important in geopolitical terms.

Major technology powers are now also fighting for access and control of digital markets. Technology is the new shaper of our economic destinies, so the technologically advanced nations (and their tech firms) are fighting hard to keep their opponents out of these markets. So just like the British and the French were competing for colonies from where they could extract resources, the Americans and the Chinese are competing aggressively for control of new digital markets. Nations are also fighting to be the major suppliers of critical technologies for the world, such as 5G, often to the exclusion of their rivals. And where needed, they will end up dividing up the markets amongst themselves (just like the European colonial powers had split up the world amongst themselves).

The major powers are also fighting over control and dominance of emerging technologies like 5G, AI, genetic engineering, and climate and food technology, which will shape future economic growth. These technologies promise to transform the destinies of nations, much like the mobile and the internet has done in the last couple of decades. Self-sufficiency, reliable access and even dominance, where possible, of those technologies, have become critical geopolitical concerns of nations.

And for that, they are building new alliances and friendships, and sometimes even breaking old ties. In addition to the traditional determinants of these relationships, such as a strategic geographical location or a shared cultural affinity, the strength of a country's technological capability, or the attractiveness and size of its technology market, will shape new friendships, alliances and enemies.

States—at least the geopolitically savvy nations—will look to ensure they are not reliant on unfriendly states for their core technology needs. Think, for example, of how the US—given its geopolitical concerns around oil supply—worked hard over the decades to build self-sufficiency and reduce, if not eliminate, its reliance on untrustworthy nations. Today, the US is working to eliminate its reliance on undependable nations for semiconductors and rare earths and other such critical resources.

The list goes on. Going forward, geopolitics and technology will merge in ways that we can probably not even fathom right now. But for now, let us examine the aspects discussed above in greater detail.

Notes

1. John Ludlow, 'The Impact of Technology on Geopolitical Risk' (November 2019), https://csuite.raconteur.net/business-risk/the-impact-of-technology-on-geopolitical-risk/, accessed on 1 October 2021.
2. Ibid.

6

The Geopolitics of Technology
Silk Routes

One of the key domains today that the global technological competition is playing out in is the control of the internet—infrastructure, content, norms, rules of conduct, standards and security. The ability to control the internet is becoming a source of state power and influence, both domestically and internationally.

A peek back into history to see the future: the telegraph and geopolitics

Neither the desire to access information, nor to control information and communication networks, is new. Access to information has been at the core of security and geopolitics for a long time. Going back centuries, governments have had a deep-rooted need for information, arising probably from their desire to retain power and legitimacy. Even the earliest rulers would maintain a network of spies and agents to know and control any likely challenges to their power.[1] Similarly, control of information networks, especially the ones leveraging technology, have often been used for strategic advantage, especially in the last 150–200 years.

The history of the telegraph provides an illustrative example of how technology has shaped the geopolitics and geo-economics of the world in the recent past. It not only impacted the relations between nations and empires, it also shaped the outcome of at least one world war if not two.

In the nineteenth and twentieth centuries, Britain had developed a monopolistic dominance of the telegraph communications network of the world. The British Eastern Telegraph Company alone manufactured between half to two-thirds of cables in the world at that time. Of the roughly thirty ships that could lay cables around the world, twenty-four were owned by the British.[2] The British, strategically, encouraged other countries such as the US and Germany to lay their cables in and around Britain, with the effect that 'their communications came under British control in wartime'.[3]

The potent combination of manufacturing expertise, ownership of physical infrastructure, strategic influence over cables routes, control of essential raw materials for manufacturing cables such as latex wrap, unmatched cable-laying and cable-repair capabilities, and domination of international standards for telegraph technology, all meant that the British control of the telegraph industry was complete.[4]

This dominance conferred at least two immensely strategic advantages on Britain. One, this 'strategic backbone to the empire' helped reinforce the dominance of British military and naval forces throughout the world and secure their colonies.[5] Two, the strategic vision and decision to control these routes proved 'prescient' during the world wars that followed the escalation of the rivalry among Europe's great powers.

In August 1914, for example, a day after Britain declared war on Germany, it cut Germany's telegraph cables, which would then remain out of service for the remainder of the war. The British leveraged the telegraph networks to isolate their opponents, cut off their communication with their respective militaries, and impose an economic blockage.[6] In fact, during both the world wars, British dominance of the telecommunication networks would prove absolutely critical.[7]

On the defence front, the British realized that their telegraph networks—especially those that passed through rival territory—were also prone to attack and espionage by their rivals, such as the French and the Russians. In 1866, the Select Committee of the British House of Commons concluded:

> That, having regard to the magnitude of the interests, political, commercial, and social, involved in the connection between this country and India, it is not expedient that the means of intercommunication by telegraph should be dependent upon any single line, or any single system of wires, in the hands of several foreign governments, and under several distinct responsibilities, however well such services may be conducted as a whole, in time of peace.[8]

The Select Committee decided to introduce 'network resilience' and 'redundancy'(the same strategies for defence continue to be utilized today). By the dawn of the twentieth century, the British government had laid an exclusive system of cables between Britain and its colonies, called the 'All Red' routes, while simultaneously building an unmatched capacity to disable the cable networks of rivals.

The telegraph, much like the internet, was not initially envisioned as a geopolitical tool. As Headrick describes, until 1850, the telegraph networks were used to 'speed up the everyday interactions between peoples', much like the internet networks of today. The rapid expansion of the telegraph network globally increased the reliance of nations (and their militaries) on the communications made possible by the telegraph. As trade using these networks increased and great power rivalry developed, as is again happening today, the major powers of the day—Britain and France then—began to value the telegraph 'as a means of projecting their will upon others'.[9] So, in many cases, governments of nations like France and Britain would end up pushing for greater emphasis on laying telegraph lines to new places, so that they could maintain 'contact with their armies on distant battlefields'.[10]

Just as technology then was shaping geopolitics, geopolitics was also shaping technology as well. Military and economic considerations would also move Japan to push for its first telegraph cable connection with the West through the Pacific Submarine Cable in 1906[11] (its Korea cable had proved to be an essential strategic asset during a war with China in the 1890s).[12] Similarly, the US had begun to grasp the military and economic significance of these telegraph networks. Realizing these networks were critical for communications between Spain and its colonies, US naval officers began to use the Caribbean telegraph stations to monitor Spanish naval movements around 1894. Then, in 1896, when the Spanish Governor-General refused to grant the US the right to use it, Lt. William W. Kimball would recommend cutting the submarine cable between Manila and Hong Kong (and also the cables on the Cuban coast for good measure).[13] In 1900, in a speech to the US Naval War College, Capt. George O. Squier of the US Army Signal Corps would state that the Spanish-American war had 'for the first time demonstrated the dominating influence of submarine cable communications in the conduct of a naval war'.[14]

The vulnerability of these lines of communication and the geopolitically risky dependence that nations such as France and Germany had 'on the goodwill of Great Britain' led many of them to attempt to build and subsidize their own All Red-style exclusive telegraph networks. Unfortunately, this telegraph arms race only served to further instigate mutual suspicion and rivalry. It would even contribute to bringing the nations to the brink of war. As Headrick describes:

> By 1914, instantaneous communications, far from smoothing out misunderstandings between the powers, only sharpened the jitters of nervous governments teetering on the brink of war. In the hopes of freeing themselves from their dependence on foreign cables, all

the great powers helped push the infant technology of radio into an early adolescence. Telecommunications, once hailed as a miracle and later regarded as a public utility, had become a political tool in the rivalry between great powers.[15]

The two world wars further accelerated the politicization and weaponization of telecommunications networks.[16] While news, business and private messages were the critical forms of information that travelled over these networks during peace time, three other forms of information—propaganda, secrets and intelligence—would start to flow over the telegraph networks.

As the emerging power of that time, the US witnessed the adverse impact British capabilities and hegemony had on the Germans in World War I. In 1914, the Americans had seen the British cable ship *Alert* cut off Germany's five Atlantic submarine telegraph cables that linked Germany to France, Spain and the Azores, and onwards to the United States itself.[17] In 1917, they had seen Germany retaliate by cutting a series of cables connecting Britain, Portugal and Gibraltar, using its U-Boats and submarines equipped with specialized cutting equipment.[18]

Witnessing these events made real the 'potential danger of the United States' being isolated from places of commercial, political, or military significance'.[19] Realizing its own potential vulnerability, the US would begin the process of laying the foundation for its own strategic communications network. It would be this foundation that would, just in a few decades, 'undergird the rise of the United States to global power in the mid-twentieth century'.[20]

World War II was in many ways 'a replay of World War I with more advanced technologies'.[21] The British again used their mastery of communications—combined with skilled decryption technology this time—to penetrate Germany's most secret codes and ciphers, even as the Americans did the same with Japan.[22] And the impact was equally significant. Famously, in 1945, as World War II came to a close, Winston Churchill stated that Bletchley Park (the precursor to Government Communications Headquarters (GCHQ), the British intelligence agency equivalent of the National Security Agency (NSA) responsible for communications decryption) had proven to be the deciding factor in the British victory.[23] With this historical context, it is not surprising then that today China is seeking to build its own Digital Silk Roads infrastructure as the foundation for its own emergence as a global power in the twenty-first century.

The geopolitics of the technology silk routes in the twenty-first century

The parallels with today are clear. The great powers of today—the US, the UK, China and Russia—have started to view the internet as a means of power projection today; therefore, ownership and control of information infrastructures like fibre cable networks, 5G networks and satellites, have become a key bone of contention. The internet infrastructure today that I refer to as the 'technology silk routes' primarily comprises undersea fibre optic cables, data centres and cloud networks. And much like we saw with the telegraph networks, the ownership, location and security of this infrastructure have become a geopolitically charged matter.

The undersea fibre optic cable network

The internet is essentially a network, connecting computers and servers using primarily undersea fibre optic cables. Since these cables are more efficient than satellites for flows of large amounts of data, over 95 per cent of the internet traffic flows across the world through cables. There are approximately just 400 oceanic cables around the world today, spanning about 1.2 million kilometres. A map of the world with the cables is shown below (Map 6.1).

The telegraph networks and then the fibre optic internet cables have been superimposed on the oceanic trading routes of the colonial and industrial eras. The first telegraph cable was laid across the Atlantic

Map 6.1 Submarine Cable Map, 2019

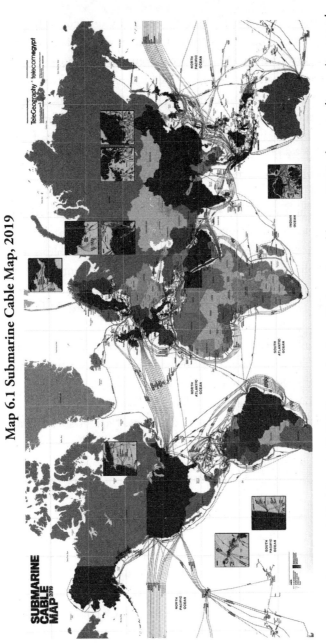

Source: 'Submarine Cable Map 2019', TeleGeography, https://submarine-cable-map-2019.telegeography.com/, accessed on 30 June 2021.

Ocean between the US and the UK over 150 years ago. At that time, colonial networks and ties shaped which routes were picked. Therefore, the British set up telegraph cables between the UK and their former and current colonies such as the US and India, and the French did the same. In more recent times, the fibre optic cable networks have been laid along the same routes as the telegraph cable network. In fact, even the landing points have remained the same in this transition from the telegraph to the fibre optic cable network.

During peacetime, these cables are just like any other piece of regional or global infrastructure like intercontinental roads or rail networks. Those who own, control and secure them have the advantage of being able to also monitor all the traffic that flows through them. In wartime, the ownership and security of these data cables—as with the telegraph cables in the nineteenth and twentieth century—matters even more, given these fibre optic cables now form the primary telecommunications backbone for all economic, political, diplomatic and military activity today.

Laying an undersea cable is a multi-year process, costing millions of dollars. The cables themselves are owned today by a mix of government and private bodies, with the latter owning the majority of them. A surge in submarine fibre optic cables has been underway since 2016, as internet traffic and cross-border data flows have boomed. Between 2016 and 2020, TeleGeograpy had estimated that 107 new submarine cables had been deployed with a value of almost $14 billion. As of 2021, estimates suggest that around 1.3 million km of cables are in service globally.[24]

Google, Facebook, Microsoft and other technology giants are quietly buying up, or investing in, this network. For example, Google owns major shares of over 100,000 km of submarine cables. In other words, Google holds partial or sole ownership of almost 10 per cent of the submarine cables. Facebook is not far behind, co-owning about 92,000 km of cables, followed by Amazon (approximately 19,000 km) and Microsoft (approximately 4,000 km).

As their requirements increase and rivalries intensify, content and cloud service providers such as Google, Facebook, Amazon and Microsoft are also increasingly building private cables to support their cloud services, especially from their servers in the US to content consumers in Asia. Global demand for underwater cable bandwidth is growing rapidly each year. In 2018 alone, US administration officials have estimated that Google, Facebook, Amazon and Microsoft spent almost $40 billion in capex on network infrastructure like undersea cables, making them effectively the largest investors now in undersea cable routes.[25]

Companies like SubCom (based in New Jersey), Alcatel Submarine Networks (Nokia-owned, based in France), Fujitsu (based in Japan), HMN Technologies (formerly Huawei Marine Networks, based in China) and NEC (based in Japan) are among the leading designers, manufacturers and operators of submarine cables. In case of a military conflict between nations in the future, the firms that manufacture, operate and repair these cables will become critical in restoring internet access if disrupted intentionally by adversaries. Countries that do not have strategic partnerships with such firms (for example, India or even Russia, or smaller nations like Vietnam or Cuba) might find themselves at a disadvantage in case of a conflict involving damage of cables by a stronger power with strategic access to these firms (e.g., the US, France, China or Japan).

Data centres and edge networks

The other backbone of the internet is data centres and edge networks. Data centres are essentially just a collection of computers and servers connected to the internet (see image 6.1). Companies like Google and Facebook own multiple mammoth data centres across the world, though these are largely concentrated in Europe and North America. As map 6.2 shows, Google only owns two data centres in Asia and one in Latin America, compared to five in Europe and thirteen in the US.

Image 6.1 Inside the data centres

Source: Google Data Centres Gallery, Google, https://www.google.com/about/datacenters/gallery/, accessed on 30 June 2021.

Map 6.2: Google global data centre network, 2021

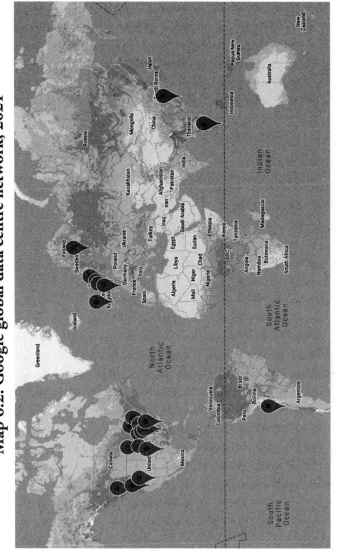

Source: Google Data Centre Locations, Google,
https://www.google.com/about/datacenters/locations/, accessed on 30 June 2021.

Map 6.3: Facebook's FNA Node Network

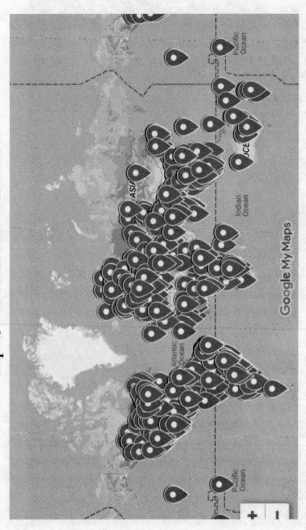

Source: 'Mapping Facebook's FNA (CDN) nodes across the world', https://anuragbhatia.com/2018/03/networking/isp-column/mapping-facebooks-fna-cdn-nodes-across-the-world/, accessed on 1 October 2021.

Then there are the edge networks or content delivery networks (CDNs). Many content providers, such as Google, Facebook and Netflix, are now increasingly resorting to building their 'private' internets. That means that they are storing content that is likely to be requested by users in a given region in privately owned regional data centres. This private infrastructure, called edge networks or CDNs, decrease the stress on the server-to-user undersea data traffic. Google has built an extensive edge node network (called the Google Global Cache, or GGC), while Facebook's equivalent network is called Facebook Network Appliance (FNA) Node Network (see map 6.3). The number of these edge nodes will range from a few hundred to a few thousand for each firm and are locally managed by ISP partners of the firms. For example, Facebook's edge nodes in India are being managed by firms such as Bharti Airtel, Jio and Idea Cellular.

Geopolitical implications

Though the undersea cables and the edge node or CDN networks have not received their due attention in strategic circles in many governments, they are a critical, yet vulnerable, component of the internet and communications infrastructure of the world today, with significant security and economic consequences.[26] From the perspective of geopolitics, a few key implications stand out from the emerging web of internet infrastructure.

First, most of the cables are owned by Big Tech firms based in the US. The US dominance of the internet networks is quite similar to the British dominance of the telegraph networks. And just like the British, the US, in wartime or otherwise, has the capability of tapping or even cutting off the internet for large or even specific parts of the rest of the world. This fear of US capabilities on this front might partly also explain why Russia has been keen on developing its own 'sovereign internet' that can continue to function even if the 'outside' internet is cut off.

Second, the security of these cables is also threatened by the capabilities of various nations to sever these cables. A *New York Times* article in 2015, for example, had pointed out that Russian submarines were detected operating near certain vital undersea cables. This had raised serious concerns among the Americans about Russian intentions to attack those cables during a conflict.[27] The damage to the broader economy could be immense from such a sabotage attack on these undersea cables.

Third, large sectors of the economy, including the financial services sectors, could 'snap to a halt' in the event of any major disruptions.[28] In a 2012 paper published by the Harvard Kennedy School, Michael Sechrist had estimated that, given that the SWIFT international wire transfer network uses these cables to transmit financial transaction data to over 195 countries, widespread disruption to undersea communications networks could sabotage daily international financial transactions worth over $10 trillion.[29]

The edge networks or CDNs also open up the opportunity for very specifically targeted attacks. For example, in June 2021, a massive internet outage affected websites such as Amazon, Reddit, Gov.uk, CNN and *The New York Times*, due to the failure of a CDN network run by a company called Fastly. Given the localized nature of CDN networks, the failure was experienced in specific locations around the world only but not others.[30] Targeted outages, therefore, also become possible.

Fourth, much like the telegraph networks, these cables and edge networks offer opportunities for espionage. An article in *The Guardian* in 2013,[31] citing documents provided by NSA whistleblower Edward Snowden, had suggested that the British agency, GCHQ, had secretly gained access to as many as 200 of these fibre-optic cables. Similarly, US agencies such as the NSA were alleged to have tapped these cables with the cooperation of the private players operating these cables.[32]

Companies that rely on secure transfer of data via these cables have designed their data flows keeping potential monitoring, intentional damage or regular outages in mind. The data flowing through these cables is now increasingly encrypted to prevent unauthorized access of the data, and companies have also built 'redundancies' into the system. That means that the same data might be distributed across multiple routes so that even if there is an outage on a particular cable, the customers are not affected. In the 1860s, you may recall, the British Select Committee had similarly recommended building redundancies in their cables given concerns of their disruption led by the Russians or the French.

But at the same time, each region is only being serviced by a finite number of cables, and decryption technologies are getting more and more sophisticated. Since the specific locations of these cables are more or less known, it increases the likelihood of such disruptions being used for political or military purposes.

Finally, the location spread of this infrastructure is being managed strategically, and also has economic, strategic and security implications. Most data centres are based in Europe and North America, though Asia has also started to catch up recently (see Map 6.4). Yet companies like Facebook have refused to set up data centres in their largest markets in Asia, such as India, due to concerns around security and the data localization requirements of nations. This indirectly also implies that the firms and countries in these continents now own the data of other continents. To the extent that this data is valuable—both economically and strategically—the countries in Asia, Africa and Latin America believe they are effectively handing over control of a strategic resource.

The battles over the internet infrastructure have begun

The US and China have already been engaged in strategic battles over the undersea cable network already, showcasing how contentious this layer of the internet infrastructure is likely to become. Countries are starting to pressurize firms within their jurisdictions to refrain from building certain links. A recent example has been the Pacific Light Cable Network project that was supposed to connect the US, the Philippines, Taiwan and Hong Kong.[33] The project was being undertaken by the

Map 6.4: Data centres around the world

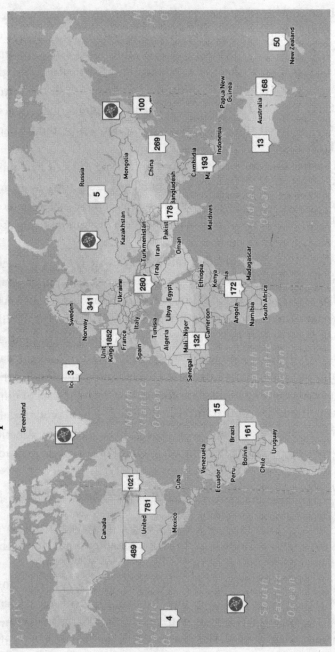

Source: 'DataCente.rs World Map', https://www.datacente.rs/, accessed on 1 October 2021.

New Jersey-based SubCom, PLDCC (a Hong Kong subsidiary of a Chinese telecom major), Facebook and Google.

Team Telecom—an executive branch group comprising the US Departments of Justice, Defense and Homeland Security, charged with reviewing the national security risks associated with foreign ownership for entities with pending applications before the Federal Communications Commission (FCC)[34]—opposed the project. The grounds put forth were concerns that the Hong Kong link of this cable would expose data flows of the US to China, and greatly benefit Chinese efforts at data espionage.[35] In August 2020, Facebook and Google fell in line, and submitted a revised plan to take the cables up to Taiwan and the Philippines but not Hong Kong.[36] Similarly, in September 2020, Facebook, Amazon and China Mobile also withdrew their bid to connect San Francisco and Hong Kong as part of the Bay to Bay Express Cable System.[37]

The pattern of who is building and laying submarine cables where in the world also follows a geopolitical divide. For example, Huawei Marine Networks (HMN)—earlier a subsidiary of Huawei but now owned by a Chinese-listed, state-level enterprise, Hengtong—is active in areas with greater Chinese influence. For example, it is currently building the Maldives–Sri Lanka Cable,[38] the Senegal Horn of Africa Cable,[39] the Pakistan–East Africa–Europe cable,[40] among others. Similarly, the Pacific Islands are also facing a similar dilemma where they are under pressure from the US to avoid HMN bids for their undersea cable projects, but HMN is often bidding at prices as low as 20 per cent below their competitors.[41] Strategic and financial objectives are clashing, creating a difficult decision for smaller nations.

While the US, Japan, France, Sweden, Singapore and China have companies that are major players in the business of laying, operating and repairing undersea cables, large internet markets and economies such as India, Brazil, Russia and Indonesia are missing completely. These countries must work out a strategy to either compete in this space or build strategic partnerships to ensure that this doesn't become their Achilles heel.

For the nations that host the major players, it is important to consider taking responsibility—or oversight—of repair capabilities of undersea infrastructure, especially at international choke points where often large amounts of data capacity are being funnelled into dense areas like major cities.[42] Instead of seeing them entirely as a commercial responsibility of players such as Facebook and Google, governments must develop a joint public–private operational plan to reduce the response time to an attack on these cables. In addition, international law must push for stronger legal protection of this infrastructure, and criminalize attacks on submarine cables.

Rishi Sunak, now Chancellor of the Treasury of the UK, in his report on undersea cables in 2017, also warned against neglect of this matter by national governments. He highlighted the deficiencies in international law (such as the United Nations Convention on the Law of the Sea) in giving states adequate jurisdiction and powers to deal with potential attacks on these cables. The current laws, Sunak argued, were more suited to an earlier era, not to the current era where these cable networks have become indispensable to the economic and national security of nations.[43]

Finally, the private tech players must also beef up the security of this infrastructure and invest in better technology for not just encryption, but detection of efforts at undersea espionage or disruption.[44] Together with governments, the private players must also consider establishing undersea cable protection zones in areas that have high value or high density of such cables. In addition, diversifying the geographic spread of the cables and landing sites—along with setting up of redundant 'dark cables'—would help build greater security for the entire system.[45]

Key Conclusions

The American experience, as a rising power on the eve of World War I, is equally instructive for our world today. Today, in many ways, China is to America what America was to Britain at that time. Despite their keenness, the Americans had not been able to build their own undersea cables directly to Europe or even other locations because of British monopolistic control of the manufacturing expertise and the essential raw materials.[46,47] The British also imposed discriminatory pricing on the cost of sending messages through the cables in South America or Asia.[48] Altogether, these real geopolitical constraints 'left the United States dependent upon foreign powers for its vital communications in a time of great need'.[49]

Clearly, the strategic thinkers in the US have learned their lessons from history. Similarly, it would not be difficult—especially for emerging powers like the Chinese today—to imagine a situation where they would end up being dependent upon the United States 'for its vital communications in a time of great need'.

Therefore, countries (and Big Tech firms) must think very strategically about the networks they rely on, and the way these networks might get impacted during periods of war or conflict. The control of the internet infrastructure today and the ability to defend one's networks and damage those of the opponents will prove extremely potent in case of a future escalation of conflict between the major powers. No wonder that Russia is working hard today to build its own 'sovereign internet' and the Chinese are busy building their own undersea fibre optic cables. The Digital Silk Roads initiative of China must be seen within this context as well.

And again, these are not concerns reserved for major powers alone. As we saw during the telegraph era, control of these information networks is just as critical for smaller nations as well. For them, the value of controlling the information flows might become evident when their independence or survival is under threat, but by that time it might be too late to act. Sensing a vacuum that might be filled by its adversaries like Russia or China, the British have started investing in boosting the cyber-defences of 'vulnerable countries' in Africa and the Indo-Pacific.[50]

Both the telegraph and the internet have gone through a very similar journey: from being largely benign tools of communication to being major contributors to increased tensions and rivalry between the major powers of the day. Governments at the turn of the twentieth century had recognized that these telecommunications networks were increasingly fundamental to national security and economic advancement, and therefore acted accordingly. And finally, it is important to remember that along with military might, it was often with communications and communications intelligence and decryption that the Americans and the British won the world wars. Some governments in the twenty-first century remember these lessons from a hundred years ago, but others might learn the hard way.

Yet, during their day, the telegraph networks also accelerated the course of war, overcoming the delays created by traditional diplomacy and other customs. Today, similarly, the internet is making rivalries more volatile, and cyberattacks too easy to carry out, all without waiting for diplomacy to do its job. One can only hope that it does not accelerate a major war like the telegraph did.

Notes

1. Daniel R. Headrick, *The Invisible Weapon* (Oxford University Press), Kindle.

2. Jonathan E. Hillman, *The Emperor's New Road* (Yale University Press), Kindle.

3. Jonathan Reed Winkler, *Nexus: Strategic Communications and American Security in World War I*, Harvard Historical Studies (Harvard University Press, 2008)Kindle, loc. 147.

4. Hillman, *The Emperor's New Road*.

5. Winkler, *Nexus*.

6. Winkler, *Nexus*.

7. Hillman, *The Emperor's New Road*.

8. Ibid.

9. Ibid.

10. Headrick, *The Invisible Weapon*.

11. Tomoko Hasegawa, 'The Pacific Submarine Cable and Its Impact on Japan in the 19th Century', Open Access Library Journal, 3: e3001. http://dx.doi.org/10.4236/oalib.1103001, accessed on 1 October 2021.

12. Daqing Yang, *Technology of Empire* (Harvard University Asia Center, 2010).

13. Jonathan Reed Winkler, 'Silencing the Enemy: Cable-Cutting in the Spanish–American War', WarOnTheRocks (November 2015), https://warontherocks.com/2015/11/silencing-the-enemy-cable-cutting-in-the-spanish-american-war/, accessed on 1 October 2021.

14. Ibid.

15. Headrick, *The Invisible Weapon*.

16. Ibid.

17. Winkler, *Nexus*.

18. Mark Stout, 'Trans-Atlantic Bandwidth: Then and Now', WarOnTheRocks (October 2015), https://warontherocks.com/2015/10/trans-atlantic-bandwidth-then-and-now/, accessed on 1 October 2021.

19. Winkler, *Nexus*.

20. Ibid.

21. Headrick, *The Invisible Weapon*.

22. Ibid.

23. Richard J. Aldrich, *GCHQ: The Uncensored Story of Britain's Most Secret Intelligence Agency* (HarperCollins GB, 2010), Kindle.

24. 'Submarine Cable 101', TeleGeography, https://www2.telegeography.com/submarine-cable-faqs-frequently-asked-questions#Cable-101, accessed on 1 October 2021.

25. John Hendel and Betsy Woodruff Swan, 'Justice Department Opposes Google, Facebook Cable Link to Hong Kong', *Politico*, June 2020, https://www.politico.com/news/2020/06/17/justice-department-hong-kong-google-facebook-cable-326688, accessed on 1 October 2021.

26. James Griffiths, 'The Global Internet Is Powered by Vast Undersea Cables. But They're Vulnerable', CNN (July 2019), https://edition. cnn.com/2019/07/25/asia/internet-undersea-cables-intl-hnk/index. html, accessed on 1 October 2021.

27. David Sanger and Eric Schmitt, 'Russian Ships Near Data Cables Are Too Close for US Comfort', *The New York Times* (October 2015), https://www.nytimes.com/2015/10/26/world/europe/russian-presence-near-undersea-cables-concerns-us.html, accessed on 1 October 2021.

28. Nicole Starosielski, *The Undersea Network (Sign, Storage, Transmission)* (Duke University Press, 2015), Kindle.

29. Michael Sechrist, 'New Threats, Old Technology: Vulnerabilities in Undersea Communications Cable Network Management Systems', Discussion Paper #2012-03, Belfer Center For Science and International Affairs, Harvard Kennedy School (February 2012), https://www.belfercenter.org/sites/default/files/files/publication/ sechrist-dp-2012-03-march-5-2012-final.pdf, accessed on 1 October 2021.

30. Alex Hern, 'Massive Internet Outage Hits Websites Including Amazon, gov.uk and Guardian', *The Guardian* (June 2021), https:// www.theguardian.com/technology/2021/jun/08/massive-internet-outage-hits-websites-including-amazon-govuk-and-guardian-fastly, accessed on 1 October 2021.

31. 'GCHQ Taps Fibre-optic Cables for Secret Access to World's Communications', *The Guardian* (2013), https://www.theguardian. com/uk/2013/jun/21/gchq-cables-secret-world-communications-nsa, accessed on 1 October 2021.

32. 'NSA Worldwide SIGINT/ Defense Cryptologic Platform', https:// archive.org/details/NSA-Defense-Cryptologic-Platform, accessed on 30 June 2021.

33. Justin Sherman, 'The US-China Battle Over the Internet Goes Under the Sea', *Wired* (June 2020), https://www.wired.com/story/opinion-

the-us-china-battle-over-the-internet-goes-under-the-sea/, accessed on 1 October 2021.

34. Michael Leiter, 'Executive Order Seeks to Modernize "Team Telecom" After Years-Long Effort', Skadden, Arps (April 2020), https://www. skadden.com/insights/publications/2020/04/executive-order-seeks-to-modernize, accessed on 1 October 2021.

35. Hendel and Swan, 'Justice Department Opposes Google, Facebook Cable Link'.

36. 'Team Telecom Recommends that the FCC Deny Pacific Light Cable Network System's Hong Kong Undersea Cable Connection to the United States', Department of Justice (June 2020), https://www. justice.gov/opa/pr/team-telecom-recommends-fcc-deny-pacific-light-cable-network-system-s-hong-kong-undersea, accessed on 1 October 2021.

37. David Shepardson, 'FCC Moves against Two Chinese Telecoms Firms Operating in US', Reuters (March 2021), https://www.reuters. com/article/us-usa-china-telecom-idUSKBN2B92FE, accessed on 1 October 2021.

38. 'HMN Successfully Completes the Marine Survey of MSC System', HMN Press Release (June 2020), https://subtelforum.com/hmn-completes-marine-survey-of-msc-system/, accessed on 1 October 2021.

39. 'HMN Kicks off Senegal Horn of Africa Regional Express Cable', HMN Press Release (April 2020), https://subtelforum.com/hmn-kicks-off-senegal-horn-of-africa-regional-express-cable/, accessed on 1 October 2021.

40. Barbara Pongratz, 'The Chinese Digital Silk Road: Analysis of Chinese State-Business Relations in New and Ongoing Public-Private Projects', http://deutsch-chinesisches-forum.de/images/thinktank/ DigitalSilkRoad_MA_Thesis_Pongratz.pdf, accessed on 1 October 2021.

41. Jonathan Barrett, 'US Warns Pacific Islands about Chinese Bid for Undersea Cable Project) (December 2020), https://www.reuters.

com/article/china-pacific-exclusive/exclusive-u-s-warns-pacific-islands-about-chinese-bid-for-undersea-cable-project-sources-idINKBN28R0KW, accessed on 1 October 2021.

42. Rishi Sunak, 'Undersea Cables: Indispensable, Insecure', Policy Exchange (November 2017), https://policyexchange.org.uk/wp-content/uploads/2017/11/Undersea-Cables.pdf, accessed on 1 October 2021.

43. Ibid.

44. Nadia Schadlow and Brayden Helwig, 'Protecting Undersea Cables Must Be Made a National Security Priority', *Defense News* (July 2020), https://www.defensenews.com/opinion/commentary/2020/07/01/protecting-undersea-cables-must-be-made-a-national-security-priority/, accessed on 1 October 2021.

45. Rishi Sunak, 'Undersea Cables'.

46. Winkler, *Nexus*.

47. Ibid.

48. Ibid.

49. Ibid.

50. 'UK to Help Vulnerable Countries against Russia, China Cyber Threat', Reuters (May 2021), https://telecom.economictimes.indiatimes.com/news/uk-to-help-vulnerable-countries-against-russia-china-cyber-threat/82572158, accessed on 1 October 2021.

7

The Battle for Markets and Emerging Technologies

The Great Tech Game—this global contest for technological, economic and geopolitical dominance—is starting to shape the world order, and underlines what experts have called 'a major shift in the arena of geopolitical rivalry to technological competition'.[1] Indeed, the US and China, more so than other countries, understand the long-term significance of the technology-driven battles that they are engaged in today.

The strategic thinkers in these nations view science and technology not just as 'drivers of growth and ultimately, geopolitical power'. Fundamentally, they believe that 'technology is the real foundation of power'[2]—as was evident from the thinking underlying the Vannevar Bush memo to US President Roosevelt in 1945.[3] But steadily, other regions and countries are beginning to grasp this view and the long-term implications for the world order as well. The Great Tech Game—the defining contest of the twenty-first century—therefore seems to be developing in front of our eyes.

225

The Competition for Technological Dominance of Markets and Technology

There are two centres of gravity in the technology world today: The West Coast of the United States and the East Coast of China. These two coasts, alone, are today home to nine of the top companies and eighteen of the top internet companies (by market cap) in the world. These two regions host the largest companies in online search, social media, messaging and communications, payments and e-commerce in the world. And these two regions have such a head start over other potential competitors in the world that they are 'the leading candidates to win in the next economic era'.[4] But the US does not seem to be keen on sharing the mantle of technological leadership with China.

The Chinese strategy for dominance of markets and technology

China believes it has a 'rare historic opportunity' to leapfrog past the US and other leading nations and gain control of several emerging technologies such as high-speed 5G internet, sensors and robotics, artificial intelligence and smart city infrastructure.[5] By establishing leadership in these emerging, transformative technologies, China is aiming to become the most advanced science and technology power in the world by 2050.

In its strategy and focus on technological dominance, the Chinese have displayed a deep understanding of the complex mechanisms through which the Europeans and the Americans have retained economic leadership in the world, especially in the critical field of technology and telecommunications. In many ways, it is seeking to replicate the Western strategies for success in the previous centuries. In addition to seeking control of the digital infrastructure, it is also seeking leadership roles in international standardization bodies, to get Chinese technology standards adopted by the rest of the world, and to actively leverage their strength and capabilities in emerging technologies such as 5G to build relationships with other like-minded regimes around the world.

Its 2016 Innovation-Driven Development Strategy, which also included its Made in China 2025 plan, has emphasized development of China's digital ecosystem and the appropriate regulatory structure for it. The Chinese government has been actively supporting its companies and their technology to enter into direct competition with US and European firms.

As part of its 'Digital Silk Road'[6] initiative, Chinese companies have played a major role in boosting internet connectivity and infrastructure in Africa, Eurasia and Latin America. Chinese state-backed banks, like the Export-Import Bank, have also provided credit lines and loans to several countries that are part of its Belt and Road Initiative (BRI). For example, the Chinese Export-Import Bank has financed 85 per cent of the China–Pakistan fibre optic project, and 100 per cent of the costs of the Nigerian 5G project to set up Huawei's 5G infrastructure there. Huawei, a firm that has run into major issues in the US, and other Chinese companies such as ZTE, are estimated to be powering almost two-thirds of the 5G networks launched outside of China.[7]

The Chinese government and Chinese companies have worked hand in hand to ensure access to new markets and customers. To this end, Chinese tech firms have also been making large investments strategically in e-commerce, payments, fin-tech and other sectors in various countries (as we saw in India for several years before the recent impasse between the two countries).

In addition to telecom networks, Chinese companies are also involved in smart city infrastructure for both commercial and strategic reasons. Many of these projects involve setting up of facial recognition and video surveillance data, combined with advanced analytics. Chinese companies like Huawei are at the front of AI- and data analytics-driven surveillance technology that is in high demand in many parts of the world. In this, it competes with suppliers from various countries such as France, Germany, Israel, the UK and the US.[8] The competition for these markets is as strategic as it is commercial.

China has also understood the importance of world-class research and development and the significant advantage a well-trained talent pool can afford its strategic objectives. So, not only has the Chinese government certified over eighty Chinese universities to conduct classified R&D, but it has also increasingly relied on its vast pool of Chinese students studying in science, technology, engineering and mathematics (STEM) fields at universities abroad, especially in countries like the US. Many state-owned enterprises also fund the studies of such students, in return for a commitment to work for those companies for a defined period of time after completing their academic work.[9]

While this understanding of Chinese objectives, and the strategies they are deploying to meet those objectives, is largely through the lens of Western scholars, it is clear that the Chinese have a plan, and are working hard towards it. In attempting to leapfrog and outflank the US, it is drawing upon strategies adopted by the challengers of previous eras as we discussed in Section I. Strategies and tactics utilized by the West in the past to achieve technological and economic dominance are informing and significantly shaping the Chinese approach. The Chinese, therefore, often view criticisms by the West of its tactics as duplicitous.

The US strategy to block China's rise

The US, on the other hand, understands its technological, economic, political and military dominance is being challenged. Just a century ago, the US was the challenger to the global hegemon, the UK. Today, China is attempting to turn the tables.

The US is therefore increasingly deploying its own multifaceted economic, technological, geopolitical and military playbook to block China's rise.[10] One, the US is increasingly severely restricting any technology flows to China, whether through acquisitions or theft/espionage. To do so, it is blocking technology acquisitions by China in all fields considered critical to economic and technological competitiveness or national security. It has done this through laws such as the Foreign Investment Risk Review Modernization Act of 2018 (FIRRMA) and other strategies outlined in the National Defence Authorization Act of 2019 (NDAA). FIRRMA, for example, enhanced the powers of the Committee on Foreign Investment in the United States (CFIUS), including the ability to apply national security considerations in reviewing foreign investments, besides widening the definition of 'critical technology' to include emerging and foundational technologies.

The increasing interconnectedness of economic, technological, defence, security and geopolitical considerations is evident from the fact that most of the countermeasures adopted by the US have been sanctioned under a defence act (NDAA). The NDAA 2019, underlining the seriousness, scale and urgency of the threat, recommends a 'whole-of-government strategy to counter China's multiple activities to undermine US capabilities and wrest technology through unfair means'.[11] A 'whole-of-government' strategy basically entails a comprehensive strategy that includes coordination amongst the different departments and branches of government.

In addition to legislation, the US has also used presidential executive orders to put in place further restrictions for Chinese military–industrial activity and espionage. In June 2021, for example, President Biden signed an executive order that further built upon restrictions outlined in Executive Order (E.O.) 13959 of 2020 by President Trump.[12] E.O. 13959 had 'declared a national emergency' to protect the American homeland and its people from the 'unusual and extraordinary threat' to the national security, economy and foreign policy of the United States arising from Chinese military–industrial complex's activities.

The US is extremely concerned over the Chinese national strategy of military–civil fusion, as part of which China's military essentially compels civilian Chinese companies to support its military and intelligence activities.[13] Given that these Chinese companies are raising capital in the United States by selling securities to US investors, the Presidential executive orders (E.O.s) have also aimed to prevent US investments financing the development and modernization of the Chinese military.

The US government has redrawn its national security export control rules in order to close any loopholes that might be exploited by China. Moreover, through E.O.s, the US has also attempted to block the development and use of Chinese surveillance technology outside China, given US claims that such technology is facilitating repression and serious human rights abuses. The US has prohibited, for instance, the activities of fifty-nine Chinese entities actively involved in the Chinese military–industrial complex.[14] This list contains around 200 Chinese companies, as of June 2021.

The US has also clamped down hard on another source of technology flows to China: espionage and theft. The economic espionage threat from China is, according to Christopher Wray, director of the FBI, 'the greatest long-term threat to our nation's information and intellectual property, and to our economic vitality'.[15] Wray has pointed out that the Chinese have adopted an 'all-tools and all-sectors' approach to its economic espionage. Using a diverse range of methods and techniques (from cyberespionage to bribing US officials) and actors (from Chinese intelligence agencies to private companies to students and researchers), the Chinese have targeted an equally diverse set of institutions (from Fortune 100 companies to Silicon Valley start-ups, and from government and academia to high tech and agriculture).

Wray has argued that the Chinese are going after not just innovation and R&D but 'anything that can give them a competitive advantage' from cost and pricing information to internal strategy documents.[16] In fact, a former National Security Agency (NSA) director, Keith Alexander, has called China's cyber-facilitated intellectual property and technology theft 'the biggest wealth transfer in history'.[17]

In response, the US is taking a similarly 'multifaceted approach'. Working closely with foreign and domestic partners, the US government is using a host of tools at its disposal. Just sample this: the US Department of Commerce in October 2019 added twenty-eight Chinese companies—including leading Chinese AI firms such as iFlytek, SenseTime and Megvii—to its 'entity list', which meant that they became subject to several trade restrictions. In May 2020, the US released a strategy document explicitly calling for active prosecution of Chinese theft of technology trade secrets and intellectual property. It also sought to put in place a strong system for preventing Chinese companies from accessing or acquiring key advanced technologies in the field of AI, quantum computing and biotechnology. The restrictions and blockage of Huawei on the 5G infrastructure front was to follow soon thereafter. In addition, the US has enhanced scrutiny of Chinese scientists and engineers working in the US.

The US government is also working closely with the private sector to share information about the Chinese economic espionage threat, help them consider their supply chain vulnerabilities, carefully choose who they do business with and on what terms, and also to solicit their help in achieving common objectives.

The economic espionage incidents—both reported and unreported—are increasing in frequency and profile. Lists of the reported incidents describe a diverse variety, ranging from Chinese hackers stealing hundreds of gigabytes of data from more than forty-five technology companies and the US government, Chinese nationals stealing trade secrets about Apple's autonomous vehicles,[18] and Chinese intelligence officers attempting to steal jet fan blade designs from General Electric.

Another key piece of the US strategy is that of decoupling its supply chains in core sectors from China, and reducing supply chain vulnerabilities. The decoupling and supply chain de-linkages are especially important from the US perspective, in view of 'China's increasing domination of global upstream and downstream 'manufacturing supply chains' in areas critical to US national security'.[19] This includes everything from semiconductors to rare earths materials.

Other than blocking China's rise, the US is also working to extend its lead by furthering innovation and competition in the tech space.

Like the 1945 Vannevar Bush memo to President Roosevelt, the NDAA 2019, a comprehensive outline of the US's intended playbook, has emphasized the need for the US to develop a long-term science and technology strategy to ensure that it stays ahead of competitors in key technology areas, such as AI and quantum computing.

In June 2021, the US Senate passed the US Innovation and Competition Act, a $250 billion bill 'aimed at countering China's technological ambitions'. In addition to an overhaul of the National Science Foundation, the Act envisions over $52 billion to fund semiconductor design and manufacturing, with President Biden arguing, 'As other countries continue to invest in their own research and development, we cannot risk falling behind.'[20] (China immediately issued a statement criticizing the bill for its 'Cold War mentality and ideological prejudice' and emphasis on seeking 'to contain China's development'.)[21]

The United States–China Economic and Security Review Commission has also been focused on prioritizing a national strategy for promoting 'supply chain transparency', especially for procurements linked to China, and reducing 'supply chain vulnerabilities'. In light of this, the US is considering formulating an industrial policy to support these objectives, which is significant because the US government has refrained from a formal industrial policy for several decades now.

As a result of these restrictive trade and export control rules, trade wars—which involve restrictions and rules such as export controls, and have been common throughout the industrial era—are now increasingly looking like technology wars. All of these steps are increasingly leading economic analysts to point towards a likely 'decoupling' of the two economies. This, as many economists have warned, could end up risking global economic upheaval, given that the world economy is now undergirded by complex cross-border interdependence in pretty much all sectors of the economy. Such decoupling could lead not just to a fresh round of protectionism and trade barriers, but also slow down global economic growth.

The tit-for-tat continues

China, in response to US accusations of economic espionage, has not just denied the accusations as being slanderous but also introduced 'tit-for-tat' penalties for cases of US economic espionage against China.[22] In July 2020, for example, China announced it was amending its criminal code to include trade secret thefts by foreign businesses, a change that Beijing could use to implicate the US and its firms in economic espionage.[23]

China has also started to create a 'blacklist' or an 'Unreliable Entities List' of foreign companies that are seen as acting against Chinese national security or business interests.[24] Entities placed on this list would be barred from investing in, or even importing or exporting anything from or into China. Employees of these companies could also be barred from entering China.[25] Though it stopped short of naming any particular US companies on the list, the threat was clear: many US companies would have 'much to lose' if China added them to this blacklist. Apple, for example, does not just manufacture and assemble most of its products in China; the Greater China region also accounts for one-sixth of its sales globally.[26]

China has already blocked many US websites and mobile apps as part of the Great Chinese Firewall, which prevents these foreign companies from accessing the vast Chinese internet user base. In addition, much like it did in 2010, China could leverage another key strength it has: world dominance of the production of rare earth elements that form a critical component of the technology manufacturing supply chains.[27]

Chinese firms are also finding ways to get around the implications of the US efforts to block their expansion, often by developing alternatives to core technology platforms developed by the US. For example, in response to Trump's bans in 2019 that denied Huawei access to Google's Android OS, Huawei announced the development of its own OS in 2019, named the HarmonyOS—a political statement in itself. Huawei launched its new HarmonyOS smartphones in February 2021.[28]

With significant market share of the Chinese (42 per cent) and Russian (25 per cent) markets, HarmonyOS could become a genuine global alternative to Android and iOS (Apple's operating system). Along the same lines, China also announced that an alternative to America's GPS satellite navigation system, called BeiDou, would be ready soon, and exceed the global standard set by the US's GPS system.[29]

As the two nations remain tightly—and surprisingly explicitly—locked in battle for dominance of technologies and markets, the tit-for-tat actions can be expected to continue. The geopolitical implications of these technology wars and tit-for-tats will be immense. Countries may also need to start picking their sides, in a dynamic eerily similar to the Cold War. From the perspective of mid-sized powers like India, it will be an era-defining decision to pick a side. As Indian foreign minister S. Jaishankar acknowledged, 'Many of the new and emerging technologies have significant implications for diplomacy, national security and global rule-making,' pointing out that 'technology, connectivity and trade are at the heart of new contestations'.[30] Similarly, even the larger powers such as Europe will need to take the decisions on future alignments keeping into account the interconnectedness today of trade, technology and geopolitics.

The geopolitical race for dominance of standards

The battle for dominance of emerging technologies and digital markets is playing out in another behind-the-scenes domain: the establishment of technological standards in international technical standards organizations.

A brief explanation about standards might help. In the early days of development of any emerging technology, different developers working on it will end up using different norms, protocols, techniques and architecture to operationalize or commercialize the technology. These are referred to as 'standards'. For example, Tim Berners-Lee, the founder of the World Wide Web, had come up with certain 'standards' such as URLs, HTTP and HTML that are still prevalent today.

'Standards' are one of the key ways in which tech firms cement their commercially advantageous positions in the industry. A prime example is IBM: the adoption of its PC standards as the industry standards became a key driver of IBM's continued profit streams from licensing that technology to PC manufacturers from all over the world for decades.

Back in the late nineteenth century, three brilliant inventors engaged in a battle that became known as 'the War of the Currents'. These inventors—Thomas Edison, Nikola Tesla and George Westinghouse—battled over whose electricity system of standards would become the industry standard. On one hand, there was the direct current (DC) standard championed by Edison, and on the other, the alternating current (AC) promoted by Tesla and Westinghouse.

Similarly, today, in the twenty-first century, we are seeing 'a Battle over Technology Standards'. This battle is being played out between technologically advanced nations (and the companies they represent) to get their standards adopted as the global industry standards. There is effectively a three-way competition between the US, China and the European Union currently underway to shape technology standards, whether it be for 5G or other emerging technologies. As Björn Fägersten and Tim Rühlig argue, 'Standard setting is today a crucial arena for commercial, normative and geopolitical conflict,'[31] and not so much a search for the most appropriate technical solutions.

This competition is primarily being played out in two ways: one, by increasing the share of standard-essential patents (SEPs) owned by a country, and two, by assuming leadership of international organizations responsible for setting the global technology standards. Most critical technical standards consist of technology that is patented or protected, or what are known as 'standard-essential patents' (SEPs). Companies that hold SEPs possess two advantages: one, it is cheaper for them to adapt their products to international standards (because they already conform to them), and two, they profit immensely from selling or licensing the SEPs to other companies looking to conform with international industry standards.[32]

Moreover, as tariff barriers are being reduced in international trade, standards have become an increasingly important geopolitical and economic tool used by nations to promote or restrict trade from other countries.[33] For example, China may mandate that technology products complying with certain specific standards may only be imported into or sold within China. Because these standards might be owned by Chinese companies, the US companies could either be denied access altogether to these standards or be charged exorbitantly for them.

Similarly, the US could influence India to adopt technology compliant with US standards. This would not only open up the whole Indian market for US companies and products, but also simultaneously deny access to companies or countries that comply with different standards. For 5G technology products currently, for example, the US and China are both pushing countries to adopt 5G standards compliant with the 5G technologies of their respective companies.

The capacity to influence technical standards-setting organizations has become a tool of power in itself, even though most countries tend to overlook it. Consequently, there is an international battle underway to gain greater leadership positions within various international standards-setting organizations. While the Europeans and Americans have used this standards-setting strategy for a long time to cement their dominance, the Chinese are relatively new to the game.

But the Chinese have taken to it like a fish to water. The Chinese Communist Party (CCP) has encouraged private actors to develop market-driven technical standards and also participate actively in international working groups within international standard-setting organizations (SSOs) such as the International Telecommunications Union (ITU), 3rd Generation Partnership Project (3GPP), International Electrotechnical Commission (IEC) and the International Standards Organization (ISO). Under the guidance of the Standards Administration of China (SAC), China has launched China Standards 2035, an initiative to develop a strategic vision for shaping standards and also boosting research on technical standards.[34]

The US and the European Union traditionally held most of these positions, but China has increasingly been exerting its influence within these organizations. Taking advantage of the US's neglect of these organizations, the Chinese have not only assumed many low-, mid- and high-level positions within them, but also built strong relationships with representatives of other countries. Chinese technology companies and institutions now have ten of fifty-seven chair and vice-chair positions at 3GPP. At the ISO, China held the Presidency (Dr Zhang Xiaogang) in 2015–18,[35] and a Chinese representative, Dr Yinbiao Shu, is IEC's president for 2020–23.[36] Similarly, Zhao Houlin has been heading ITU as its secretary-general since 2014.

Still, a disproportionate share of leadership positions (over 60 per cent) within these organizations is still held by the EU, which is often considered a 'regulatory superpower'.[37] In comparison, the US and Japan typically hold just roughly over 10 per cent each of the positions, for example, in the ISO and IEC technical committee secretariats. Moreover, EU representatives dominate the strategically important secretariat positions in the technical committees of these organizations. But China is also strategically increasing its share rapidly within the secretariats, having roughly doubled its share in the last decade.[38]

As Björn Fägersten and Tim Rühlig note, China has acquired levels of influence similar to individual European countries such as Sweden, Germany, France and the UK. Only Germany and the US hold more secretariat positions than China. China, however, significantly outperforms all other emerging economies such as India, Indonesia, Brazil and Russia in these organizations.[39]

Currently, China aims at internationalizing its domestic standards that revolve around infrastructures such as smart cities, machine construction, ICT, and mobility such as self-driving cars.[40] However, the energetic efforts of China to shape standards do not obviously guarantee success. Chinese proposals in these organizations are sometimes characterized as being of very low quality, though with heavy R&D investments, the quality of the Chinese proposals will likely improve over time.

Access to the large Chinese market itself makes mutual standard recognition attractive to many countries. China has also promoted adoption of its technical standards through the Belt and Road Initiative (BRI) and bilateral agreements. It has smartly linked adoption of its standards to participation in the BRI, calling for the same technical standards to be used across all BRI member states. China has signed memorandums of understanding (MoUs) on standards with several countries, such as Vietnam, Myanmar and Indonesia, which are likely to adopt Chinese technical standards given Chinese technology is cheaper than Western alternatives. By some estimates, China has already signed eighty-five agreements with forty-nine countries and regions on mutual standards recognition.

The Americans have taken a strongly confrontational view of Chinese efforts to gain further influence in the standards-setting organizations, whereas the Europeans have been adopting a slightly more accommodative approach. The Europeans believe that a strongly confrontational approach risks China stepping out of existing SSOs and forming their own. In addition to losing access to a large market, the legitimacy and credibility of the international organizations the Europeans currently dominate, will suffer.

To tilt the balance back towards them, the US will start to assign a lot more importance to these technical SSOs than it previously did, and gun for its own candidates for leadership positions. Other countries with stakes in technical governance and standards should also start to think strategically about increasing their own membership and leadership in these SSOs. In fact, a country like India, especially given its depth of technical talent, must move quickly to assume leadership of technical committees and secretariats within these organizations.

The race for AI dominance: Will the US win or China?

The AI revolution is likely to unleash an era of enormous productivity increases.[41] Increasingly being seen as the 'electricity' of our era, AI will have extremely broad applicability in our lives and also spawn a wide variety of productivity-enhancing applications. Realizing the transformative power of AI, countries (and companies) are racing to prepare for dominance. While the battle over 5G infrastructure and markets seems to be a zero-sum game between the US and China, the race for dominance of artificial intelligence technology (AI) is not necessarily so. Still, it is becoming yet another battlefield for technological dominance between the two largest geopolitical tech powers: the US and China.

According to venture capitalist and author Kai-Fu Lee, the world of artificial intelligence is set for bipolar leadership, with China and the United States being the two poles. These two countries have the right combination of factors for success, such as venture capital ecosystems, large user bases, abundant data, talented entrepreneurs, AI researchers and emerging AI firms, that other countries don't. Therefore, they are likely 'currently incubating the AI giants that will dominate global markets and extract wealth from consumers around the globe'. Lee postulates that the AI world might very well end up being a winner-takes-all outcome, leading to unimaginable concentration of wealth in the hands of a few, driving widespread unemployment and social disorder in the process.[42]

Betting on China

Two main schools of thought have emerged on who might prevail in this particular battle. One school of thought, represented by Kai-Fu Lee, suggests that China will be the predominant AI superpower in the world. China is significantly ramping up AI investment, research and entrepreneurship. According to Lee, in recent years the Chinese start-up ecosystem, boosted with capital and investments from VC firms, their tech giants, and the Chinese government, has caught 'AI fever'.[43]

The Chinese government has poured its might into this mission. In fact, it has made winning at 'AI theory, technology and application' the centrepiece of its China 2035 plan.[44] Further, the CCP has also pushed local provincial governments to follow its lead as well.[45] Similarly,

Chinese VC firms have responded to this clarion call, pouring record amounts into AI start-ups. In fact, China makes up for 48 per cent of all AI venture funding globally, surpassing even the United States.[46]

Advancements in the field of AI rely upon either development in underlying AI technologies and frameworks, such as deep learning, reinforcement learning and transfer learning, or alternatively, in incredible and innovative applications of these technologies to real-life problems.

According to Andrew Ng, a pioneer in AI, the state of AI today can be compared to when Thomas Edison figured out how to harness electricity. As we saw in Chapter 3, electricity was a transformative technology in and of itself. But it was the ability to harness it in and for different contexts that revolutionized not just the average household but also the factories, industries and other commercial establishments of the time. In the last quarter of the nineteenth century, the US (and other countries) benefited from entrepreneurs coming up with innovative ways of applying the power of electricity.

Similarly, in the first half of the twenty-first century, today's AI entrepreneurs are attempting to do the same by leveraging AI frameworks such as deep learning and neural networks. Lee believes that advances in the core AI technologies have slowed, but development of applications is on the rise. Therefore, he terms the current phase as the 'age of implementation'.[47] The hard work of research, according to Lee, has already been done. 'It's now time,' he argues, 'for entrepreneurs to roll up their sleeves and get down to the dirty work of turning algorithms into sustainable businesses.'[48]

And in that, Lee believes, China has the advantage. He thinks two key factors will allow China to break out of the stereotype of the 'copycat who lagged far behind the cutting edge'.[49] One, China's e-commerce and other transactional platforms are generating a lot more data than their US counterparts. So, data—and lots of different types of data—will be abundantly available in the Chinese ecosystem. Two, he believes that the scrappy entrepreneurs of China undergo their baptism by fire in what he views as the most cutthroat start-up environment. American entrepreneurs, compared to their Chinese counterparts, have it easy. 'These entrepreneurs,' Lee argues, 'will be the secret sauce that helps China become the first country to cash in on AI's age of implementation.'[50] Lee's predictions are affirmed by a PricewaterhouseCoopers (PwC) study that has estimated that of the $16 trillion that AI deployment is expected to add to global GDP by 2030, China is projected to add $7 trillion, compared to $3.7 trillion for the US.[51]

Former Google CEO Eric Schmidt, who has been serving as chairman of the US National Security Commission on Artificial Intelligence, has affirmed Lee's view that China is progressing extremely smartly and aggressively on AI. During testimony before the Senate Armed Services Committee, Schmidt shared his assessment that the United States is 'one or two years ahead of China, not five or ten', and that the Chinese are well ahead in certain areas such as facial recognition. As a result of this assessment, he urged the US government to expedite development of emerging technologies, including AI.[52]

Betting on the US

However, others, such as Carl Benedikt Frey and Michael Osborne, argue that Kai-Fu Lee is overestimating the ability of China in the field of AI. The school of thought represented by Frey and Osborne believes that the key to artificial intelligence lies not in the quantity of data that can be fed into algorithms but rather in the efficiency with which the algorithms are trained to learn from that data. According to them, algorithms driving data efficiency, and not data abundance, are the holy grail of AI development.[53]

Frey and Osborne also draw a reference from the industrial era to explain the state of AI development today. They believe that while Thomas Newcomen developed a coal-powered steam engine many decades before James Watt, Watt's invention is credited because his separate condenser technology was what made the technology efficient for the first time. According to them, AI is still waiting for its 'separate condenser moment'.

As per this view, the research in core AI technologies still has a long way to go to become anywhere near as efficient as humans are. They therefore conclude that the leader or winner in AI depends far less on who has access to the most data than on who will be the first to get to the most efficient ways of learning from data.

Further, they reject the idea that authoritarian governments are better able to foster AI innovation than democratic ones, and by extension, that AI technology will fundamentally favour authoritarian governments. Continued progress in AI will require radical innovation and open bottom-up-driven research. They believe that open, free societies like the US are in fact more likely to witness such innovation. The same reasons that drove Europe to foster the Industrial Revolution will help the US lead the AI revolution, according to them. And while China might definitely be strong at building infrastructure swiftly, its strong top-down state-led approach will eventually hamper innovation and dynamic research in this case.[54]

Both arguments seem to have merit. But if the evolution of the internet economy is any indication, we can expect that for the foreseeable future, the US and China will continue their individual paths towards becoming major AI superpowers, leveraging their respective strengths.

Can the Others Catch Up?

Is Kai-Fu Lee right that the AI world will be one where the winner-takes-all, and we are in the throes of a Great Divergence yet again? Or, as I have explored a few times in previous chapters, is convergence between the current leaders and likely laggards possible?

Many markets within the digital economy (even pre-AI) are winner-takes-all, as is evident from the market dominance of firms such as Google, Microsoft, Facebook, Alibaba and Amazon. These Big Tech firms that are running our searches, social media, communications, news, e-commerce, payments and mobility platforms are accumulating boundless data about billions of people across the world. And in the world of AI, the more data you have, the richer your insights, the more patterns you can detect, and the better predictions you can make. Therefore, armed with this data, capital that they have in abundance, a knack for attracting and retaining the best AI talent in the world, and product developers and managers who understand the consumer needs, it is not unreasonable to predict that some of the same Big Tech firms will be the winners in the AI revolution.

At the level of nations, however, the story might look different, though it will be an uphill exercise. Despite all the data that exists today in the world, I believe we are still at the very early stages of data accumulation. Over the next few years, the amount of data that will get created is likely to grow exponentially, especially as we move towards an IoT, sensor-rich, 5G world. Nations today, therefore, have an opportunity—even a duty, I'd argue—not just to think about how to leverage existing data but also to 'generate data'.

Nations could learn a lot from Big Tech firms on how to generate and use data. Nations are often sitting on vast troves of data that unfortunately either doesn't get tracked or retained, or remain in silos. Take, for example, traffic patterns based on toll bridge cameras and sensors; education and healthcare data; land use data; data about the various public services; and all the other statistics that governments capture about their citizens, businesses and economic activity in general.

Nations have misplaced their focus on trying to grab back the data they feel Big Tech firms have extracted about their citizens. Instead, alternative data policy frameworks such as 'data trusts' (under which users own and manage their data) and 'digital data commons' (which envisions collective data ownership) are worth exploring to ensure a more equitable distribution of economic gains from such data. Governments must also take a longer-term view on data, and simultaneously think about how they can generate and leverage data sets at a massive scale. This data will be the platform upon which a country's AI destiny might be set.

For instance, the Indian government's efforts to generate more structured and linked data through the IndiaStack, and the vision for data exchanges upon which innovative applications could be built are an attempt in this direction. Speaking at a tech conference, Rajeev Chandrasekhar, the junior minister of India's IT ministry, pointed out that India generates about 20 per cent of the world's data and is one of the fastest data-generating and data-consuming economies in the world. These data sets, if made available to researchers, represent 'a once-in-a-generation opportunity' to leverage the data for the Indian economy's benefit, according to Chandrasekhar.[55]

AI laggard nations could also just focus on developing innovative, inherently useful products and applications leveraging AI technologies developed by others. As Andrew Ng has argued, you might launch a product with limited data, but the product itself—if adopted well—will generate reams of data over time. The product will get better with time and more data being fed into AI algorithms that identify patterns and insights to make it better. This might be the 'AI flywheel' or the 'virtuous cycle of AI'.

Some analysts have also argued that interpreting the competition over AI as an 'arms race' fundamentally misjudges the transnational nature of AI research and development, and the technological interdependence of today's world.[56] As Graham Webster has argued, unlike the US and USSR during the Cold War, in which science and technology developed on largely autonomous paths, the tech ecosystems of the US and China are part of a 'globally intertwined ecosystem'. They warn that the winner-takes-all view of AI will hurt the advancement of international research, development and manufacturing. This would be mutually damaging, and end up being a race to the bottom for everyone in the AI community.[57]

That said, pioneers of AI such as Yoshua Bengio (who along with Geoff Hinton and Yann LeCun has championed deep learning as a technology) have acknowledged that 'AI research by itself will tend to lead to concentrations of power, money, and researchers'.[58] Bengio has also expressed his regret about the unfairness being experienced by AI researchers in developing nations who not only lack resources but also access to a community of fellow researchers.

At the end of the day, realistically, we are likely to see a Great Divergence with the rise of AI and other emerging technologies, where the data- and AI technology-rich will get richer and the data and AI technology-poor will get poorer. Nation states, when it comes to core and strategic objectives, are less prone to cooperation than they are to unabashedly pursue their own national interest. Therefore, we can expect the competition for digital markets, standards, data access and emerging technologies to only further intensify as the Great Tech Game progresses.

Notes

1. Smita Purushottam, 'US–China Geotechnology Race and the Lessons for India', ICS Occasional Paper No. 24 (2019). https://www.icsin. org/uploads/2019/02/05/b57720af41345138ec4a73830943bc8f. pdf, accessed on 1 October 2021.

2. Ibid.

3. 'Science: The Endless Frontier', A Report to the President by Vannevar Bush, Director of the Office of Scientific Research and Development (July 1945), https://www.nsf.gov/od/lpa/nsf50/ vbush1945.htm#ch6.3, accessed on 1 October 2021.

4. François Candelon and Martin Reeves, 'The New Digital World: Hegemony or Harmony?', BCG Henderson Institute (November 2017), https://www.bcg.com/publications/2017/strategy-globalization-new-digital-world-hegemony-harmony, accessed on 1 October 2021.

5. 2020 Report to Congress of the US–China Economic and Security Review Commission (December 2020), https://www.uscc.gov/ sites/default/files/2020-12/2020_Annual_Report_to_Congress.pdf, accessed on 1 October 2021.

6. Adam Segal, Prepared Remarks Before the US–China Economic Security Review Commission, Hearing on 'A "China Model?"

Beijing's Promotion of Alternative Global Norms and Standards' (13 March 2020), https://www.uscc.gov/sites/default/files/2020-10/March_13_Hearing_and_April_27_Roundtable_Transcript.pdf, accessed on 1 October 2021.

7. Ibid.

8. Ibid.

9. Dr Christopher Ford, 'Remarks on Technology and Power in China's Geopolitical Ambitions', Testimony to the US–China Economic and Security Review Commission (June 2019), https://www.uscc.gov/sites/default/files/Ford_USCC Testimony_Final.pdf, accessed on 1 October 2021.

10. Purushottam, 'US–China Geotechnology Race'.

11. Ibid.

12. 'Executive Order on Addressing the Threat from Securities Investments that Finance Certain Companies of the People's Republic of China', The White House (June 2021), https://www.whitehouse.gov/briefing-room/presidential-actions/2021/06/03/executive-order-on-addressing-the-threat-from-securities-investments-that-finance-certain-companies-of-the-peoples-republic-of-china/, accessed on 1 October 2021.

13. 'Addressing the Threat From Securities Investments That Finance Communist Chinese Military Companies', Executive Order 13959, Executive Office of the President of the United States (12 November 2020), https://www.federalregister.gov/documents/2020/11/17/2020-25459/addressing-the-threat-from-securities-investments-that-finance-communist-chinese-military-companies, accessed on 1 October 2021.

14. 'Non-SDN Chinese Military-Industrial Complex Companies List', Office of Foreign Assets Control, Department of the Treasury, US Government (June 2021), https://www.treasury.gov/ofac/downloads/ccmc/nscmiclist.pdf, accessed on 1 October 2021.

15. Christopher Wray, 'Responding Effectively to the Chinese Economic Espionage Threat', Remarks delivered at the Department of Justice

China Initiative Conference, Center for Strategic and International Studies, Washington, D.C. (6 February 2020), https://www.fbi.gov/news/speeches/responding-effectively-to-the-chinese-economic-espionage-threat, accessed on 1 October 2021.

16. Ibid.

17. Ford, 'Remarks on Technology and Power'.

18. 'Survey of Chinese-linked Espionage in the United States Since 2000', Center for Strategic and International Studies, Washington D.C., Updated November 2020, https://www.csis.org/programs/technology-policy-program/survey-chinese-linked-espionage-united-states-2000, accessed on 1 October 2021.

19. Purushottam, 'US–China Geotechnology Race'.

20. Thomas Franck, 'Senate Passes $250 Billion Bipartisan Tech and Manufacturing Bill Aimed at Countering China', CNBC (June 2021), https://www.cnbc.com/2021/06/08/senate-passes-bipartisan-tech-and-manufacturing-bill-aimed-at-china.html, accessed on 1 October 2021.

21. 'China's NPC Says US Innovation and Competition Act Is Doomed to Fail', *Global Times* (June 2021), https://www.globaltimes.cn/page/202106/1225798.shtml, accessed on 1 October 2021.

22. Phillip Wen, 'China Denies "Slanderous" Economic Espionage Charges from US, Allies', Reuters (December 2018), https://www.reuters.com/article/us-china-cyber-usa-ministry-idUSKCN1OK03Y, accessed on 1 October 2021.

23. Cissy Zhou, 'China Sharpens Economic Espionage Penalties in "Tit-for-tat Provision" against US Accusations of Trade Secret Theft', *South China Morning Post* (July 2020), https://www.scmp.com/economy/china-economy/article/3092939/china-sharpens-economic-espionage-penalties-tit-tat-provision, accessed on 1 October 2021.

24. Keith Bradsher and Raymond Zhong, 'After Trump's TikTok Ban, China Readies Blacklist of Foreign Companies', *The New York Times* (September 2020), https://www.nytimes.com/2020/09/19/

technology/china-tiktok-wechat-blacklist.html, accessed on 1 October 2021.

25. 'Anti-Foreign Sanctions Law of the People's Republic of China', adopted at the 29th meeting of the Standing Committee of the 13th National People's Congress (10 June 2021), http://www.npc.gov.cn/npc/c30834/202106/d4a714d5813c4ad2ac54a5f0f78a5270.shtml, accessed on 1 October 2021.

26. Bradsher and Zhong, 'After Trump's TikTok Ban, China Readies Blacklist'.

27. 'China–US Trade War: Beijing Escalates Tit-for-tat with Washington', BBC News (December 2020), https://www.bbc.co.uk/news/business-55132425, accessed on 1 October 2021.

28. Arjun Kharpal, 'Two Years after Launch, Huawei to Roll Out its Google Android Rival to Phones—With Big Challenges', CNBC (February 2021), https://www.cnbc.com/2021/02/23/huawei-harmonyos-google-android-rival-to-roll-out-to-phones-in-april.html, accessed on 1 October 2021.

29. 'China's BeiDou Navigation System to Provide Unique Services', XinhuaNet (December 2019), http://www.xinhuanet.com/english/2019-12/27/c_138661877.htm, accessed on 1 October 2021.

30. 'MEA Sets Up Emerging Technologies Division', *The Economic Times* (January 2020), https://economictimes.indiatimes.com/news/politics-and-nation/mea-sets-up-emerging-technologies-division/articleshow/73063773.cms, accessed on 1 October 2021.

31. Björn Fägersten and Tim Rühlig, 'Geopolitics of Standards', Swedish Institute of International Affairs, https://www.ui.se/english/research/europe/geopolitics-of-standards/, accessed on 1 October 2021.

32. Fägersten and Rühlig, 'China's Standard Power and Its Geopolitical Implications for Europe', Swedish Institute of International Affairs, https://www.ui.se/globalassets/ui.se-eng/publications/ui-publications/2019/ui-brief-no.-2-2019.pdf, accessed on 1 October 2021.

33. Information Technology Standards, https://www.encyclopedia. com/computing/news-wires-white-papers-and-books/information-technology-standards, accessed on 1 October 2021.

34. 'Next Generation Artificial Intelligence Development Plan, Issued by State Council', *China Science & Technology Newsletter*, no. 17 (September 2017), http://fi.china-embassy.org/eng/kxjs/P020171025789108009001.pdf, accessed on 1 October 2021.

35. 'Zhang Xiaogang, President of ISO', *China Daily*, https://www.chinadaily.com.cn/m/qingdao/2017-06/23/content_29862586.htm, accessed on 1 October 2021.

36. IEC website, https://www.iec.ch/leadership, accessed on 1 October 2021.

37. Fägersten and Rühlig, 'China's Standard Power'.

38. Ibid.

39. Ibid.

40. Ibid.

41. Kai-Fu Lee, *AI Superpowers: China, Silicon Valley, and the New World Order* (HMH Books, 2018), Kindle.

42. Ibid.

43. Ibid.

44. Ibid.

45. Ibid.

46. Ibid.

47. Ibid.

48. Ibid.

49. Ibid.

50. Ibid.

51. Ibid.

52. Jodi Xu Klein, 'Ex-Google CEO Eric Schmidt Stresses "Urgency" in Countering China on Artificial Intelligence as US–China Tech War Continues', *South China Morning Post* (February 2021), https://www.

scmp.com/news/china/article/3122857/us-china-tech-war-former-google-ceo-eric-schmidt-stresses-urgency, accessed on 1 October 2021.

53. Carl Benedikt Frey and Michael Osborne, 'China Won't Win the Race for AI Dominance', *Foreign Affairs* (June 2020). https://www.foreignaffairs.com/articles/united-states/2020-06-19/china-wont-win-race-ai-dominance, accessed on 1 October 2021.

54. Frey and Osborne, 'China Won't Win the Race'.

55. Rajeev Chandrasekhar, Remarks at 'CyFy 2021', Observer Research Foundation (October 2021), https://www.youtube.com/watch?v=IHhQbmSKlXk, accessed on 20 October 2021.

56. Justin Sherman, 'Essay: Reframing the US–China AI "Arms Race"', *New America* (March 2019), https://www.newamerica.org/cybersecurity-initiative/reports/essay-reframing-the-us-china-ai-arms-race/, accessed on 1 October 2021.

57. Graham Webster, 'The US and China Aren't in a "cold war", So Stop Calling it That', *MIT Technology Review* (19 December 2018), https://www.technologyreview.com/2018/12/19/138211/the-us-and-china-arent-in-a-cold-war-so-stop-calling-it-that/, accessed on 1 October 2021.

58. Yoshua Bengio, 'Interview with Will Knight: One of the Fathers of AI Is Worried about Its Future', *MIT Technology Review* (November 2018), https://www.technologyreview.com/2018/11/17/66372/one-of-the-fathers-of-ai-is-worried-about-its-future/, accessed on 1 October 2021.

8

The Golden Age of Cyberespionage

Technology is transforming another key aspect of geopolitics: espionage and warfare. Even as nations compete for the new valuable resources of data and technology, those same resources ironically are enabling the 'golden era of espionage' as well as transforming warfare.

The rapid growth of data (and data flows) and the proliferation of personal devices such as laptops and mobile phones have enabled new forms of digital espionage. Espionage did not evolve much in the two millennia between Sun Tzu's writing of 'On the Use of Spies' in his classic *The Art of War* sometime around the third century BCE and the Industrial Revolution. But pervasive telecommunication networks, and most recently, mobile phone and computer-led communications, have been game-changers. If in the past human intelligence, or human spies, were the key, today, encryption and decryption are the key. Pun intended.

In the nineteenth and twentieth century, the telegraph and radio did to espionage what the proliferation of mobile phones, internet technology and data are doing to it today. The telegraph and radio were more powerful (though less thrilling) than any previous method of espionage. As communication and information flow became cheaper and easier, there was now more information to track and monitor.

As technology historian Daniel Headrick pointed out to me, these technologies allowed leaders to control and monitor armies and fleets remotely, thus enabling global wars for the first time in history.[1]

Twenty-first-century warfare might very well be defined by the increasing frequency, scale and intensity of cyber-attacks. Wars will not just be fought with technology, but also over technology. The rules, doctrines and the nature of cyberwar will be very different from conventional war. In addition to the territorial borders and trading routes, nations have to now defend and secure their data, technology and critical infrastructure. Advanced encryption (cyber-defence) and superior decryption capabilities (cyber-offence) have become a key strategic skillset and a key geopolitical competitive advantage for nations.

Espionage: The Age of Cryptography

Why has encryption (and decryption) become so important?

Global data flows—the cross-border flows of information—are skyrocketing. As a Harvard Belfer Center report stated, 'Information is now the world's most consequential and contested geopolitical resource.'[2] Encryption technologies to secure the data and decryption capabilities to still 'listen in' have therefore become a massive priority for most governments.

A peek back

Cryptography, developed early in the twentieth century, came into its own around the time of the two world wars. The leading superpower of the time, Britain, set up its Government Code and Cipher School (GC&CS) in 1919 right after World War I. GC&CS would end up evolving into GCHQ, the British intelligence arm focused on cryptographic and communications intelligence.[3] The US equivalent of the GCHQ, the National Security Agency, was set up in 1952. The NSA grew out of the US's signals and communications intelligence (SIGINT and COMINT, respectively) efforts during World War II, and is today the world's largest collector of foreign signals intelligence.

The mass surveillance by intelligence agencies in the internet era, which has often shocked the world, had its origins in the period around World War I. The British, for example, intercepted over seventy million cables, twenty million wireless messages and a billion letters during World War I.[4] During the Cold War, GCHQ, the NSA, and other European partners leveraged SIGINT extensively to penetrate Soviet military secrets and plans. Soon after World War II, the SIGINT alliance between the nations comprising the 'Five Eyes'—Australia, Britain, Canada, New Zealand and the United States—formed a 'key but secret bulwark of international stability'.[5] Their intelligence, experts argue, 'shaped deterrence and defence against the Soviet Union'.[6] And together, their work shaped many significant events and their outcomes, including the Hungarian Revolution, the Cuban Missile Crisis, and others.

As encryption technologies started to become more widely used in the late 1990s and early 2000s by private technology companies, the NSA and its counterparts kicked into action. The NSA, in particular, decided to invest heavily—by some accounts, billions of dollars—in developing its ability to crack these encryptions in order to retain their ability to 'eavesdrop' in the internet-era, the same way it had been doing for decades with earlier telecommunication technologies such as radio and the telephone. As cyberespionage expert James Bamford points out, the NSA's operations are eerily similar to the FBI's operations under J. Edgar Hoover in the 1960s, where the FBI used wiretapping extensively to identify vulnerabilities and ultimately neutralize their targets.[7]

In 2013, Edward Snowden, a former contractor with the NSA, leaked documents that showed that 'the agency has circumvented or cracked much of the encryption, or digital scrambling, that guards global commerce and banking systems, protects sensitive data like trade secrets and medical records, and automatically secures the e-mails,

Web searches, Internet chats and phone calls of Americans and others around the world'.[8]

Intelligence agencies such as the US's NSA and the British GCHQ break encryption either by getting access keys from the technology companies, or by sneakily putting in 'backdoor' entry provisions. Backdoor access essentially refers to secret access via backdoor channels given by the owners of certain applications or information to agencies like the NSA. The private technology sector has often complied with the NSA's requests. But given a few instances where the private sector refused, the NSA has then either hacked its way in covertly or alternatively, approached the courts for permission to get 'backdoor' access to encrypted applications.

A *New York Times* article in 2013 drew upon some 'top secret' documents leaked by Edward Snowden that apparently confirmed as much. The article argued that a particular loophole, which allowed the NSA to decrypt encrypted data, was allegedly 'part of a $250-million, decade-long covert operation by the agency to weaken and undermine the integrity of a number of encryption systems used by millions of people around the world'.[9]

The NSA is not alone in demanding or attempting to sneakily get backdoor access. Other intelligence agencies also do the same. But while such backdoors enable agencies like the NSA to eavesdrop, they also enable other groups to use these weaknesses to break through the encryption technologies as well, therefore threatening the security of these very American communications. Moreover, these groups might be the same groups that the NSA hopes to work against by using these backdoor access provisions.

This is nothing new. Historian Alfred McCoy has outlined a detailed history of the US government's surveillance programmes over the past several decades, which makes clear that 'backdoors' in some form or the other have been used by surveillance agencies for a long time.[10] The difference this time is that the impact of these backdoors is more widespread than ever before. As an NSA document of 2007 stated, 'In the future, superpowers will be made or broken based on the strength of their cryptanalytic programs.'[11]

Geopolitical implications of the golden age of espionage

As nations (and even Big Tech firms) get better at encryption, enhanced decryption capabilities to break through that encryption become even more critical. This has led to a cryptographic arms race and a Cold War-esque escalation in capabilities amongst both intelligence agencies and Big Tech firms.

This cryptographic arms race could have major geopolitical implications. As Edward Lucas of *The Economist* argues, espionage through technology has made it easier for states like China, Iran or Russia to spy on democratic countries and vice versa. Today, all the major and minor powers—including the US, UK, China, Russia, Iran, North Korea, Israel and many others—have significant cyberespionage capabilities. The scope of cyberespionage has also expanded beyond just communications to include all economic, industrial, research and military activities that rely on information networks.

Yet, it is also important to remember, as the Carnegie Endowment's George Perkovich highlighted to me, that the digital intelligence and espionage capabilities—and the outcomes they can actually effect—are often over-emphasized. Despite the enhanced capabilities today, Perkovich argues that we often still fail to gauge and respond to many of the big-picture changes in the world—whether it is refugee crises, crises in conflict zones such as Afghanistan, or even climate change. Former Indian National Security Advisor Shivshankar Menon similarly highlighted to me how the history of wars in recent decades—whether Vietnam, Afghanistan or many others—suggests that the technologically superior nation has often not won. This is partly, Menon argued, because of an over-reliance on the power of technology to achieve military objectives against much less technologically reliant opponents.

The home field advantage

As espionage becomes more focused on cryptographic capabilities, countries with several large technology firms with such expertise are likely to experience the 'home field advantage'. Compared to countries such as China, the UK, Japan, Russia and Israel, the NSA likely enjoys the biggest 'home field advantage' given its alleged relationship with over 100 US tech companies that collectively form and control the primary backbone for global telecommunications.[12] In fact, the United States today enjoys 'a capacity for global surveillance far beyond the British Empire's yield from its control of transoceanic telegraph cables'.[13] Through this, the US has sought to achieve the same strategic advantage that dominance of global telegraph networks had granted the British during the world wars.

This capacity can be a strategic advantage even during peacetime. For example, the NSA's surveillance capabilities often give the US a significant 'diplomatic advantage'. The Snowden revelations indicated that the NSA had actively conducted surveillance of the communications of global political leaders of over thirty-five nations around the world, including former Brazilian President Dilma Rousseff, German leader Angela Merkel, former Mexican President Felipe Calderón, former Indonesian President Yudhoyono, former French President François Hollande and others.

Countries can use this capability not just strategically, but also tactically. For example, during diplomatic negotiations at the UN on the issue of the US invasion of Iraq in 2002–03, the NSA allegedly was monitoring Secretary-General Kofi Annan's conversations while also listening in to the so-called 'Middle Six' Third World nations on the UN Security Council at the time. The US then allegedly used the information gleaned by listening in as the representatives of these nations communicated with their home countries to gauge which way they might vote. Where the US was worried, on the basis of this information, about the countries that might vote against, those countries could then be offered 'a highway, a dam or a favourable trade deal'.[14] As surveillance expert James Bamford put it, this kind of surveillance capability is akin to being at a poker game, and one player knowing exactly what cards the other players had.

Do the technology superpowers have an advantage in the golden age of espionage?

The balance of power in the world of espionage could shift quickly if any nation develops advanced cryptographic technologies ahead of others. Countries that are the most advanced technologically stand to become 'cryptographic superpowers'.[15]

Modern encryption technology relies on certain mathematical problems, such as factoring large numbers so intractable that computers would not be able to crack these problems fast enough. For decryption, computers with sufficient and fast computing capacity, such as supercomputers or quantum computers, are required.

Supercomputers are essentially massive, often room-sized, computers that are used for complex military and scientific tasks, including breaking codes, modelling climate change and simulating nuclear tests.[16] Supercomputers, with their impressive capacity to process data at mind-boggling speeds, can perform the code-breaking calculations required to break encryption several times more efficiently than regular computers.[17] The same supercomputers are critical for the advancement of AI as well. But supercomputers are expensive to build, costing anything from hundreds of millions of dollars to over a billion dollars.

Not surprisingly, supercomputers have not just become 'a symbol for both technical and economic competitiveness' but are also at the heart of the escalating competition between the United States and China over technology.[18] Countries with the largest supercomputers would have an exponentially faster and easier way to decrypt the encrypted data and communications of the other, and as a corollary, better encrypt their own data.

The key players in the supercomputer race today are the US, China and Japan. The intelligence agencies of these countries, such as the NSA, are already using their supercomputers for cracking encryption codes. Of the top 500 supercomputers in the world, China has an estimated 226, while the US has an estimated 114. Together, the two countries account for almost 70 per cent of the total supercomputing capacity in the world.

China has emerged as a key player in this race only in the last five years. China launched its supercomputing push just over a decade ago, initially absorbing foreign technology largely. In 2015, after Washington did not permit Intel to sell its microprocessor chips to four supercomputer labs in China, the latter started building home-grown microprocessors.[19] Three Chinese companies—Lenovo, Inspur and Sugon—now figure in the top five manufacturers, while Cray (owned by Hewlett Packard Enterprise—HPE) and HPE are the American companies in the top five. China has also become by far the largest commercial user of supercomputers (for uses such as drug discovery and AI applications), while the US and Japan are still largely using supercomputers for research (such as space research and climate modelling). Incidentally, India (three), Brazil (four), Russia (two) and Indonesia (zero) are lagging behind significantly on this front. [20]

As with other technologies like 5G and AI, the geopolitical game has become not just about building the largest supercomputers, but also blocking the competitors' advances in supercomputing. Arguing that Chinese supercomputing companies are helping the Chinese build modern weapons such as nuclear weapons and hypersonic weapons, the US Commerce Department put seven such firms on its 'Entity List'.[21] This prevents these companies from buying any components such as chips or microprocessors from US companies without US government approval. But even as the US, Europe and Japan work hard to regain their edge in supercomputing, the Chinese will continue to push the frontiers of supercomputing as well.

Cyberwarfare (and the Future of Warfare)

Technology is shaping the future of warfare. The objectives of war haven't changed, but as Indian National Security Advisor Ajit Doval has pointed out, 'wars are now fought with other means'.[22] The fourth revolution in military affairs (RMA), which envisions connected and autonomous military systems, is transforming the role technology can play in providing conventional armies superiority over others. But the nature of warfare itself is changing, as cyberwarfare is becoming more and more important vis-à-vis other domains of warfare. Much has been written about the fourth RMA by military experts, so I don't delve deeper into that and instead focus on the way cyberwarfare may be transforming the future of war.

In 2007, cyberwar or cyberattacks didn't even get a mention in the Global Threat Assessment prepared by the US intelligence agencies. But just a decade later, it had made its way to the very top of the global threats faced by the US in their assessment. The last time the threat assessment was shaken up this rapidly was when the Soviets tested the nuclear bomb in 1949, altering perceptions of the nuclear threat instantly for the US.

As David Sanger explains, cyber weapons are 'so cheap to develop and so easy to hide that they have proven irresistible'.[23] In a world where everything is networked or connected—from phones to electrical grids to satellites—intelligence agencies have realized that everything can be disrupted remotely, if not destroyed. The magnitude and potential impact of cyber weapons has therefore started to match the threat perceptions associated with nuclear attacks.[24]

Cyberwar is entirely different in nature from conventional war or even, for that matter, nuclear war. First, the weapons of cyberwar are not super expensive to develop. So, the capabilities gap between the richer countries and the others has narrowed. Even a country like North Korea can pull off a brazen cyberattack with much fewer resources than the US. As professor of cybersecurity at Tufts, Susan Landau told me, cyberwarfare has proven to be a great levelling agent.

Second, the more digitally connected your economy and institutions are, the more at risk you are. So, ironically, the more digitally advanced countries like the US are more at risk. Third, not unlike terrorist attacks, it is difficult to attribute the cyberattacks easily to its originators. And even if you are able to attribute the attack to a hacker group, it is hard to establish their relationship with a nation state.

Fourth, unlike nuclear or conventional weapons, it is harder to assess or judge the cyberwar capabilities of a group or a nation because they are mostly hidden and distributed amongst various state and non-state actors. Fifth, cyber weapons can be stolen by others fairly easily, unlike missile systems or tanks or even nuclear weapons. This has raised the spectre of widespread cyber capabilities, as opposed to being concentrated amongst major powers. Sixth, the extent or scope of the damage that cyber weapons can inflict is still evolving rapidly. Though until two decades ago, cyberattacks were minor in nature, they now involve major disruptions in the economy as the Colonial Pipeline ransomware attack showed (more on that later).

Seventh, the dynamics of a cyber conflict are very different from conventional warfare. Most cyber conflicts, including disinformation campaigns, are occurring daily without being considered as war, and remain in the 'gray area between war and peace'.[25] As Prof. Landau pointed out to me, while more technologically advanced nations like the US have become much better at attribution of cyberattacks, many small nations are not. Finally, since cyberattacks often target infrastructure owned by the private sector—whether it be in the form of power grids, data, internet networks, or routers—so cyber-defence requires a level of public–private cooperation and coordination that was not necessarily needed in earlier eras.

The rise of new geopolitical actors

Given the rising importance of technology in shaping geopolitics, a whole new set of state and non-state actors are becoming important in shaping relations between nations, and the hierarchies of power and influence.

Firstly, within governments generally and the intelligence communities specifically, each government's cyber-intelligence agencies are becoming more powerful vis-à-vis other intelligence agencies of that nation. For example, the NSA in the US, GCHQ in the UK, GRU in Russia, the Israeli 8200 Unit and the Chinese PLA Units 61398 and 61486 have become more powerful and influential in their respective countries.

Second, the world is seeing the emergence of new types of actors. Two new types are worth noting: proxy actors, who initiate cyber-campaigns against nation states and even corporations on behalf of their sponsor governments, and Big Tech firms as well as cybersecurity firms. Examples of the former include Shadow Brokers, who have been known to act on behalf of the Russian GRU. In terms of technology firms, both network and hardware firms such as Cisco, Qualcomm, HP, Dell and Apple, as well as software giants such as Facebook, Google, Microsoft and Amazon, are amongst the emerging dominant players in the US. In addition, cybersecurity firms such as Symantec and FireEye or even Israel's NSO (as the Pegasus incident demonstrated) are increasingly playing critical roles in coordination with their respective governments, and also foreign governments, as customers.

For China, similarly, the Big Tech firms like Alibaba, Baidu, Tencent and others are becoming natural partners for their intelligence agencies, along with hardware firms developing, for example, supercomputing capabilities, as discussed earlier. The Chinese Military–Industrial Complex (CMIC) Companies List published by the US Department of Treasury is instructive in demonstrating the wide expanse of private actors that are critical players in geopolitics now globally. The list includes companies from sectors such as mobile and satellite communications, aerospace, aviation, navigational technology, engine and heavy machinery manufacturers, marine technology, microelectronics and semiconductors, optronics, nuclear power, and other fields.[26] State-run companies such as China Electronics Technology Group (CETG), telecommunications giants such as Huawei, other electronic surveillance technology companies such as Hytera Communications (radio systems), Hikvision and Zhejiang Dahua Technology (world's second-biggest surveillance camera maker) are also allegedly active members of this CMIC.[27]

Challengers such as China and Russia are learning from and attempting to replicate the perceived success of the US's own model of the military–industrial complex (USMIC, due to the merger of the modern industrial firms with the modern military).[28] The USMIC has traditionally included a wide range of private firms such as Lockheed Martin, Raytheon Technologies, Boeing, General Dynamics and Northrop Grumman, whose annual revenues range between $30 billion and $100 billion. The USMIC (often also referred to as the 'private military contractors') has been considered a critical component of the US victory over the Soviet Union during the Cold War, the US response to the 9/11 attacks, and the wars in Iraq and Afghanistan.

With the rise of the digital age, the nature of the USMIC has also evolved. The Intelligence and National Security Alliance (INSA), established in 2005, is a powerful but not widely known coalition of private companies working collaboratively with the NSA and the broader US security establishment. A brief survey of the INSA website shows that aside from the traditional USMIC actors, its list of corporate members includes IT services firms such as Booz Allen Hamilton and Accenture, but also tech firms such as Amazon Web Services, Microsoft, Adobe, CISCO, Dell EMC, Intel, IBM, Oracle, Verizon, Cloudera and Salesforce.[29] The current group might be more aptly referred to as the Military–BigTech complex (MBC) or, as others have termed it, the Cyberintelligence–Military Complex (CMC). The MBC, which many call a 'shadow NSA,' is not just different but even more dangerous than the military–industrial complex.[30]

Unlike the US and, increasingly now, China, few other countries have leveraged the strengths of their respective private sector firms to boost their own capabilities in this space.

New incidents: Cyberattacks

Cyberattacks have been increasing in frequency and scope. Just in the last decade or so, the key incidents in the cyber-domain have included attacks in Estonia, Georgia, and Ukraine, the Snowden leaks, WikiLeaks, the Shadow Brokers theft of NSA cyberweapons, the allegedly US–Israeli-led Stuxnet attack on the Iranian centrifuges and on the North Korean-built Syrian nuclear facilities, and the NotPetya attack. Most incidents have either been Distributed Denial of Services (DDoS) attacks or ransomware incidents.[31,32]

The incidents are not always attacks. In some cases, like the Shadow Brokers incident, the hacker group Shadow Brokers actually stole secrets from the NSA and published information about major vulnerabilities in Cisco routers, Linux mail servers and Microsoft software (including most prominently the NSA hacking tool known as EternalBlue). [33] In the months that followed, several other hacker attacks relied on EternalBlue, including a major ransomware attack known as WannaCry.[34]

Table 8.1: New geopolitical cyber-actors and incidents in the last 10–15 years

Type	Illustrative examples
Government players	NSA, CIA, Computer Services Corporation (CSC), CyberCommand (DoD), GCHQ, Israeli 8200, GRU (Unit 26165 and 74455), Chinese Equivalent (PLA Unit 61398, 61486), Iran IRGC and MOI
Proxy actors/ Hacker groups	APT 3 and APT 10 (Chinese), Shadow Brokers (Russian), Longhorn, Intrusion Truth, Cyber Caliphate
Private actors	Big Tech firms and their data and cybersecurity teams such as Microsoft's Threat Intelligence Center (MSTIC) and Security Response Center (MSRC). Cybersecurity software firms such as CrowdStrike, Dragos, Cylance, FireEye, Symantec, Cyxtera

Type	Illustrative examples
Non-profit organizations and individuals	WikiLeaks, Joshua Schulte and Julian Assange, Edward Snowden
Spyware and cyber-incidents	Sandworm, WannaCry, Stuxnet, NotPetya, Estonia, Georgia, Snowden leaks, WikiLeaks, Ukraine, Iraq, Iran centrifuges, Syrian nuclear facilities, Shadow Brokers
Types of cyberattacks	DDoS, Ransomware, Wiper, Malware, etc.

Source: Author compilation, various sources.

In May 2021, in one of the largest, most prominent cyberattacks on critical US infrastructure, a ransomware attack on Colonial Pipeline, a top US oil pipeline operator, forced it to halt systems for its 5500 miles of pipeline for several days. Given Colonial's pipelines carry around 45 per cent of the US East Coast's fuel supplies across to fourteen states,[35] the disruption caused chaos across gas stations in many states. The US Federal Bureau of Investigation (FBI) issued a statement confirming that DarkSide, a criminal ransomware gang, was behind the cyber-extortion attempt.[36] Eventually, after several days of being unable to get its main systems up and running, Colonial Pipeline had to pay roughly $4.4 million in cryptocurrency to the attackers who were holding its computer systems hostage. (Later, the US Justice Department would state that it had recovered over half of that ransom amount).[37]

Around the same time as the attack on Colonial Pipeline, a US-based meat company allegedly paid a ransom of $11 million after a similar attack caused a shutdown of plants that process roughly one-fifth of the US's meat supply.[38] Earlier, in February 2021, a water treatment plant in Florida had been attacked, while a major (allegedly) Russian attack earlier on Texas-based SolarWinds, a technology company, had led to the US imposing sanctions on Russia.[39] All these incidents showcase not just how sophisticated the attackers are but also the incredibly dangerous impact these attacks can now have on the economy and lifelines of a country, whether it be food, electricity or fuel.

A blind spot for most countries

Unlike nuclear weapons, whose development and conditions of use were debated heavily in the public realm, especially after their first use in World War II, the same has not happened yet for cyber weapons. Geopolitical analysts lament the 'absence of the kind of grand strategic debates surrounding cyber that dominated the first nuclear age'.[40]

Much like any other technological change, the capabilities in the cyber domain are also evolving and growing so rapidly that governments and citizens are unable to understand what's happening, much less come together to devise a coherent strategy or response. As David Sanger explains, 'Rarely in human history has a new weapon been adapted with such speed, customized to fit so many different tasks, and exploited by so many nations to reshape their influence on global events without turning to outright war.'[41]

One of the reasons for this has been the secretive, invisible nature of the weapons. Countries and governments, especially the intelligence and military agencies who have been managing the cyberweapons, have been very reticent about their capabilities, choosing instead to only highlight the attacks that they have been the victims of. When the United States engages in cyberattacks, they're called 'cyber network exploitations', but when Americans are the targets, they are called 'cyberattacks'.[42]

Cyber weapons also 'come in many subtle shades, ranging from the highly destructive to the psychologically manipulative'. Many governments have until recently focused on the cyberthreats with the highest destructive potential, such as threats to nuclear installations. But it is the 'dialled down cyber weapons' that are being used daily by nations 'not to destroy an adversary but rather to frustrate it, slow it, undermine its institutions, and leave its citizens angry or confused'.[43] These are the harder ones to protect against, as they are employed in ways that do not cross the threshold that would lead to retaliation.[44]

In any case, there is still hardly any agreement or consensus in the international community on whether and when cyber-incidents constitute an act of war, a terrorist attack or mere incidents of cyber-espionage or cyber-vandalism. Governments, in any case, often just deny the attacks ever took place. For example, reports suggested that in the midst of the tense border clashes between India and China in May 2020, a Chinese government-linked hacker group, RedEcho, had targeted India's critical power grid system.[45] This malware attack caused a major power outage in India's financial capital, Mumbai. However, the Indian power ministry denied any such attack. While the India–China clashes were considered a military conflict, it is unclear how the Indian government would have internally categorized the malware attack.

As the Colonial Pipeline and the SolarWinds attacks have demonstrated, the vulnerabilities are expanding rapidly as well, given the increased digitization of all societies, corporations, infrastructure and governments. As Rob Joyce, the first cyber czar appointed by US President Donald Trump in 2016, explained, 'so much of the fabric of our society rests on the bedrock of our IT. We continue to digitize things; we store our wealth and treasure there; we run operations; we keep our secrets all in that cyber domain.'[46]

The implications for this lack of general consensus are manifold. For one, many governments and leaders have been experimenting with 'short-of-war aggression'. Most countries' frequent denials of attacks, lack of transparency about their cyber-capabilities, and unwillingness to accept some constraints have made it impossible to even begin the process of negotiation of widely accepted norms of cyber-behaviour.[47]

Though nations benefit from this strategic ambiguity in that it helps them buy time while 'stretching both technological and normative boundaries',[48] yet this state of uneasy equilibrium is quite risky and unprecedented. Even minor cyberattacks could end up escalating into serious disasters. As a recent report by the Carnegie Endowment for International Peace pointed out, cyber operations or attacks, whether by China against the United States, or vice versa, can easily provoke countries and escalate sharply into a conventional or nuclear war, even if one or both countries actually desired to avert such a disaster.[49]

Countries need to sit up and take note

Countries around the world, big and small, need to sit up and take note. War is no longer just conventional war, and information operations are, for any modern military leader, a key component of war strategy and execution. Unfortunately, despite living in an age of digital or cyber conflict, few countries have a strong handle on how cyberwarfare is reshaping global power.[50]

For national security establishments around the world, it is essential to anticipate potential attacks and have a clear and well-thought-out playbook for both defensive and offensive cyber and information operations. Developing strategic doctrine around cyber- and information-warfare, therefore, is the most immediate and important imperative for all major and minor cyber-powers of the world.

Most countries—and their military and political leaders, not to mention their strategic communities—have not quite grasped this simple point well enough. For example, David Sanger criticizes the US leadership for being 'remarkably slow to adapt to the new reality'.[51] The US knew, and understood, the nature of information and cyberwarfare that the Russians had unleashed in Estonia and Georgia a decade ago. Yet it somehow believed that the Russians would either not be capable of, or dare, crossing over the Atlantic and applying some of the same techniques to an election in the United States.[52] But as Brad Smith, president of Microsoft and author of *Tools and Weapons*, has argued, 'the internet has made everyone each other's next door neighbour'.[53]

In fact, analysts have argued that the absence of clearly planned responses to such cyberattacks have led adversaries of the US to continue to use cyber weapons to hurt the US, knowing that there is little price to be paid and that it will not trigger a direct military response.[54] Examples abound, from North Korea attacking Sony or China stealing the private details of over 21 million US citizens. And because 'Washington remains befuddled', cyber weapons have just become a new form of guerilla terrorism.[55] Though President Biden has moved to increase investment in cybersecurity, a clearer, more comprehensive strategy is yet to be put in place.

This is not true just for the US. This status quo of befuddlement and inaction needs to change across all countries. Nations will have to defend and secure their data and technology (in addition to the conventional land, territorial borders and trading routes that had to be traditionally secured anyway). Offensive capability now will not just mean the ability to project power far away from your borders through intercontinental ballistic missiles or naval carriers, but also your ability to acquire your opponent's data and technology. That will become a key competitive advantage, in geopolitical terms.

The emerging cyber powers

In some ways, where we are in cyberwar today is where we were with military aircraft around World War I. Until a few years ago, only a few countries had effective cyber armies. The state-on-state cyberattacks over the last decade, by many estimates, have exceeded at least a couple of hundred (counting only the public state-on-state ones). Sanger argues that 'as in World War I, this glimpse into the future has led nations to arm up, fast'.[56] Now, at least thirty countries have cyber armies.[57]

While a few countries—such as the 'Seven Sisters' of cyberwar, the US, China, Russia, Britain, Iran, Israel and North Korea—have been amongst the most active, several other nations are trying to catch up. Harvard's Belfer Center has developed a National Cyber Power Index (NCPI), which measures the comprehensive ability and intent of a cyber-actor to achieve various cyber-objectives such as surveillance, cyber-offence, cyber-defence, manipulation of the information environment, foreign intelligence collection, defining international standards, and commercial and industrial gain.

According to the NCPI 2020, the most comprehensive cyber powers, in order of power, are the US, China, UK, Russia, Netherlands, France, Germany, Canada, Japan, Australia.[58] Chart 8.1 plots the cyber power measures for thirty countries included in the index basis their intent and capabilities. Notably, emerging tech powers like India are ranked quite low on both intent and capability, as is Iran, even though it is often touted as a major cyber-threat for the US.[59]

This assessment of India, for example, has been confirmed by other cybersecurity experts. According to Chris Sedgwick of Talion, a cybersecurity firm, 'The sophistication of the various Indian cyber threat actors [does] not appear to be in the same league as China or Russia, and rather than having the ability to call on a cache of 0-day exploits to utilise, they have been known to use less sophisticated—but still effective—techniques such as decoy documents containing weaponised macros.' At the same time, India's cyberespionage is also limited by its geographic focus majorly on its South Asian neighbours and China, with some of the prominent Indian APT groups being SideWinder, Dropping Elephant and Viceroy Tiger.[60]

Cyber-commands in militaries

No modern military, Sanger has concluded, can afford to live without cyber capabilities, much like after 1918, no nation's army could live without airpower.[61] Starting in 2012, the US was among the first to start building what it called the 'Cyber Mission Forces' as part of the US Cyber Command (USCYBERCOM, formed in 2009). Comprising 133 teams, totalling more than 6,000 troops,[62] the Mission Forces have combat teams to support offence, defence and protection of the DoD information network.[63] USCYBERCOM is seeing a rapid rise in its importance: in 2018, it was elevated to the status of one of eleven combatant commands of the US Department of Defense (DoD), and

Chart 8.1 Plot of Cyber Power Rankings across Capability and Intent

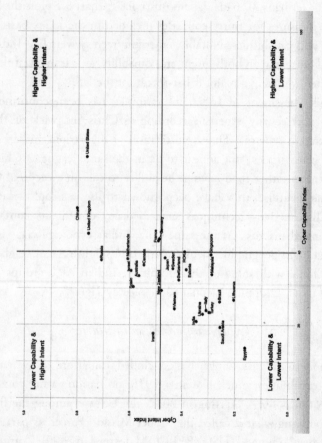

Source: Julia Voo et al., 'National Cyber Power Index 2020', Belfer Center for Science and International Affairs, Harvard Kennedy School (September 2020), https://www.belfercenter.org/sites/default/files/2020-09/NCPI_2020.pdf, accessed on 30 June 2021.

in 2021, its commander, Gen. Paul M. Nakasone, hinted that there would be a further growth in personnel as well.[64]

Other major cyber powers, especially Russia and China, are also aggressively building up both offensive and defensive capabilities. In 2015, China had also set up the Strategic Support Force (SSF) as the fifth branch of China's People's Liberation Army to oversee the space, cyber and electronic warfare force. Though information about the SSF is sparse, SSF is envisioned as a 'new-type combat force' (*xinxing zuozhan liliang*, 新型作战力量), set up due to the transformative evolution of the nature of warfare. Not unlike the US, China has emphasized the integration of the SSF and its information capabilities within joint operations, including the strategic frontiers of space and cyber to ensure that it is not at a disadvantage vis-à-vis the US military forces.[65,66]

Other countries are at different stages, but we can reasonably expect most minor and major powers to have cyber-armed divisions operational within the next decade. For example, India appointed its first chief for its Defence Cyber Agency in 2019 though it is unclear whether the agency is fully operational yet.[67]

New doctrines

New emerging military doctrines incorporate the elements of cyberwarfare and information operations. In the US, the Cyberspace Solarium Commission has recommended the adoption of the doctrine of 'layered cyber deterrence', which aims to reduce both the probability and impact of any significant cyberattacks. To this end, the commission report has recommended shaping responsible behaviour in cyberspace by forming strong alliances, securing critical infrastructure and networks in partnership with the private sector to boost resilience, and imposing costs through retaliation against actors who conduct cyberattacks.[68] This strategy of 'proactive defense operations in cyberspace' has been advocated by a Harvard Belfer Center report as well.[69]

Deterrence—a strategy that has arguably worked during the nuclear era—does not, however, quite work in the same way in the cyber era. The offensive capabilities also have to be matched with equally powerful defensive capabilities in cyberwarfare. The entire phenomenon of cyber war continues to be shrouded in such secrecy that states do not know each other's capabilities or strength—a piece that was critical in establishing deterrence during the nuclear era. While the US government, for example, continues to call out Russian and Chinese hackers, it refuses to divulge any details of its own cyber-offensive capabilities.

Putin's Russia, on the other hand, is credited with the new 'hybrid war' doctrine that integrates cyber and information operations. Both US and Russian military leaders have emphasized the critical role that 'Information Operations' are starting to play in the twenty-first-century battlefields. (Information Operations refers broadly to the use of information-related capabilities to both influence, shape, disrupt, corrupt and usurp the decision-making of adversaries while protecting one's own.)[70] As Russian General Gerasimov has pointed out, 'information technology essentially is becoming one of the most promising types of weapons.'[71]

Syria, unfortunately, has been witness to these new emerging doctrines of information operations and hybrid wars. Prior to the alleged US–Israeli cyberattack on the North Korean-built nuclear facility in Syria, Israel had pre-emptively manipulated Syria's air defence network. The Syrians' view of their own air defence network had no resemblance to the actual happenings, as F-15 Eagles and F-16 Falcons attacked the facility. The Syrians' Russian-built air defence systems had been hacked, and as a result, fooled. On the other hand, when Russia intervened in the Syrian civil war, General Gerasimov cited it as an example of a successful intervention where a small Russian expeditionary force was supplemented with information operations.[72]

Two uses of cyber war in aiding conventional war have also become evident. One, by disabling or confusing the enemy's defences through cyberattacks or cyber weapons, conventional attacks can be made easier, or rather, their likelihood of success can be increased. Two, propaganda can be used to demoralize the enemy prior to an actual military attack, as the US did before it invaded Iraq in 1991. Increasingly, cyberwar might simply be the prelude to conventional attacks, as the Russian attack in Georgia in 2008 or the US–Israeli attack on the Syrian nuclear facility illustrated.

Cyberwar might actually replace short conventional wars as well-planned cyberattacks can now severely paralyze a nation's economic, political and military systems. The 2008 Russian attack on Georgia remains one of the most chilling examples of state-on-state cyberattacks. Prior to their conventional army moving in, as well as during the conflict, the Russians allegedly carried out what in cyber-parlance are known as Distributed Denial of Service (DDoS) attacks.[73] They overwhelmed the Georgian routers with inbound attacks in order to severely restrict outbound internet traffic. No email, news or information could go out of the country. Georgia effectively no longer had access or control to the '.ge' domain. In order to hurt the Georgian banking sector, the Russians also initiated barrages of information to international banks. Expectedly, those banks, to protect their own systems, shut all connections to Georgian banks, including the settlement systems. Georgia's banking operations, followed by credit card and mobile phone systems, were paralyzed. The Kremlin denied the involvement of its agencies.[74]

This incident was over a decade ago, which is a lifetime in cyber terms. The cyber capabilities of countries have increased exponentially since then. The more worrying fact, therefore, is that these incidents are like just the trailers, not the movie. As Clark and Knake point out, 'the Russians are probably saving their best cyber weapons for when they need them, in a conflict in which NATO and the United States are involved.'[75]

Key Conclusions

Like guerilla warfare during the Cold War and terrorism in the post-Cold War period, cyberattacks might become the preferred route for countries and groups that suffer from asymmetric power dynamics. In a world where conventional (including nuclear) power remains concentrated amongst a few nations, cyberterrorism and non-state actor-led cyberattacks can reasonably be expected to increase in frequency and intensity. To achieve a period of relative stability through a balance of cyber-power, a few things have to fall into place.

One, given the much broader nature and scope of cyberattacks in recent years, significantly greater cooperation and coordination are needed between various arms of government, technology firms, cybersecurity firms, and even non-governmental organizations. The silos—both in the private sector and public sector—that contain information about attacks as well as expertise to tackle such attacks must be broken down. As Brad Smith has also pointed out, this necessitates 'a renewed conversation about policies for sharing threat intelligence and information about specific cybersecurity incidents'.[76] Many private cybersecurity firms (in addition to their government counterparts) have actually been able to develop cybersecurity solutions that are slowly making their way into the market.[77] Adoption still remains low, and that must become a priority for governments, regulators, companies and individuals.

Moreover, the onus of securing the defence of privately owned computer systems and connected industrial networks must lie on the private owners themselves. The government's role would need to be limited to support the private players with law enforcement, information sharing, diplomacy and, where needed and appropriate, military force. This would be in contrast to the dominant role that the government takes in the case of nuclear or air security.

The key difference is that the cyber domain and the connected networks are built, owned, managed, controlled and operated by a multitude of players. Supreme responsibility of the government would necessarily have to be accompanied by supreme control of the cyber domain by the government. Not only would that be anathema to many of the tech players, such centralized control of the infrastructure and choke points could also make the job of hackers that much easier. Big questions still remain around how to put in place these obligations and responsibilities on private sectors firms, and what incentives, if any, must accompany such obligations.

Two, as Clark and Knake suggest, a balance between offensive and defensive cyber technology has to emerge. Some countries today are more capable on the offence or attack front, while some are focused entirely on defence. Some, like Henry Kissinger recommended several decades ago, are focused on the optimal 'offence-defence mix' that can provide them the greatest flexibility.[78]

Military theorists believe if offensive capabilities continue to have an advantage over the defensive ones, then conflict will ensue. On the other hand, when it is either costlier to attack, or the chances of your attacks inviting much greater blowback are much higher, then greater stability is expected. Therefore, countries must start thinking of developing sufficient defences to cyberattacks, and also the imposition of major costs on attackers (whether state-backed or otherwise).

Three, cybersecurity best practices must be applied more broadly by individual and institutional users, and not just by governments and tech firms. Brad Smith has pointed out that simple mechanisms such as multi-factor authentication (MFA), for example, successfully deter most cyberattacks and prevent any significant loss of sensitive data. Yet, as a Microsoft study found, only 20 per cent of their customers use MFA currently. The OTP (one-time password) mechanism that is quite commonly used for online transactions in India is also a type of MFA.

Finally, governments around the world have to come together to set the rules of the game. I discuss this in detail in a subsequent section, but suffice it to say that if governments do not set the rules or fail to take coordinated action when certain lines are crossed, then user confidence in the cyber-systems might take a severe hit.

Notes

1. Headrick, *The Invisible Weapon.*

2. Eric Rosenbach and Katherine Mansted, 'The Geopolitics of Information', Belfer Center for Science and International Affairs, Harvard Kennedy School, May 2019, https://www.belfercenter.org/publication/geopolitics-information, accessed on 1 October 2021.

3. John Ferris, *Behind the Enigma* (Bloomsbury Publishing, 2020), Kindle.

4. Ibid.

5. Ibid.

6. Ibid.

7. 'Surveillance and Scandal: Time-Tested Weapons for US Global Power', *The Nation* (January 2014), quoted in Alfred McCoy, https://www.thenation.com/article/archive/surveillance-and-scandal-time-tested-weapons-us-global-power/, accessed on 1 October 2021.

8. 'N.S.A. Able to Foil Basic Safeguards of Privacy on Web', *The New York Times* (5 September 2013). https://www.nytimes.com/2013/09/06/us/nsa-foils-much-internet-encryption.html?pagewanted=all&_r=0, accessed on 1 October 2021.

9. 'How a Crypto "Backdoor" Pitted the Tech World Against the NSA', *Wired* (September 2013), https://www.wired.com/2013/09/nsa-backdoor/, accessed on 1 October 2021.

10. Alfred McCoy, 'Obama's Expanding Surveillance Universe', TomDispatch (July 2013), https://tomdispatch.com/alfred-w-mccoy-obama-s-expanding-surveillance-universe/, accessed on 1 October 2021.

11. 'N.S.A. Able to Foil Basic Safeguards', *The New York Times.*

12. McCoy, *In the Shadows.*

13. Ibid.

14. Ibid.

15. Edward Lucas, 'The Spycraft Revolution', *Foreign Policy* (April 2019), https://foreignpolicy.com/2019/04/27/the-spycraft-revolution-espionage-technology/, accessed on 1 October 2021.

16. Don Clark, 'Japanese Supercomputer Is Crowned World's Speediest', *The New York Times* (June 2020), https://www.nytimes.com/2020/06/22/technology/japanese-supercomputer-fugaku-tops-american-chinese-machines.html, accessed on 1 October 2021.

17. 'How a Quantum Computer Could Break 2048-bit RSA Encryption in 8 Hours', *MIT Technology Review* (May 2019), https://www.technologyreview.com/2019/05/30/65724/how-a-quantum-computer-could-break-2048-bit-rsa-encryption-in-8-hours/, accessed on 1 October 2021.

18. Steve Lohr, 'Move Over, China: US Is Again Home to World's Speediest Supercomputer', *The New York Times* (June 2018), https://www.nytimes.com/2018/06/08/technology/supercomputer-china-us.html, accessed on 1 October 2021.

19. Steve Lohr, 'China Extends Lead as Most Prolific Supercomputer Maker', *The New York Times* (June 2018), https://www.nytimes.com/2018/06/25/technology/china-supercomputers.html, accessed on 1 October 2021.

20. 'TOP500 Event at ISC High Performance 2020 Digital', https://www.top500.org/news/top500-event-isc-high-performance-2020-digital/, accessed on 1 October 2021.

21. Campbell Kwan, 'US Adds Seven Chinese Supercomputing Organisations onto Entity List', ZDNet (April 2021), https://www.zdnet.com/article/us-adds-seven-chinese-supercomputing-organisations-onto-entity-list/, accessed on 1 October 2021.

22. Ajit Doval, 'Warfare Areas Shifting from Frontier to Civil Societies: NSA', *The Tribune* (October 2021), https://www.tribuneindia.com/news/nation/warfare-areas-shifting-from-frontier-to-civil-societies-nsa-331015, accessed on 29 October 2021.

23. David Sanger, *The Perfect Weapon* (Harper Collins, 2019), Kindle.

24. Ibid.

25. Ibid.

26. 'Non-SDN Chinese Military-Industrial Complex Companies List', Office of Foreign Assets Control, Department of the Treasury, US Government (June 2021), https://www.treasury.gov/ofac/downloads/ccmc/nscmiclist.pdf, accessed on 1 October 2021.

27. Katsuji Nakazawa, 'Xi, Huawei and China's Powerful Military-Industrial Complex: How Beijing Harnesses the Private Sector for National Security', *Nikkei Asia* (December 2018), https://asia.nikkei.com/Editor-s-Picks/China-up-close/Xi-Huawei-and-China-s-powerful-military-industrial-complex, accessed on 1 October 2021.

28. James Ledbetter, *Unwarranted Influence: Dwight D. Eisenhower and the Military Industrial Complex* (Yale University Press, 2011).

29. INSA Website (July 2021), https://www.insaonline.org/about/members/, accessed on 1 October 2021.

30. Tim Shorrock, 'How Private Contractors Have Created a Shadow NSA', *The Nation* (May 2015), https://www.thenation.com/article/archive/how-private-contractors-have-created-a-shadow-nsa/, accessed on 1 October 2021.

31. Zak Doffman, 'How China's Most Dangerous Cyber Threats Are "Made In America"', *Forbes* (February 2021), https://www.forbes.com/sites/zakdoffman/2021/02/22/dangerous-chinese-cyber-threats-against-microsoft-windows-users-were-made-in-america/?sh=401db8f17632, accessed on 1 October 2021.

32. Laura Hotala and Rae Hodge, 'Congress Confronts US Cybersecurity Weaknesses in Wake of SolarWinds Hacking Campaign', CNet (February 2021), https://www.cnet.com/news/congress-confronts-us-cybersecurity-weaknesses-in-wake-of-solarwinds-hacking-campaign/, accessed on 1 October 2021.

33. Bruce Schneier, 'Who Are the Shadow Brokers?', *The Atlantic* (May 2017), https://www.theatlantic.com/technology/archive/2017/05/shadow-brokers/527778/, accessed on 1 October 2021.

34. Lily Hay Newman, 'The Leaked NSA Spy Tool That Hacked the World', *Wired* (July 2018), https://www.wired.com/story/eternalblue-leaked-nsa-spy-tool-hacked-world/, accessed on 1 October 2021.

35. David E. Sanger et al., 'Cyberattack Forces a Shutdown of a Top US Pipeline', *The New York Times* (May 2021), https://www.nytimes.com/2021/05/08/us/politics/cyberattack-colonial-pipeline.html, accessed on 1 October 2021.

36. 'FBI Confirms Cyberattack on US Pipeline Carried Out by DarkSide', AlJazeera (May 2021), https://www.aljazeera.com/economy/2021/5/10/cyberattack-on-us-pipeline-carried-out-by-criminal-gang-report, accessed on 1 October 2021.

37. David Uberti, 'How the FBI Got Colonial Pipeline's Ransom Money Back', *Wall Street Journal* (June 2021), https://www.wsj.com/articles/how-the-fbi-got-colonial-pipelines-ransom-money-back-11623403981, accessed on 1 October 2021.

38. Ibid.

39. Erum Salam, 'Cyber-attack Forces Shutdown of One of the US's Largest Pipelines', *The Guardian* (May 2021), https://www.theguardian.com/technology/2021/may/08/colonial-pipeline-cyber-attack-shutdown, accessed on 1 October 2021.

40. Sanger, *The Perfect Weapon*.

41. Ibid.

42. Ibid.

43. Ibid.

44. Ibid.

45. Amidst the tense border tension between India and China, a Chinese government-linked group of hackers targeted India's critical power grid system through malware. See *Mint* (March 2021), https://www.livemint.com/news/india/chinese-hackers-targeted-india-s-power-through-malware-us-firm-11614608839562.html, accessed on 1 October 2021.

46. Quoted in *The Perfect Weapon*, David E. Sanger.

47. Sanger, *The Perfect Weapon*.

48. Ilina Georgieva, 'The Unexpected Norm-setters: Intelligence Agencies in Cyberspace', *Contemporary Security Policy* 41, no. 1 (9 October 2019): 33–54, https://www.tandfonline.com/doi/full/10.10 80/13523260.2019.1677389.

49. Ariel Levite, et al., 'China–US Cyber-Nuclear C3 Stability', Carnegie Endowment for International Peace (April 2021), https:// carnegieendowment.org/files/Levite_et_all_C3_Stability.pdf, accessed on 1 October 2021.

50. Sanger, *The Perfect Weapon*.

51. Ibid.

52. Ibid.

53. Brad Smith and Carol Ann Browne, *Tools and Weapons: The Promise and Peril of the Digital Age*, (Hodder & Stoughton, 2021), p. 22

54. Ibid.

55. Ibid.

56. Ibid.

57. 'List of Cyber Warfare Forces', Wikipedia, https://en.wikipedia.org/ wiki/List_of_cyber_warfare_forces, accessed on 1 October 2021.

58. Julia Voo et al., 'National Cyber Power Index 2020: Methodology and Analytical Considerations', Belfer Center for Science and International Affairs, Harvard Kennedy School (September 2020), https://www.belfercenter.org/sites/default/files/2020-09/ NCPI_2020.pdf, accessed on 1 October 2021.

59. Ibid.

60. John Leyden, 'Indian Cyber-espionage Activity Rising Amid Growing Rivalry with China, Pakistan', *The Daily Swig* (February 2021), https://portswigger.net/daily-swig/indian-cyber-espionage-activity-rising-amid-growing-rivalry-with-china-pakistan, accessed on 1 October 2021.

61. Sanger, *The Perfect Weapon*.

62. 'DOD Fact Sheet: Cyber Mission Force', US Army Cyber Command (February 2020), https://www.arcyber.army.mil/Info/Fact-Sheets/Fact-Sheet-View-Page/Article/2079594/dod-fact-sheet-cyber-mission-force/, accessed on 1 October 2021.

63. 'Defense Primer: Cyberspace Operations, Congressional Research Service', CRS Report IF10537, updated December 2020, https://fas.org/sgp/crs/natsec/IF10537.pdf, accessed on 1 October 2021.

64. Mark Pomerleau, 'Will the Cyber Mission Force Soon Receive More Personnel?', C4ISRNet (May 2021), https://www.c4isrnet.com/cyber/2021/05/14/will-the-cyber-mission-force-soon-receive-more-personnel/, accessed on 1 October 2021.

65. Adam Ni and Bates Gill, 'The People's Liberation Army Strategic Support Force: Update 2019', *China Brief* 19, no. 10, Jamestown Foundation (May 2019), https://jamestown.org/program/the-peoples-liberation-army-strategic-support-force-update-2019/, accessed on 1 October 2021.

66. '2020 Report to Congress of the US–China Economic and Security Review Commission' (December 2020), https://www.uscc.gov/sites/default/files/2020-12/2020_Annual_Report_to_Congress.pdf, accessed on 1 October 2021.

67. 'India Set to Have Defence Cyber Agency in May; Rear Admiral Mohit to Be Its First Chief', ANI News (April 2019), https://www.aninews.in/news/national/general-news/india-set-to-have-defence-cyber-agency-in-may-rear-admiral-mohit-to-be-its-first-chief20190430102739/, accessed on 1 October 2021.

68. 'US Cyberspace Solarium Commission Report' (March 2020), https://www.solarium.gov/report, accessed on 1 October 2021.

69. Rosenbach and Mansted, 'The Geopolitics of Information'.

70. Joint Chiefs of Staff, *Information Operations* Joint Publication 3-1, (Washington, DC: Joint Chiefs of Staff, 2014), I-1

71. Valery Gerasimov, 'Genshtab planiruet udary po tzentram prinyatiya reshenii, puskovym ustanovkam i "pyatoi kolonne"' [The General Staff Plans Strikes on the Centres of Decision-Making, Launchers,

and the 'Fifth Column'], *Voyenno-Promyshlennyy Kurier*, no. 9 (2019), https://vpk-news.ru/articles/48913, accessed on 1 October 2021.

72. Andrew Kramer, 'Russian General Pitches "Information" Operations as a Form of War', *The New York Times* (March 2019), https://www.nytimes.com/2019/03/02/world/europe/russia-hybrid-war-gerasimov.html, accessed on 1 October 2021.

73. John Markoff, 'Before the Gunfire, Cyberattacks', *The New York Times* (August 2008), https://www.nytimes.com/2008/08/13/technology/13cyber.html, accessed on 4 October 2021.

74. Richard A. Clarke and Robert Knake, *Cyber War: The Next Threat to National Security and What to Do About It* (HarperCollins e-books, 2010), Kindle.

75. Ibid.

76. Smith and Browne, *Tools and Weapons*, p. 17.

77. Clarke and Knake, *The Fifth Domain* (Penguin Publishing Group, 2019), Kindle.

78. Henry Kissinger, *Nuclear Weapons and Foreign Policy*, Kindle.

9

New Friends, Old Enemies, Shifting Alignments

The confluence of technology and geopolitics, and the race for technological leadership, are leading to new conflicts, new orientations and new alliances. The frameworks or organizing principles underlying the alliances and partnerships of the previous era were, for example, democracies versus authoritarian states, capitalist versus communist states, and oil exporters and importers. Relationships were based on factors such as strategic geographical considerations, economic interests, common political systems, or historical cultural affinities. While some of these principles might remain relevant, new principles will emerge as well.

Now, countries are rethinking their own strategic interests and objectives, in the context of the technology-driven era of geopolitics. New permutations and combinations are on the table that might have seemed completely out of the question earlier. Partnerships are also being formed based on the nations' technological capabilities and the attractiveness of technology markets. Technology, as Shivshankar Menon emphasized, must become a bigger part of the strategic calculus of countries.

The intensification of the US–China geopolitical competition—much like the Cold War rivalry of the US and Soviet Union—will also become a major driver of alliances and partnerships. Certain existing alliances and relationships, such as the one between the US, Western Europe and Japan, will be reinforced. Similarly, China will double down on some existing friendships, but also strike new partnerships to assist it in its quest for dominance. At the same time, several major shifts are likely as well. The Russia–China relationship and the US–India relationship, for example, are likely to see major transformations. This shuffling will fundamentally reshape the world order over the next decade or two.

New Emerging Frameworks for Alignments and Contests

Framework 1: Techno-democracies vs techno-authoritarian states

The world, in the twentieth century, was divided into democracies and authoritarian states. In the tech era, the US and UK and other allies are attempting to continue with that same world view: democracies should band together against authoritarian states. According to this world view, the world will be divided into techno-autocracies and techno-democracies. The former, autocracies that are using technology to enhance surveillance and further cement their control over their populace, are threatening the latter, that is, those democracies that are using technology less for surveillance but more for economic development of their populace while respecting the traditional democratic values of free speech and privacy.

The argument goes that techno-autocracies are leveraging technology for furthering their autocratic control. Examples cited by the techno-democracies include the Chinese using facial recognition technology to surveil its citizens or profiling the Uighurs, or Russia proposing a 'Sovereign Internet'. Even more worryingly for techno-democracies, techno-autocracies are leveraging technology to prop up autocratic regimes elsewhere. Chinese companies such as Yitu, CloudWalk and the partly state-owned Hikvision are offering sophisticated AI-enabled surveillance and facial recognition systems to like-minded regimes in Africa, Eurasia and Latin America.[1] China is working hard to spread its 'techno-dystopian expansionism'[2] around the world, leveraging initiatives such as the BRI.

The threat to techno-democracies is not emanating from China alone. Russia-watchers such as Alina Polyakova have warned that the US's laser focus on controlling Chinese surveillance technology exports might allow the stealthy spread of the Russian model of digital authoritarianism. Russia's low-tech model of post hoc surveillance of the internet and telecom networks known as the System of Operative Search Measures (SORM) could prove to be more attractive to aspiring techno-autocracies.[3] While being more affordable and easier to install and integrate, SORM is equally effective as the Chinese model of mass filtering and pre-planned firewalling of information. Russian companies such as MFI Soft have been selling SORM-based technologies to other countries for as cheap as US $20,000, a price that is particularly attractive to resource-strapped authoritarian leaders.[4]

According to the leaders of techno-democracies, the writing is on the wall: 'If democracies fail to advance their own principles and interests with equal determination, digital authoritarianism threatens to become the new reality for all of us.'[5] Understanding the gravity of this trend, the new Biden administration in the US has developed an ambitious plan for an alliance of 'techno-democracies' as a way to counter the expansion of tech-enabled authoritarianism.[6] The proposed 'T-12 alliance' would include the technologically advanced democracies of Australia, Britain, Canada, Finland, France, Germany, India, Israel, Japan, South Korea and Sweden, along with the United States.[7]

Western media outlets, such as *The Economist* and *Financial Times*, have sounded the clarion call for an alliance of techno-democracies to 'take on China in the techno-sphere'[8] and 'keep Chinese tech at bay'.[9] Based on initial behind-the-scenes ideation efforts, the T-12 will work to set up an international technology finance corporation to help techno-democracies and their allies resist the lure of China's Digital Silk

Road initiative, in addition to a new global standard-setting body to frame a safe and open technology architecture for the world. The T-12, in a modern-day version of trade zones, might also set up 'trust zones' that would allow easier sharing of research and emerging technologies with countries that agree not to buy Chinese or Russian technology.[10]

The deeper question, however, is whether the West is exhibiting intellectual laziness or haste in continuing to rely on a Cold War–era ideological and values divide. If the foundations of these new alliances are not well-thought-out, they are likely to suffer from inherent contradictions and fault lines that could hurt their cohesion later. Moreover, a techno-democratic alliance might preclude many countries in the Middle East, Africa, Latin America and other regions that it is critical for the US to win over. The US has in the past also found ways to support and ally with non-democratic regimes where strategic interests dictate, so this dilemma is not new.

Furthermore, many techno-democracies also possess public surveillance capabilities powered in part by big data and AI, and some have in fact been surveilling their own citizens as well.[11] Mass digital surveillance is a key tool for all intelligence agencies today, and values such as freedom of speech and privacy are often violated both by techno-democracies and techno-autocracies. Technology developed by US and Israeli firms is being used widely by countries like Mexico and Saudi Arabia to monitor dissent, promote pro-government narratives on social media, and run disinformation campaigns.[12] So naturally, questions arise about whether the two groups are actually different enough from each other to provide a robust intellectual basis for the divide.

Framework 2: Digital sovereignty (national internets) vs a global, open, interoperable internet

An alternative organizing framework is offered by the ongoing debate between cyber-sovereignty (nations controlling their national internets) and an open, globally interoperable internet. For the most part, this yields a similar divide, with techno-autocracies defending the former and techno-democracies largely advocating for the latter. As Richard Haass, president of the influential Council on Foreign Relations (CFR), puts it, 'The fight is on to determine the internet's future,' with the United States advocating for an open, global internet while China and Russia are championing a more regulated, national internet.[13]

Under this framework, the world would be divided on the basis of a normative battle: should nations be able to frame their own rules on how their citizens use emerging technologies such as the internet, AI, 5G and genetic engineering? Countries, mostly techno-autocracies like China, Russia, Iran and others, believe in this concept of cyber- or techno-sovereignty. In Russia, for example, its conception of a 'sovereign internet' allows the country's internet to be self-contained and centrally controlled by the government. China has, in any case, its Great Firewall that allows it to control what its citizens access on the internet.

Countries, mostly techno-democracies like the US and the UK, firmly believe instead in the concept of an open, globally interoperable internet. As envisioned by its founders, the internet was meant to promote values of openness and free speech, and minimize the role of government. While the US and Europe are in broad agreement about an open and interoperable internet, potential fault lines do exist within the alliance of T-12 techno-democracies on this set of values.

Key amongst the T-12 democracies with a different opinion is India. During recent tussles between Big Tech firms and the Indian government, India—like China—has categorically asserted that it will not 'compromise its digital sovereignty'.[14] Though India's definition of digital sovereignty does not envision a 'sovereign internet' (like Russia's) or a Great Firewall (like China's), it does envision greater sovereign control over privacy, data and free speech.

Indeed, the internet has often worked in ways to undermine the control exercised by governments.[15] Even the US does envision greater sovereign control over Big Tech firms. But countries like India and China, and other developing countries that have had colonial experiences, are much more sensitive about ensuring that no foreign countries or corporations start to exert influence or violate laws in ways that might be reminiscent of the colonial era. And there, the US and Western European countries might find key allies like India to not always be on the same page.

Framework 3: Techno-nationalism (every country for itself!)

Related to the concept of 'digital sovereignty' and 'data sovereignty' is the emerging idea of 'techno-nationalism'. Techno-nationalists view technology and data as a key tool and driver of economic growth, and hence consider them as national resources.[16] In many ways, techno-nationalists are the modern-day avatars of trade protectionists, and are rethinking their own strategic interests and objectives in the context of the new technology-driven era of geopolitics.

Techno-nationalists aim to prevent unbridled cross-border data flows, because they see that as reducing the ability for them to use the data generated within their nations for their own national economic growth and employment. Visuals of colonialism—where resources of colonies were extracted by foreign powers and corporations—dominate in conversations, and unrestricted cross-border data flows often get termed as 'data colonialism'.

Here again, India has more in common with China than with the US. China, like India, is keen on ensuring sovereign control over corporations and adherence to national laws. Like India, it is also keen on ensuring that the value from the data generated within China must not be extracted by foreign powers, and rather accrue to its own citizens and the national economy. Both China and India believe in the concepts of digital sovereignty, data sovereignty and techno-nationalism. Data localization, that is, the physical storage and processing of data where it is being generated, is a key pillar of their quest for data sovereignty.[17]

On the other hand, the US, the European Union and other developed nations such as Japan are keen on ensuring unrestricted cross-border data flows, and easier access for their technology firms to enter markets without tariffs or other restrictions. That is essentially the techno-globalist view. The US and European nations, as the status quo tech powers, benefit economically from a techno-globalist view. But that pits them against developing countries that do not want to compromise this once-in-an-era opportunity to leapfrog on growth and productivity. These emergent countries, rightly so, want to ensure that the benefits of this technological era accrue to them as well, and not just to the Big Tech firms that call the US home.

Gideon Lichfield, editor-in-chief of the *MIT Technology Review*, defines techno-nationalism as 'the urge for nations to amass technological prowess and use it as an instrument of geopolitical power'.[18] It is evident that the US is also techno-nationalist, as is apparent from its strategy to keep Chinese companies out, and its emphasis on preventing Chinese entities from having access to US data. Techno-nationalists believe that no country can afford to let competitors pull ahead on technological strength.[19] This is in sharp contrast to earlier decades, where the world view around technology primarily seemed to be that technology, like globalization, is making the world flatter, closer, more open and more equal.

Not just India, China and Russia, but most countries are increasingly viewing technology as the key to gaining and sustaining power. Techno-nationalism, therefore, threatens to make our world an 'every country for itself' kind of world. India's external affairs minister, S. Jaishankar, also affirms that view in his book, *The India Way*, arguing that the uncertainties of the evolving world order are incentivizing nations to focus on their own narrow self-interest.[20] Countries would partner with other nations depending on who can best help them climb up the technological ladder, more so than the countries that they might have historical or cultural ties with. The US and Israel would therefore become more important partners for India than, let's say, the Soviet Union and Palestine.

In a way, it would be eerily similar to the early days of colonialism or industrialization. Each of the Western European colonial powers was engaged in a bitter rivalry to gain the most territories and boost their industrialization efforts, as a way to generate the most wealth for their nations. Commonality of political ideology or values and principles would matter little. And, like that era of European power rivalry, techno-nationalist approaches, adopted by all nations today, would threaten to create new divides between even existing allies or strategic partners.

Framework 4: It's the technology cold war, stupid!

The major players in today's world order—the US, Europe, China and Russia—are today engaged in a once-in-a-era fight for global technological and economic leadership and geopolitical influence. Many a change is afoot on the global chessboard, as each of these powers—as well as the smaller and mid-sized powers—are realizing that alliances, friendships, partnerships and animosities are all in a major state of flux. We are in a process of transition and a period of disequilibrium in the field of international relations.

As a CSIS report has argued, 'The world order is fragmenting without a clear organizing principle to follow.'[21] While we have discussed some of the potential new organizing principles, it is also evident that these organizing principles are ultimately still too new, and yet to be properly defined. Ultimately, as the CSIS report points out, 'within this transforming geopolitical landscape, the most important variables at play are the relative influence and leadership of the United States and China, and the bilateral relationship between these countries'.[22] It is this organizing principle that might define in the most immediate term the alliances and groupings that will dot the world order. And therefore, like the post-World War II Cold War era, all the other countries would need to pick a side.

Ultimately, these are just four examples of new organizing frameworks for alliances and partnerships. Nations will need to prioritize new principles in this era of technological competition. These choices will ultimately determine their friends and partners and, as a corollary, their opponents and adversaries—and most importantly, the new world order.

Reinforcing, Strengthening and Expanding Existing Alliances

US-led alliances

Alliances have been a core part of the US strategy for world dominance since the world wars when the US first shed its traditional approach of eschewing alliances. The US seems to be continuing with that approach in the twenty-first century as well, especially under the new Biden administration, which believes that rebuilding common ground with US allies and partners will form the foundation for a much more effective strategy for dealing with China.[23]

For example, the Group of Seven (G7), the pre-eminent grouping of the world's wealthiest countries (UK, USA, Canada, Japan, Germany, France and Italy), have come together with several new initiatives to prepare itself for the competition with China.

Prominent amongst the recent initiatives launched at the G7 Summit in June 2021 is the Build Back Better World (B3W) Initiative to finance infrastructure projects in the developing world and restrict the influence of China and its Belt and Road Initiative.[24] US President Biden and UK Prime Minister Johnson called the initiatives a 'democratic alternative' and the demonstration of 'the benefits of democracy' respectively.

The fact that the US also acceded to a long-standing EU demand for a global minimum tax suggests a quid pro quo, with both sides agreeing to come together as 'democracies' and fight the autocratic values of a common adversary. (Whether the global minimum tax regime actually does get implemented, and whether tax havens such as Ireland agree to comply with such regimes, remains to be seen.) The selection of invitees to this G7 Summit (Australia, India, South Korea and South

Africa) was also instructive, given all countries are from the Indo-Pacific region that the US considers to be strategically critical now.

During the Trump era, Europe was increasingly feeling isolated or neglected by the US but this changed with the Biden administration. As President Biden announced, on the eve of the 2021 NATO Summit:

> The transatlantic alliance is the strong foundation on which our collective security and our shared prosperity are built. The partnership between Europe and the United States, in my view, is and must remain the cornerstone of all that we hope to accomplish in the twenty-first century, just as we did in the twentieth century.[25]

Europe is reaching out to the US by meeting it more than halfway on cybersecurity and overall geopolitical concerns, but definitely expects the US to concede to some of its demands on matters such as taxation, data governance and anti-trust. The Europeans are now likely to be much more enthusiastic partners for the US and its global agenda. If the recent Munich Summit in 2021 is any indication, the US also wants the Europeans to assist them in the strategically important Indo-Pacific region.

As the economic, political and strategic centre of gravity of the world moves from the Atlantic Ocean to the Indo-Pacific, the Americans have realized that they need the Europeans' assistance there. This new strategy is being reflected in key changes underway within NATO as well. The 2022 NATO Summit is expected to adopt a 'new strategic concept' for NATO, which will firstly guide NATO's actions to counter threats emanating from Russia and China, and secondly, enhance practical cooperation with the Transatlantic Alliance's partners in the Indo-Pacific, such as Australia, Japan, New Zealand and Korea.

Though the US wants its European allies to contribute to the security of the Indo-Pacific region, the Europeans have not done anything like that since the end of the colonial era.[26] But the Europeans seem to be seriously considering engaging actively with the Indo-Pacific region.

The British and the French still have territorial holdings in that region, but their colonial history will remain a consideration. Such a shift, while obviously beneficial to the US, would also make the European powers more relevant on the global stage.

In light of the increasingly frequent and disruptive cyber threats being faced by its members from Russia- and China-backed hacker groups, NATO is also preparing to adopt a new cyber defence policy to ensure the Alliance's cyber-resilience.[27] In addition, the US is also upgrading and expanding its intelligence-based alliances. One of the most longstanding post-World War II alliances of the US is the Five Eyes, which is the intelligence-sharing arrangement between the US, UK, New Zealand, Australia and Canada.

With the NSA and GCHQ at the core of this alliance, the Five Eyes command 'almost unlimited intelligence power'.[28] In recent years, recognizing the growing cyber-surveillance capabilities of other countries that might be useful for Five Eyes, efforts have been made to expand the Five Eyes network. With China again as the threat focus, the US has been pushing for inclusion of India, Japan and South Korea in this alliance. The US and India, for example, have signed the three foundational agreements—for sharing geospatial intelligence (BECA-GI), logistics exchange (LEMOA) and communications compatibility (COMCASA)—that the US transacts with close military allies.[29] This is being seen as the stepping stone for India to be included into the Five Eyes++ grouping.

There are already precedents for such expansion and inclusionary groupings, such as the groupings known as the Nine Eyes (Five Eyes, plus Denmark, France, Netherlands and Norway) and the Fourteen Eyes (Nine Eyes, plus Germany, Belgium, Italy, Spain and Sweden) also known as the Sigint Seniors Europe (SSEUR). The Sigint Seniors Europe have a Pacific counterpart, as well, now. Founded in 2005 by the NSA, the founder-members of the SIGINT Seniors Pacific (SSPAC) were the Five Eyes as well as South Korea, Singapore and Thailand. India is believed to have joined the grouping in 2008. The Snowden leaks have indicated that India, despite being one of the newest entrants, is performing very well as part of this intelligence alliance:

> The results have been positive: RAW is now a regular contributor of SSPAC information reports and NTRO has also begun sharing bilaterally, and occasionally via SSPAC. RAW has produced the highest volume of reports for SSPAC next to the US and its information has garnered positive feedback from multiple SSPAC members.[30]

Together, these intelligence alliances, albeit unknown to most people, are some of the most powerful coalitions or alliances that exist in the world today.[31] Some intelligence analysts have also warned that these intelligence alliances are not all they are made out to be. As Brigadier Kuldeep Singh has argued, 'The US has a patchy record on information/ intelligence-sharing—even within NATO; a fair amount of what it shares is aimed at furthering its own national interests, or enhancing the threat perception in the minds of nations it is seeking as an ally.'[32] These contemporary intelligence-sharing alliances, he believes, can end up being double-edged weapons, as shared access to secure/classified information can reveal a member country's own vulnerabilities, which can later be leveraged against that nation when the strategic interests of the nations might not overlap anymore.[33]

Creating new alliances or groupings

The US has also embarked on laying the foundations for new groupings, some of which could end up becoming the foundational groupings for the new world order. The new grouping with the most potential to become a long-lasting one is the Quadrilateral Dialogue (popularly known as the 'Quad'), comprising its traditional allies, Japan and Australia, and an emerging strategic partner, India.

The Quad, first conceptualized in 2007, began as a platform for joint naval and rescue exercises in the Asia Pacific, but is now expanding beyond just military cooperation to security, economic, intelligence and technology cooperation. The initial years saw some hiccups, as Australia and India both were hesitant to formally get involved in a seemingly anti-China grouping. But as China's ties with each of the Quad members, including Australia and India, have become increasingly tense, they have shed their ambivalence.[34]

Even as China has heavily criticized the Quad, the Quad has grown in importance in recent years. In November 2020, just a few months after the India–China border clashes in Ladakh, the Quad members' navies participated in their first joint naval exercise in over a decade. In March 2021, President Biden hosted the first-ever Virtual Summit of the Quad with the leaders of all member countries demonstrating an alignment of shared concerns about China's increasingly assertive behaviour in the region.[35]

The Quad also serves as a great example of a twenty-first-century alliance that is coming together on technology-driven considerations as well. In addition to cooperation on vaccine production and climate change, the Quad is focusing on shared technological innovation and collaboration on supply chain issues through its Working Groups.[36] The supply chain issues being discussed in the Quad revolve squarely around the US–China technological competition. The Quad countries are aligned on building a supply chain of semiconductors and microchips, which is not dependent on China. Traditional US allies such as South Korea, Japan and Taiwan, which are the largest manufacturers of semiconductors and microchips in the world, will be core to this effort. In addition, the US and its allies are propping India up as an alternative manufacturing hub for semiconductors and chips.[37] Similarly, Australia might chip in with its significant reserves of rare earths (China has the largest.)[38] Collectively, the Quad and other US allies could reduce, if not eliminate, their reliance on China for critical raw materials.

But the traditional dimensions of alliances shall also persist. The US, drawing upon the success of NATO in the Cold War era, might envision the Quad to become the nucleus of a NATO-style security framework for the Indo-Pacific region. Many analysts have in fact argued that the Quad could evolve into a NATO-plus-OECD-type grouping for Asia, with a strong security, economic and technological focus.

However, the hesitation of India to enter into a formal alliance might still remain a roadblock for the Quad to turn into a formal military or security alliance. AUKUS (Australia–UK–US), a formal security pact between the three countries in September 2021, has emerged as an additional new alliance in the Asia-Pacific region. In his remarks announcing the 'next-generation' partnership, President Biden recalled the 100 years of history of the three countries' forces fighting shoulder to shoulder since World War I while looking forward to AUKUS helping the allies expand their 'edge in military capabilities and critical technologies, such as cyber, artificial intelligence, quantum technologies, and undersea domains.' Moreover, in a not-so-subtle reference to the US's intent to bring its European and Asian allies together, Biden also pointed out that 'that there is no regional divide separating the interests of our Atlantic and Pacific partners.'[39]

It would therefore not be surprising to see groupings such as AUKUS and the Quad work closely with NATO and other allies of the US. Moreover, the evolution of the AUKUS and Quad's relationship with ASEAN, the existing grouping of South East Asian nations, is also worth watching out for. Many South East Asian countries do not want to be in a state of overdependence on China. Yet, China is leveraging its strong economic ties within ASEAN to push back against the Quad. How China will respond to AUKUS remains to be seen.

Differences still do exist within these US-led alliances, old and new, that will need to be ironed out. Europe, for example, has been at the forefront of the privacy and data protection laws, with its General Data Protection Regulation (GDPR) laws being considered as a template for the world. Similarly, in December 2020, the EU unveiled the landmark

Digital Services and Markets Acts, which require Big Tech to take more responsibility for the goods and content distributed or sold on their platforms, besides also attempting to prevent them from giving unfair preference to their own services over competition. The Acts have also envisaged high punishments for non-compliance: penalties of up to 10 per cent of global revenues of the firms, and even forced divestiture of certain parts of their businesses.[40]

However, the US has been reticent to follow in Europe's footsteps, presumably because of opposition domestically from the US-based tech firms. Even the Global Minimum Tax proposals agreed in principle by the Biden administration are running into opposition in the US Congress, with many business groups urging delay.[41] At the same time, the US, much like Europe, has had a steady build-up of bipartisan support for anti-trust action against Big Tech firms.

Similarly, India is also starting to see the early signs of both anti-monopoly regulation as well as initiation of judicial cases alleging predatory pricing and anti-competitive practices amongst the Big Tech firms. The US-led alliances and partners will likely begin coordinating on this issue to preserve the dominance of the state in the tug of war with the Big Tech firms.

Neither will all new groupings or alliances survive. One such example is the Trump-era '5G Clean Network', a technological alliance of states as well as major telecom companies around the world that pledge to keep the 5G network infrastructure free from Chinese telecom majors such as Huawei. Though the grouping was eventually relegated to the archives of the US Department of State website, it still offers some interesting insights into the future of alliances and networks.

While traditional alliances have only involved nation states, this technology-focused alliance had over fifty countries and 170 telcos and tech giants from around the world sign up to the Clean Network. This included some of the world's largest telcos such as Reliance Jio in India, SK in Korea and O2 in the United Kingdom, and also tech giants such as Oracle, HP, NEC, Fujitsu, Cisco and SoftBank. As the battle for technological dominance evolves, and Big Tech firms become key geopolitical actors, this model of cross-sector or multi-stakeholder alliances will gain importance.

China-led partnerships

China has traditionally eschewed formal alliances, relying instead on the fundamental guiding principles of its foreign policy: independence and self-reliance. However, it has started to realize that the US and its allies would vastly overpower a rising China with no allies or partners. To stand its own ground, a more assertive China under Xi Jinping has begun forging a framework for strategic partnerships to secure its own share of steady, reliable friends in the international world order.

The most ambitious multilateral structure being pushed by Beijing is the Belt and Road Initiative (BRI). Envisioned as a global infrastructure drive to promote greater economic linkages, the BRI seeks to position China in the centre of key economic supply chains. The size of investments and infrastructure envisioned within the BRI are staggering, with some estimating it to be seven times bigger than the US's Marshall Plan to rebuild post-World War Europe.[42] The Chinese-architected BRI is still only a quasi-international institution. And while China is aiming for these institutions to be a substitute for the US-architected institutions, the membership rules and obligations for the BRI are still not well-defined.

The current composition of the BRI is also interesting, especially when seen against the membership of the now-shelved 5G Clean Network Initiative. Most of the members of the BRI are countries in Latin America, Africa, Middle East, Central and East Asia, and Eastern Europe (see Map 9.1). The Clean Network's presence, on the other hand, was strongest in North America, Western Europe and East Asia—almost a mirror image of the BRI (see Map 9.2).

Map 9.1: Map showing countries participating in BRI, 2019

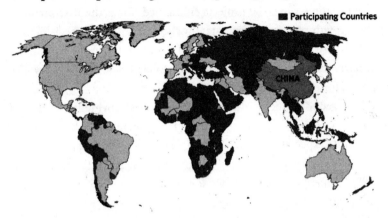

Source: 'Casting an Eye on the Belt and Road Initiative', Stratfor (August 2019), https://worldview.stratfor.com/article/casting-eye-belt-and-road-initiative-china-infrastructure, accessed on 30 June 2021.

Map 9.2: US-led 5G Clean Network map, July 2020

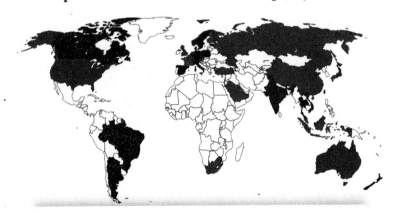

Source: 'Technology gets political', Bloomberg,

https://www.bloomberg.com/toaster/v2/charts/d6a021c6eb7c4f68a6afdab1c7783ab9.html, accessed on 4 October 2021.

If executed properly, the BRI could help China kill multiple birds with one stone. One, the projects envisioned under the BRI provide a global growth plan for China's state-owned enterprises, especially those that have driven the rapid expansion of China's own domestic road, rail and ports infrastructure. China notably today has seven of the world's top ten construction companies.[43]

Two, geopolitically and economically, it has provided a framework for China's (and Chinese companies') engagement with the rest of the world, especially the developing part of it. Projects that would otherwise just be standalone road construction projects being carried out by Chinese companies have now assumed strategic and economic significance.

China also plans to utilize the BRI in its quest for technological leadership. China announced the addition of 5G technologies to the BRI agenda when Xi Jinping announced the 'Digital Silk Road' in May 2017. It hopes to leverage BRI membership to push a common set of technology standards for all BRI countries, in effect creating an alternative digital trade zone to the one being envisioned by the T-12 democracies.

To make the BRI a success, execution will be key. The financial sustainability of many of the infrastructure projects undertaken by Chinese companies abroad is always in question. Analysts have pointed out that the Chinese companies are often happy to build the infrastructure, financed through loans provided by Chinese state-run banks, and the destination nations are happy to have that infrastructure built. For both sides, the costs and financing issues become something to be handled by those who come later.

In addition to the globally oriented BRI, the Chinese are also forming and taking the leadership in several regional plays such as the Shanghai Cooperation Organization (SCO) and the China–Pakistan Economic Corridor (CPEC). Within the SCO, China is focused on building East–West connectivity projects, while Russia is focused on North–South connectivity.[44] Similarly, CPEC is most focused on infrastructure development, especially from China's western provinces to the Pakistani deep-sea ports of Gwadar and Karachi. China will seek to grow the SCO and CPEC beyond their current infrastructure focus, but they are still quite far from becoming major alliances or international institutions of influence.

A potential Russia–China alliance

A potential Russia–China alliance is probably the most significant new alliance that could reshape the world order. It could seriously threaten the global dominance of the US and also disrupt the strategic calculations of many of the US's allies and partners.

For several decades, Russia and China had not been close friends or partners, and that had served the US very well for a long time. In fact, the US's success in driving a wedge between the then-Soviet Union and China in the 1960s and 1970s had been a game-changer. That one masterstroke itself, arguably, tilted the outcome of the Cold War towards the US.

But now Russia and China are witnessing a relative improvement in relations. Russia's pivot towards China was partly triggered by the shutting down of opportunities of cooperation with the West after Russia's annexation of Crimea in 2014. Russia increasingly began to realize that greater competition between Beijing and Washington would direct more US resources into the Asia-Pacific region and away from what Russia considers its vital interests in Europe.[45]

Moreover, realizing the difficulty of single-handedly taking on the United States and its allies, the Chinese and Russian governments are increasingly finding common ground in their world views. They have banded together, based on their mutual disgruntlement with the US-dominated international order that they feel works against them. They both have common strategies for techno-nationalism, a sovereign internet, and use of the internet to consolidate and retain power. The alignment of their interests and increasing convergence of their strengths could be a 'force multiplier for both'[46] and magnify the challenge they pose to the United States.[47]

The extent of their strategic alignment now is reflected not just in the fact that Putin and Xi Jinping have met over thirty times in the last six years, but also in a characterization by the Russian President in 2019 of the Sino–Russian relationship as 'an allied relationship in the full sense of a multifaceted strategic partnership'.[48] Russia and China are also increasing their cooperation in the cyber realm, recently declaring 2021 as the 'Year of Russian–Chinese Scientific, Technical and Innovation Cooperation'.[49]

They have also stepped up their cyber-offensive capabilities as a way to counter the superiority of the US conventional forces. Russia is adopting Huawei's technology and infrastructure for 5G. Huawei is investing heavily in Russia, including the setting up of research labs and centres at Russian universities.[50] China is also looking to tap skilled Russian engineers and mathematicians for their tech and defence industry companies, especially since they are increasingly being deprived of talent from the US and Europe.

The Russians and Chinese are aligned on another aspect: cyber-sovereignty. China has for several years had the Great Firewall of China in place that blocks many non-Chinese apps and significant amounts of content from being accessible to its citizens.

Over the years, Russia has introduced landmark regulations, all aimed at creating a restricted and controlled internet, including the Sovereign Internet Law. The idea here is simple: Russia wants to have an internet that can operate, even if it is completely cut off from the world.

Despite significant alignment in interests and vision of the future of the internet, one of the constraints, however, for the Russian–Chinese partnership is that it needs to be one of equals. Going against that is the fact that Russia has started to lag greatly behind China and other nations in AI and other emerging technologies.[51] This poses a quandary for the Russians, who wish to remain independent players in geopolitics and also, most importantly, never wish to be a junior or inferior partner in a relationship.

For China, a strategic alliance or partnership with Russia would largely be a beneficial move. But for Russia, it poses a dilemma. If the US–China tensions divide the world into two blocs, then Russia would have no choice but to join the China-led camp. But as Dmitri Trenin of the Carnegie Moscow Center argues, this would not necessarily be a very favourable outcome either for Russia, as it would also move closer to being a junior partner in that camp.[52]

At the same time, it would be important for the US and its allies and partners to prevent a Sino–Russian alliance. In fact, the Biden–Putin summit in June 2021 in Geneva is widely being seen as a sign that both countries are keen to bury the hatchet and restore at least some sense of 'predictability and stability' in their relations.[53] The Biden–Putin summit was a clear indication that the US wants to focus on the much bigger challenge that China poses to it, and not have to fight on two fronts simultaneously with China and Russia.[54]

Furthermore, a US–Russia détente could have a serious impact on the fast-evolving Asian geopolitical map. Reducing tensions between Europe and Russia would also free up Europe to help the US in the Indo-Pacific region. Furthermore, India and Japan would both benefit greatly from not having Russia ally with China, or even get too shackled to it. Delhi's own space for strategic manoeuvring gets limited if Russia is aligned too closely with China, leaving Delhi no option but to remain closely aligned with Europe and the United States.[55]

The New Digital Battlegrounds: The Digital Swing States

Whether the parallels to the Cold War are appropriate or not, the US and China are increasingly acting as per Cold War frameworks. The Chinese have kept US companies out of China for long, and recently, the US has put in place strict measures to keep the Chinese out of the US. As a result, the tech cold war is being played out in the 'new digital battlegrounds' or the 'digital swing states'.

As per a methodology designed by NewAmerica.org, the top digital swing states are Brazil, Indonesia, Mexico, India and Singapore. A region-wise analysis would suggest that the new digital battlegrounds are Africa, South East Asia, Eastern Europe and Central Asia.[56] As Tim Maurer and Robert Morgus point out, focusing on swing states such as Brazil, India, Indonesia and Turkey could pay off massively for the US and China. The choices these countries make on emerging technological frameworks could decisively influence the direction of the tech-shaped world order.[57]

All the swing regions of the world today—whether it be the Middle East, Africa, Southeast Asia, Eastern Europe or Central Asia—are increasingly faced with a similar Cold War-esque strategic choice to make: to join the US/Europe camp, to join the China camp, or to delicately balance between the two. Joining a particular camp offers the benefit of greater economic, security, military and technological benefits from that camp, but limits the strategic autonomy and flexibility that some countries value in foreign and domestic policy. Remaining 'non-aligned' in today's world might keep both camps interested in wooing you, but will not bring the exclusive benefits that come from being an insider. The case study of one of the digital battlegrounds will illustrate how the battle for global support amongst the major powers is likely to play out.

Case study: The digital battleground of Latin America

For some time now, Latin American leaders have attempted to build and maintain friendly ties with both Washington and Beijing. Given their geographic proximity to the US but also their growing economic dependence on China, this had seemed like the pragmatic stance and a winning formula.[58] But recent developments, especially the US's aggressive stance towards China, have increasingly made such fence-sitting an unviable strategy for Latin American nations.

On the one hand, the US has been explicitly and implicitly warning Latin American nations with 'consequences', in addition to pointing out the likelihood that Chinese companies such as Huawei will help the Chinese spy on them. The historical influence of the US in the region has been immense. For example, of the almost fifteen countries that do not recognize China (and recognize Taiwan instead), nine are in Latin America and the Caribbean.

On the other hand, China has been aggressively pushing back, accusing the US of treating Latin America as its backyard, and positioning itself as the saviour of the sovereignty of the Latin American nations. China is already Latin America's largest trading partner, with the Chinese middle class driving demand for, among other things, Uruguay's beef, Chilean copper, Colombian oil and Brazilian soya. Nineteen governments across Latin America and the Caribbean have joined Xi Jinping's signature Belt and Road Initiative (BRI). This economic relationship has brought political dividends as well for China.

In the last four years, three countries—Dominican Republic, El Salvador, Panama—have recognized China instead of Taiwan. These new-gained friends not only offer support and votes for the Chinese (and their candidates for leadership positions) at multilateral institutions, but they also present an opening for the Chinese tech firms to embed their standards-setting technologies into the regional infrastructure.[59]

The US has not been taking the Chinese push in Latin America lying down. Recently, for example, it launched its own América Crece initiative in direct competition with the BRI to help catalyse private sector investment in energy and other infrastructure projects across Latin America and the Caribbean.[60] When push comes to shove, history suggests that the US will work hard to limit external influence in what it sees as its backyard.

The Latin American nations realize that no matter which side they eventually take, 'it will inevitably harm one of their two most important geopolitical relationships'.[61] Therefore, they are likely to continue to either try and play a balancing game, or extract their pound of flesh for siding with only one side outright. However, strategic affairs expert C. Raja Mohan astutely pointed out to me that as the US–China relationship becomes increasingly confrontational, it will become increasingly difficult for most nations to play this balancing game.

Digital swing state: Is India today the China of the 1970s?

Of the digital swing states, India stands out as an extremely interesting, and relevant, case study. In some ways, the US is looking at India as the game-changing swing state, as it likely saw China in the 1970s.

The US–India strategic partnership seems to have many parallels with the US–China alliance struck by Nixon and Kissinger in the 1970s. In the 1970s, China was a state that shared many similarities with the Soviet Union (the key US opponent) but was poorer and hungry to be the leader of the communist world. The Chinese and the Soviets had fought a war recently. So, it was the perfect candidate for the US to ally with, and open up a second front for the Soviet Union on its border.

Today, India is the poorer Asian neighbour of China (the key US opponent now) and shares several similarities with China. At the same time, China and India have had several face-offs on their disputed border in recent years. In many ways, it is the perfect candidate for the US to ally with to open up a second front for China on its border. The US doesn't want to have two simultaneous battlefronts with China and Russia, but it does want China to have multiple battlefronts to fight on.

The US–India relationship had been improving significantly and steadily for the last two decades, even as the India–China relationship had been getting more tense and jittery over the last decade. Yet, there was no certainty, until just three or four years ago, that India would firmly place itself in the US camp.

Around 2014–15, the Chinese Big Tech firms had started to become some of the largest investors in the Indian start-up ecosystem, giving tough competition to the largest American and Japanese investors. There was this sense that the alignment, at least from a technology sector standpoint, might actually change. Indian entrepreneurs had started visiting the Chinese start-ups and tech firms in China instead of Silicon Valley firms, and had come back amazed at their scale.

Moreover, the Chinese market seemed more aligned with the challenges and opportunities in the Indian market, so entrepreneurs started to follow the China example. Suddenly, start-up pitches were drawing analogies with Chinese companies rather than Silicon Valley companies. And tech start-up conferences were now swarming with young Chinese professionals from Alibaba, Tencent and other such Chinese Big Tech firms.

But then came the border skirmishes in Ladakh and Doklam between India and China. These events might have been the consequences of India moving into the US camp or the triggers for it. Regardless, India has now moved quite deep into the US camp, and that is a big achievement for the US. It is, I believe, as significant a move as the Nixon–Kissinger achievement in getting China on board in the 1970s, and could potentially be the game-changer on the world map.

The US has been able to change India's orientation towards the US camp much more decisively than it ever had in the past. But India must think very carefully about what the alliance with the US will mean for its strategic autonomy. As Shivshankar Menon has argued in his recent book, *India and Asian Geopolitics*, the current world dynamics, in fact, make strengthening our strategic autonomy—and working closely with all major powers—an even bigger imperative for India.[62] India must also remain prepared for the longer-term when alignments or strategic calculations shift again, as they inevitably do.

The Future of Alliances

The frameworks for alliances, as well as the nature and future of alliances, are changing. The dominant framework for alliances and partnerships remains uncertain for now. However, it is clear that the Great Tech Game and the growing geopolitical, economic and technological competition between the US and China will shape future alliances and orientations.

Traditionally, alliances or partnerships have been determined by either economic or security considerations, strategic geographical locations, or historical cultural affinities. But a new dimension has been added. Countries that are important from a technology perspective—either as large digital markets or as technologically advanced nations or having critical resources for technology supply chains—are also assuming greater importance as potential allies and partners.

India, for example, has become a much more attractive ally, given these changed considerations. It is more than just a large-value digital market that the Big Tech firms—American, European and Chinese—all want a share of. It is also a strategically important swing state in the battle for technological and geopolitical dominance between the US and China. Earlier, Pakistan's strategic geographical location (vis-à-vis Afghanistan) meant that the US was always quite keen to maintain good relations with Pakistan at the same time as it stepped up its strategic partnership with India. But now, India is just that much more important, especially given the new technology- and China-driven considerations, for the US. Not surprisingly, we are seeing Pakistan move deeper into the China camp, and India firmly into the US camp.

Future alliances in the twenty-first century will be more than military alliances. As Mira Rapp-Hooper suggests, alliances that go beyond military dimensions and work together on technological, space, intelligence and cyber dimensions will end up being more effective and productive. For such cooperation, as new groupings like the Quad and AUKUS are beginning to do, allies will not necessarily need to raise their defence spending. Rather, they could contribute significantly through existing resources such as intelligence agencies, foreign ministries, technology firms and professionals, hacker groups, and national security establishments.[63]

A strategic rethink will therefore be needed for all countries, big and small, as technology will shape the nature and *raison d'être* for alliances. Countries that manage to build unique cyber weapons or cyber-capabilities will be in demand. Certain countries such as Australia will also be desirable as allies or partners because of the endowment of rare earths that they possess. (Sample this: In September 2021, soon after the announcement of the AUKUS pact, President Biden remarked that 'the United States has no closer or more reliable ally than Australia.'[64]) Similarly, the Netherlands will become a critical partner, given that Dutch multinational ASML is the world's largest supplier of photolithography systems for the semiconductor industry.

In contrast, the geographical proximity of an ally, or its armed forces, will not matter as much in an era dominated by cyberwarfare. Similarly, the demand for military technology cooperation will be as much about cyber weapons and cyber-defence and cyber-intelligence capabilities as about conventional weapons, if not more.

The potential allies will expect the US and China to share the financial burden of ensuring their cybersecurity if they are to join their camp. And the US is likely to see this simply as a cost of doing business, much like it had during the Cold War. In fact, we can reasonably expect both the US and China to become global providers of cyber-safety for their allies and friends.

It would be interesting to see how the framework for alliances develops in this context. How will the US design this framework? What new division of responsibilities will it seek to put in place? What will it provide in terms of shared services, and what will it expect its allies to be responsible for? Will certain new partnerships (e.g., AUKUS) alienate some others (e.g., France)? The lessons from its legacy alliances from the Cold War and post-Cold War era could serve to be quite instructive in this regard.[65]

On the other hand, how is China expected to respond to this aggressive attempt of the US to build cyber-alliances? Will it continue to eschew formal alliances and continue its pattern of techno-economic diplomacy, as embodied by the BRI? Could it be that China would adopt a hybrid model, whereby it strikes formal alliances with some players (such as Russia) and partnerships or friendships with other smaller nations?

Regardless, alliances will be a key determinant of who wins this new Great Game for technological and geopolitical leadership. Much like the over fifty alliances of all kinds forged by the US during the Cold War, the US is likely to attempt to win the war for technological leadership by beating China at the alliance game.

Notes

1. Steven Feldstein, 'The Global Expansion of AI Surveillance', Working Paper, Carnegie Endowment for International Peace (September 2019), https://carnegieendowment.org/files/WP-Feldstein-AISurveillance_final1.pdf, accessed on 4 October 2021.

2. Michael Abramowitz and Michael Chertoff, 'The Global Threat of China's Digital Authoritarianism', *The Washington Post* (November 2018), https://www.washingtonpost.com/opinions/the-global-threat-of-chinas-digital-authoritarianism/2018/11/01/46d6d99c-dd40-11e8-b3f0-62607289efee_story.html, accessed on 1 October 2021.

3. Alina Polyakova, 'Russia Is Teaching the World to Spy', *The New York Times* (December 2019), https://www.nytimes.com/2019/12/05/opinion/russia-hacking.html, accessed on 1 October 2021.

4. Ibid.

5. Abramowitz and Chertoff, 'The Global Threat of China's Digital Authoritarianism'.

6. David Ignatius, 'Biden's Ambitious Plan to Push Back Against Techno-Autocracies', *The Washington Post* (February 2021), https://www.washingtonpost.com/opinions/bidens-ambitious-plan-to-push-back-against-techno-autocracies/2021/02/11/2f2a358e-6cb6-11eb-9ead-673168d5b874_story.html, accessed on 1 October 2021.

7. Jared Cohen and Richard Fontaine, 'Uniting the Techno-Democracies: How to Build Digital Cooperation', *Foreign Affairs* (November/December 2020), https://www.foreignaffairs.com/articles/united-states/2020-10-13/uniting-techno-democracies, accessed on 1 October 2021.

8. 'Democracies Must Team Up to Take on China in the Technosphere', *The Economist* (November 2020), https://www.economist.com/briefing/2020/11/19/democracies-must-team-up-to-take-on-china-in-the-technosphere, accessed on 1 October 2021.

9. 'US, Europe and UK Must Unite to Keep Chinese Tech at Bay', *Financial Times*, https://www.ft.com/content/bc7abf86-f13e-4025-a120-004361aef21a, accessed on 1 October 2021.

10. Ignatius, 'Biden's Ambitious Plan'.

11. Ibid.

12. Steven Feldstein, 'The Virus that Split the World', *MIT Technology Review* 123, no. 5 (September/October 2020), https://wp.technologyreview.com/wp-content/uploads/2020/08/MIT-Technology-Review-2020-09.pdf, accessed on 1 October 2021.

13. Robert Knake, 'Weaponizing Digital Trade Creating a Digital Trade Zone to Promote Online Freedom and Cybersecurity', Council Special Report No. 88 (September 2020), https://cdn.cfr.org/sites/default/files/report_pdf/weaponizing-digital-trade_csr_combined_final.pdf, accessed on 1 October 2021.

14. '"India Won't Compromise Its Digital Sovereignty": Ravi Shankar Prasad', *Hindustan Times* (June 2021), https://www.hindustantimes.com/india-news/india-won-t-compromise-its-digital-sovereignty-ravi-shankar-prasad-101622919207459.html, accessed on 1 October 2021.

15. James Andrew Lewis, 'Sovereignty and the Evolution of Internet Ideology', Center for Strategic and International Studies (CSIS), Washington DC (October 2020), https://www.csis.org/analysis/sovereignty-and-evolution-internet-ideology, accessed on 1 October 2021.

16. Anirudh Burman and Upasana Sharma, 'How Would Data Localization Benefit India?', Carnegie Endowment for International Peace (India) (April 2021), https://carnegieindia.org/2021/04/14/how-would-data-localization-benefit-india-pub-84291, accessed on 1 October 2021.

17. Ibid.

18. Gideon Lichfield, 'From the Editor', *MIT Technology Review* 123, no. 5 (September/October 2020), https://wp.technologyreview.com/wp-content/uploads/2020/08/MIT-Technology-Review-2020-09.pdf, accessed on 1 October 2021.

19. Feldstein, 'The Virus that Split the World'.

20. S. Jaishankar, *The India Way: Strategies for an Uncertain World*, (HarperCollins India, 2020), p. 12.

21. 'Four Scenarios for Geopolitical Order in 2025–2030: What Will Great Power Competition Look Like?', CSIS (September 2020), https://www.csis.org/analysis/four-scenarios-geopolitical-order-2025-2030-what-will-great-power-competition-look, accessed on 1 October 2021.

22. Ibid.

23. Demetri Sevastopulo, 'US vs China: Biden Bets on Alliances to Push Back Against Beijing', *Financial Times* (March 2021), https://www.ft.com/content/cf71feb2-297f-4e3a-8627-b89931cc6a80, accessed on 1 October 2021.

24. Michael D. Shear, Zolan Kanno-Youngs and Marc Santora, 'G7 Leaders Come Together on a Global Minimum Tax and Democratic Ideals', *The New York Times* (June 2021), https://www.nytimes.com/2021/06/13/world/europe/g7biden-china-influenc-.html, accessed on 1 October 2021.

25. 'Fact Sheet: NATO Summit: Revitalizing the Transatlantic Alliance', The White House, US Government (June 2021), https://www.whitehouse.gov/briefing-room/statements-releases/2021/06/13/fact-sheet-nato-summit-revitalizing-the-transatlantic-alliance/, accessed on 1 October 2021.

26. Ibid.

27. Ibid.

28. Aldrich, *GCHQ*.

29. Kuldip Singh, 'What Do Indian Soldiers Stand to Gain from India–US BECA Deal?', *The Quint* (October 2020), https://www.thequint.com/voices/opinion/india-united-states-geospatial-intelligence-deal-implications-indian-armed-forces, accessed on 1 October 2021.

30. 'NSA's Changing Counterterrorism Relationship with India', Edward Snowden Documents (June 2009), https://edwardsnowden.com/docs/doc/SIDtoday-2009-06-15-NSAs-Changing.pdf, accessed on 1 October 2021.

31. Ryan Gallagher, 'The Powerful Global Spy Alliance You Never Knew Existed', *The Intercept*, 'March 2018', https://theintercept.com/2018/03/01/nsa-global-surveillance-sigint-seniors/, accessed on 1 October 2021.

32. Kuldip Singh, 'What Do Indian Soldiers Stand to Gain from India-US BECA Deal?'.

33. Ibid.

34. Jagannath Panda, 'India and the "Quad Plus" Dialogue', Royal United Services Institute (RUSI) (June 2020), https://rusi.org/commentary/india-strategic-quad, accessed on 1 October 2021.

35. Sheila A. Smith, 'The Quad in the Indo-Pacific: What to Know', Council on Foreign Relations (May 2021), https://www.cfr.org/in-brief/quad-indo-pacific-what-know, accessed on 1 October 2021.

36. Ibid.

37. Nick Wadhams, 'Biden Putting Tech, Not Troops, at Core of US–China Policy', *Bloomberg Quint* (March 2021), https://www.bloombergquint.com/business/biden-putting-tech-not-troops-at-center-of-u-s-china-strategy, accessed on 1 October 2021.

38. Taisei Hoyama and Yu Nakamura, 'US and Allies to Build "China-free" Tech Supply Chain', *Nikkei Asia* (February 2021), https://asia.nikkei.com/Politics/International-relations/Biden-s-Asia-policy/US-and-allies-to-build-China-free-tech-supply-chain, accessed on 1 October 2021.

39. Remarks by President Biden, Prime Minister Morrison of Australia and Prime Minister Johnson of the United Kingdom Announcing the Creation of AUKUS, https://www.whitehouse.gov/briefing-room/speeches-remarks/2021/09/15/remarks-by-president-biden-prime-minister-morrison-of-australia-and-prime-minister-johnson-of-the-united-kingdom-announcing-the-creation-of-aukus/, accessed on 30 September 2021.

40. Ryan Browne, 'Europe Tries to Set the Global Narrative on Regulating Big Tech', CNBC (December 2020), https://www.cnbc.com/2020/12/16/europe-tries-to-set-the-global-narrative-on-regulating-big-tech.html, accessed on 1 October 2021.

41. Richard Rubin, 'Global Tax Deal Heads Down Perilous Path in Congress', *Wall Street Journal* (July 2021), https://www.wsj.com/articles/global-tax-deal-heads-down-perilous-path-in-congress-11626008186, accessed on 1 October 2021.

42. Hillman, *The Emperor's New Road*.

43. Ibid.

44. Asoke Mukerji, 'India and the Shanghai Cooperation Organisation', ORF Raisina Debates (December 2020), https://www.orfonline.org/expert-speak/india-shanghai-cooperation-organisation/, accessed on 1 October 2021.

45. Michael Kofman, 'The Emperors League: Understanding Sino–Russian Defense Cooperation', WarOnTheRocks (August 2020), https://warontherocks.com/2020/08/the-emperors-league-understanding-sino-russian-defense-cooperation/, accessed on 1 October 2021.

46. Samuel Bendett and Elsa Kania, 'The Resilience of Sino-Russian High-Tech Cooperation', WarOnTheRocks (August 2020), https://warontherocks.com/2020/08/the-resilience-of-sino-russian-high-tech-cooperation/, accessed on 1 October 2021.

47. Andrea Kendall-Taylor, David Shullman and Dan McCormick, 'Navigating Sino-Russian Defense Cooperation', WarOnTheRocks

(August 2020), https://warontherocks.com/2020/08/navigating-sino-russian-defense-cooperation/, accessed on 1 October 2021.

48. Ibid.

49. Ibid.

50. Samuel Bendett and Elsa Kania, 'The Resilience of Sino-Russian High-Tech Cooperation'.

51. Ibid.

52. Yohei Ishikawa, 'Putin's Real Intention in Talking Up a Russia-China Alliance', *Nikkei Asia*, December 2020, https://asia.nikkei.com/Editor-s-Picks/Interview/Putin-s-real-intention-in-talking-up-a-Russia-China-alliance2, accessed on 1 October 2021.

53. Anthony Zurcher, 'Biden–Putin Summit: Awkward Conversation Looms in Geneva', BBC (June 2021), https://www.bbc.com/news/world-us-canada-57244860, accessed on 1 October 2021.

54. C. Raja Mohan, 'Asia's Stakes in the Biden–Putin Summit, Foreign Policy' (June 2021), https://foreignpolicy.com/2021/06/11/biden-putin-summit-asia-india-china-japan-us-russia-detente-quad/, accessed on 1 October 2021.

55. Ibid.

56. NewAmerica.org, https://www.newamerica.org/cybersecurity-initiative/reports/digital-deciders/understanding-the-clusters-through-data/, accessed on 1 October 2021.

57. Tim Maurer and Robert Morgus, 'Tipping the Scale: An Analysis of Global Swing States in the Internet Governance Debate', CIGI Internet Governance Papers, Paper No. 7 (May 2014), https://www.cigionline.org/sites/default/files/no7_2.pdf, accessed on 1 October 2021.

58. Oliver Stuenkel, 'Latin American Governments Are Caught in the Middle of the US–China Tech War', ForeignPolicy.com (February 2021), https://foreignpolicy.com/2021/02/26/latin-america-united-states-china-5g-technology-war/, accessed on 1 October 2021.

59. Ciara Nugent and Charlie Campell, 'The US and China Are Battling for Influence in Latin America, and the Pandemic Has Raised the Stakes', *Time* (February 2021), https://time.com/5936037/us-china-latin-america-influence/.

60. 'Growth in the Americas or América Crece', US State Department (August 2019), https://www.state.gov/wp-content/uploads/2019/11/America-Crece-FAQs-003-508.pdf, accessed on 1 October 2021.

61. Oliver Stuenkel, 'Latin American Governments Are Caught in the Middle of the US–China Tech War', ForeignPolicy.com (February 2021), https://foreignpolicy.com/2021/02/26/latin-america-united-states-china-5g-technology-war/, accessed on 1 October 2021.

62. Shivshankar Menon, *India and Asian Geopolitics: The Past, Present* (Brookings Institution Press, 2021), p. 373.

63. Mira Rapp-Hooper, 'Rethinking America's Alliances for the Future' (June 2020), https://www.worldpoliticsreview.com/trend-lines/28852/rethinking-america-s-alliances-for-the-21st-century, accessed on 1 October 2021.

64. Patrick Wintour, 'US has "no closer ally than Australia", says Biden after AUKUS pact', *The Guardian* (September 2021), https://www.theguardian.com/world/2021/sep/21/us-has-no-closer-ally-than-australia-says-biden-after-aukus-pact, accessed on 30 September 2021.

65. Bruno Tertrais, 'The Changing Nature of Military Alliances', *The Washington Quarterly* (Spring 2004), https://csis-website-prod.s3.amazonaws.com/s3fs-public/legacy_files/files/publication/twq04springtertrais.pdf, accessed on 1 October 2021.

PART FOUR

~

SETTING THE RULES OF THE GREAT TECH GAME

'Governments of the Industrial World, you weary giants of flesh and steel, I come from Cyberspace, the new home of Mind. On behalf of the future, I ask you of the past to leave us alone. You are not welcome among us. You have no sovereignty where we gather … We must declare our virtual selves immune to your sovereignty, even as we continue to consent to your rule over our bodies.'

—John Perry Barlow's 1996 Declaration of the Independence of Cyberspace, Davos, Switzerland (1996)[1]

'In a lot of ways Facebook is more like a government than a traditional company.'

—Mark Zuckerberg, CEO of Facebook (2017)[2]

10

The Tug of War: States vs Big Tech

Stretching back millennia, there has been a constant tug of war between states and private players. Conflicts between large, monopolistic corporations and governments have happened before. Just in the last two to three centuries, oil, telecom, rail and steel companies have battled it out with the governments of their time. Prior to that, the Dutch and British East India Companies were formidable players on the global stage. Before them, influential commercial or trading families, such as the Medicis in Italy, have challenged the writ of governments.

That same conflict has assumed a bigger scale today as states and Big Tech firms battle it out. Unlike steel tycoons or oil barons, however, the tech titans influence a much larger swathe of our society, economy and the polity. Big Tech firms have accumulated more wealth, power and influence than any other group of corporations in history. In the process, these firms have inevitably started to rub the wrong way that one institution that prides itself as the legitimate repository of power and influence: the government or the state.

Big Tech is mounting the biggest challenge in history to states and governments, on multiple levels. At one level, the most tactical one, the battle is about data ownership, privacy, content moderation, taxes and regulation. At a deeper level, the tug of war is about power, influence, wealth and control. But at the most fundamental level, the battle is about ideology, beliefs and world views about how the world and our society ought to be governed.

The world view, the ideologies, the values and the principles upon which Big Tech firms operate are often at loggerheads with governments and often even entire nations. Few private players in recent history, with the exception of the likes of the East India Company, have sought to become an alternative government. But Big Tech firms are also audaciously attempting to create alternative forms of governance. This is leading to questions of who—Big Tech firms or democratically elected governments—is better positioned to define the public good, shape the nature of the digital commons, and protect the values and rights of citizens?

However, governments have a long legacy of having emerged victorious in various battles, both against private players and often against their own citizens. History tells us that when private players have come up against governments, they have, for various reasons, eventually lost. The Medicis ultimately lost; the Rockefellers did too, as did the East India Company and AT&T. Sure enough, some private players have entered politics, become political dynasts even. But the state's institutions have eventually reigned supreme.

Sensing the scale and unprecedented nature of the challenge being mounted by Big Tech firms to their legitimacy and authority, governments of all hues are fighting back, leveraging the various tools at their disposal, such as stringent regulation, bureaucratic entanglement, higher taxation, shaping public opinion and launching awareness campaigns.

This is not to say that the private players will not fight back. In the face of government onslaught, private players often either just infiltrate government to influence it from the inside, or in some cases even bring it down. Big Tech is fighting back, publicly and also behind the scenes. They have more information, more money, more influence and more resources than any of their predecessors. This will not be an easy fight, and it won't conclude this year or the next. We are in this for the long haul. Will our future be a repeat of the past? Will governments prevail over Big Tech? What implications will this battle have for the political destiny of nation states, and the geopolitics of our world?

Tech Becomes Big, Rich and Powerful Tech

Big Tech firms—such as Amazon, Facebook, Google, Microsoft, Apple and others—are not just big; they are also rich, powerful, influential and ambitious. These words are not used lightly, as you shall see.

Let's start with 'big'. Ninety per cent of searches on the Web start with Google, the gatekeeper to the World Wide Web. Almost 95 per cent of young people online below the age of thirty are either on Facebook or Facebook-owned Instagram. Google and Facebook together garner close to 90 per cent of all online ad spending. Facebook, Instagram and WhatsApp have a combined user base of almost 3.5 billion users, almost half of the world's population. Amazon controls almost 50 per cent of online commerce in the US, and it is still not the biggest. Alibaba's global sales are over three times that of Amazon.

Let's move on to 'rich'. Dominance of their respective sectors has made these firms (and those running and backing them) rich. Almost 80 per cent of corporate wealth today is held by just 10 per cent of firms. The GEs, GMs and ExxonMobils of the world have given way to Big Tech firms, which comprise over 25 per cent of the value of the S&P index. The top five Big Tech firms hold almost $600 billion in cash reserves. Apple's market cap is around $2 trillion (that's more than the GDP of countries such as Italy, Russia, Canada and South Korea), while that of Microsoft, Alphabet (Google) and Amazon is above $1.5 trillion. In the two decades between 2000 and 2019, Microsoft and Apple distributed around US $750 billion to their shareholders through dividends and share buybacks.

According to the Forbes billionaire list, the top ten richest people in the world include seven tech firm founders and CEOs: Jeff Bezos (no. 1, $177 billion), Elon Musk (no. 2, $151 billion), Bill Gates (no. 4,

$124 billion), Mark Zuckerberg (no. 5, $97 billion), Larry Ellison (no. 7, $93 billion), Larry Page (no. 8, $91 billion), and Sergey Brin (no. 9, $89 billion). As Joel Kotkin argues, compared to oil or auto companies, where no single direct shareholder owns over 1 per cent of the stock, the tech titans 'control portions of their companies that would turn most oilmen or auto executives green with envy'.[3]

On to 'powerful'. On the Forbes list, 'The World's Most Powerful People', Jeff Bezos of Amazon comes in at no. 5, after Xi Jinping, Vladimir Putin, Donald Trump, and Angela Merkel, but before the Pope. Bill Gates at no. 7 and Larry Page at no. 10 round off the list. Other than political leaders (and one religious leader), the three tech founders are the only other category that makes it to the top ten. The tech titans are taking on influential political leaders, such as the US President. Twitter and Facebook earlier in 2021 banned US President Donald Trump from their platforms, cutting off his access to his millions of followers. That's the President of the United States of America, leader of the most powerful nation on earth.

Now, let's talk about 'influence'. The Big Tech firms' meteoric rise over the last two decades and accompanying accumulation of wealth and power have also helped them gain unparalleled influence outside the field of technology, specifically in society, politics and foreign policy. Big Tech firms are funding think tanks, trade associations, advocacy organizations, journalists and academics. Facebook and Amazon are now the two biggest individual corporate lobbyists in Washington, leaving behind competition from Big Oil, Big Tobacco, Big Telecom firms and arms companies.

Their influence also derives from the billions of users they have on their platforms, who use their technology to do everything from one-on-one private communications to public organizing of protests and mass movements. Big Tech firms are influencing foreign governments and elections, and shaping foreign policies of nations. Not to mention that the data they own and their algorithms allow them to influence and shape their users' behaviour, values and beliefs. The list goes on. As author Rana Foroohar points out, Big Tech firms have become like the

Too-Big-To-Fail banks who have gone practically unregulated and are 'flexing [their] considerable political and economic muscle to ensure that things stay that way'. [4]

The Tug of War Between Governments and Big Tech Firms

Peek into history: The cultural foundations of Silicon Valley

The current battle between Big Tech and states can actually be traced back to the cultural foundations of Silicon Valley. Silicon Valley, as we know it today, was shaped by the hippie and counterculture movements of the 1960s in the US. The emerging tech community was driven by utopian ideas about technology as a force for good for all. The early creators dreamt of 'a world healed by technology, brought together into a peaceful model of collaboration', aptly captured by Marshall McLuhan in his book and the term he coined, 'Global Village'. Technology was seen as a democratizing force, that would make information free, more transparent, and also enhance the power in the hands of the citizens vis-à-vis the government. Greed, profit and riches were not the goals. [5]

The early days of Silicon Valley were decisively anti-government or at least libertarian, believing that the government was and should be largely irrelevant. As Brand put it, 'Our line was sort of: Ask not what your country can do for you—do it yourself! Leave the country out of it.' [6] The heady days of the 1990s would witness such strongly anti-government, libertarian rhetoric pronounced quite publicly. John Perry Barlow's 1996 famous Declaration of the Independence of Cyberspace would openly challenge the sovereignty of governments and national boundaries. Along with the early libertarian influences in Silicon Valley had come a fear and abhorrence of the surveillance state. Freedom of speech and privacy was paramount, and early advocacy groups such as the Electronic Frontier Foundation opposed government overreach in communications. [7]

Yet, there were also many inherent contradictions, some of which exist till today. On the one hand, technologists wanted to create a world free from the influence of governments and mega-institutions (even the likes of IBM); on the other, they envisioned a global village bound by technology and cyberspace. This grand vision of a global village, by definition, would have to be large and monopolistic. As Franklin Foer pointed out, after all, 'there can be only one global village'.[8]

As Foer and Zuboff have argued, 'Silicon Valley's craving for monopoly stretches back, strangely enough, to the counterculture of the 1960s, where it emerged from the most lyrical of visions of peace and love.'[9] Echoes of these grand visions, along with their inherent contradictions, abound in Facebook's vision of a global community and Google's quest for organizing the entire world's information.

The inevitable tug of war

The state and Big Tech, at least in the US, were eventually going to clash over privacy, freedom of speech, and monopoly. This tug of war is shaped by local and historical contexts of each country, and factors such as the nature of the technology sector, the dominant political and social values, the existing relationship between governments and corporations, and the prevailing approach to technology adoption. For example, some countries, especially authoritarian, state-driven economies, tend to have a more symbiotic relationship between the private and public sectors. Others, like India and the US, for example, have a deep-rooted suspicion of big business. To better understand how this tug of war is playing out, I examine some specific battles that have played out recently.

Australia takes on Google and Facebook

In December 2020, Australia tabled in its Parliament the News Media and Digital Platforms Mandatory Bargaining Code ('News Code'). This legislation would require platforms such as Google and Facebook to negotiate a fair payment arrangement with traditional news organizations in Australia for using their news content.

Google and Facebook had already agreed to pay for news elsewhere in the world. But in this case, they would be bound under much stricter bargaining procedures compared to other countries where they usually determined the amounts they would pay. The platforms worried about the financial risk this would entail, but also about the precedent of state-arbitrated pricing.[10] Others, such as Tim Berners-Lee, were concerned about the violation of the fundamental principle to link freely on the Web.[11]

Google threatened to withdraw its search engine from Australia completely. Facebook took an even more aggressive, impulsive approach, and hit back with a news blackout. It blocked all news links on its platform for Australian users, including the posts of Australia's emergency services, state health departments, fire services and various non-profits. The Australian Prime Minister Scott Morrison took to Twitter in response:

> These actions will only confirm the concerns that an increasing number of countries are expressing about the behaviour of Big Tech companies who think they are bigger than governments and that the rules should not apply to them. They may be changing the world, but that doesn't mean they run it.[12]

Meanwhile, competitive dynamics amongst the Big Tech players meant that Microsoft Bing immediately jumped into the fray. In an interview with the ABC network, the Australian communications minister, Paul Fletcher, highlighted how the Microsoft CEO, along with other senior executives, had reached out to the Australian Prime Minister and expressed their interest in expanding Bing's services in Australia. Brad Smith, president of Microsoft, announced that Bing was prepared to adhere to the new Australian laws. Acknowledging that the internet and social media had not been kind to the free press, Microsoft also offered their high-quality search service at much lower margins than Google and gave a greater share to the press.[13]

Within a day of Bing's public offer, Google reversed its stance and committed to staying in Australia. (Competition does work!) By the end of February 2021, the Australian Parliament had passed the News Media Bargaining Code into law, but notably with a few amendments. It was clear from the amendments that Facebook and Google were able to exert sufficient influence over the Australian Parliament to claw back some of what they wanted. William Easton, MD of Facebook Australia and New Zealand, expressed satisfaction that the government had agreed to a number of changes that addressed their core concerns.[14] In return, Facebook lifted its news ban, and signed preliminary agreements with a few Australian publishers. Google also struck content licensing deals with some of Australia's largest news publishers, such as Rupert Murdoch's News Corp.[15]

The way this battle played out was instructive. One, if any Big Tech firm threatens to withdraw or not comply with government regulations, a competitor tech firm might be willing to step in, at reduced margins, no less. Governments can (and will) exploit the rivalry between the tech firms, not just to boost competition but also to distribute the value more widely across the ecosystem. Two, Big Tech firms need to defend their markets and market shares aggressively. Even as they try and negotiate hard and threaten to walk away, they are willing to negotiate. They do not want to let go of their profits or market dominance that easily. Most importantly, a fairer distribution of the online pie is possible, though it will need the joint, collective and sustained efforts of many stakeholders.

UK forces Uber to combine flexibility with benefits

In February 2021, Uber lost a key five-year-long legal battle in the UK. The Supreme Court of the UK ruled that Uber cab drivers be classified as 'workers' and not as 'independent contractors', rejecting

Uber's argument that it served merely as a payment collection agent and/or booking agent for the drivers on its platform.

'Workers' in the UK is a categorization that lies somewhere between a full-time employee and an independent contractor. In classifying Uber's drivers as workers, the Supreme Court relied on the evidence that Uber fixed the drivers' remuneration, dictated the contractual terms of service, restricted a driver's freedom to choose when and where to work, and exercised a significant degree of control over the driver's services, including restricting the ability of a driver to establish any longer-term relationship with passengers.[16] Uber's 70,000 drivers in the UK will now get minimum wage, holiday pay and pension plans. The estimated cost of $500 million, a 'gut punch' for Uber's prospects in the UK, led to Uber's shares falling by over 4 per cent in early trading.[17]

More importantly, this judgement has immense implications for the 'gig economy'. The 'gig economy' in tech parlance refers to the proliferation of workers such as cab drivers, service professionals, and delivery executives who tend to work as freelancers or under short-term contracts in temporary, flexible jobs. Most countries require employees to be given benefits such as health insurance or provident fund contributions, but not to independent contractors or freelancers. Globally, tech platforms—such as Uber, Amazon, Flipkart, UberEats, Deliveroo, Swiggy, Ola and Lyft—have taken advantage of this loophole to keep their costs lower than traditional competitors.

Similarly, countries around the world, such as the European Union, India and others, are also considering, if not they have already passed, new rules to better protect the rights of their gig economy workers. In contrast, measures like Proposition 22 in California have exempted Uber and other gig economy platforms from reclassifying drivers as employees.[18] Platforms are now seeking a middle ground, whereby they entitle the drivers to benefits but not assign them 'employee' status, which might entail further restrictions on the platforms.[19]

Recognizing the direction in which the wind is blowing, the approach being taken by Uber is to acknowledge that they need to yield some ground, yet find a middle ground that works for their business also. Uber's CEO, Dara Khosrowshahi, acknowledged that 'the status quo of independent work is simply not good enough'. The flexibility offered by platforms such as Uber, he argued, is insufficient and 'should not come at the expense of social protections'. But he blamed outdated employment laws for creating this trade-off and urged for the necessary labour reform.[20] In May 2021, Uber 'made history' by allowing its drivers to join one of the UK's biggest trade unions, GMB. GMB union hailed this development, highlighting that 'gig economy companies don't have to be a wild west on the untamed frontier of employment rights'.[21]

The lessons from this victory for gig workers are clear. First, gig economy workers need better rights and social benefits. During the industrialization era, the early years, even decades, were a period of blatant exploitation of labour migrating into the industrial towns from villages to become 'factory workers'. It took governments a while to legislate to provide protections to labour, many of which are still in place today. Similarly, in the technology era, it is taking governments time, but eventually, they will need to legislate to provide social protections to the new 'gig workers'.[22] Labour laws will need to recognize and adapt to this shift from 'factory workers' to 'gig workers'.

Second, like the landmark news laws in Australia, such decisions will have a cascading impact on other similar platforms and other countries. In most countries, it will now be a matter of when, not if. Third, while such reforms do hurt these platforms financially, they do not pose existential risks to these platforms. In the process, however, a fine balance between flexibility and social protections, and between the old and new frameworks for employment might be achieved.

India takes on WhatsApp

In February 2021, India, one of the world's largest technology consumer markets, notified the Information Technology Rules, 2021. The intent of the Indian government for this legislation was to deal more effectively with several problems arising from the widespread use of primarily foreign-owned social media platforms. These included, for example, the persistent spread of fake news, incitement of violence, disrespectful religious content, misuse of social media by terrorists, and absence of a robust and straightforward grievance redressal mechanism.[23]

Parts of the legislation ran counter to some of the core principles, such as privacy espoused by the Big Tech firms. WhatsApp, for example, filed a lawsuit against the Government of India in the Delhi High Court, primarily taking exception to Clause 4(2) of the legislation. This clause required intermediaries to help identify the first 'originator' of the information when required by a court order. According to WhatsApp, this clause would require it to break its end-to-end-encrypted (E2EE) protocols, which it couldn't do, to protect the sacred right of its users to privacy.

The Indian government immediately clarified that it recognized privacy as a fundamental right (a fundamental right is considered 'sacred' under the Indian Constitution) and that it had no intention to violate the privacy of its citizens. That said, the then-minister for information technology, Ravi Shankar Prasad, emphasized 'the responsibility of the government to maintain law and order, and ensure national security'.[24] Further, Prasad argued that fundamental rights are not absolute rights and are always subject to reasonable restrictions.[25]

The classic privacy–national security trade-off was at play. Even though the government clarified that the clause would be used only as a last-resort measure in the case of 'very serious offences', from WhatsApp's perspective, this battle of values would have global ramifications. If its parent, Facebook, were to break its E2EE protocols for any one country, then that would open the 'backdoor', literally, for other governments to coerce them into doing the same for them. Further, creating these loopholes in their encryption protocols means that other, non-legitimate actors might also be able to exploit those loopholes. Ultimately the privacy of communications between WhatsApp's users would be compromised, and undercut WhatsApp's USP as an entirely secure and private communications platform.

India knew that many other countries around the world were pushing Facebook to open up 'backdoors' into its E2EE protocols. This included the UK, US and Australia, with whom India, as a member of the Quad and certain intelligence alliances, likely coordinates its technology policy actively. An open letter to Facebook from the US attorney general and secretary of Homeland Security, the UK home secretary, and Australia's Home Minister Peter Dutton had in fact demanded that Facebook not proceed with implementing end-to-end encryption across its messaging platforms 'without including a means for lawful access to the content of communications to protect our citizens'.[26]

India's rules could have been part of a coordinated effort by governments to secure their 'eyes and ears' into E2EE platforms such as WhatsApp. Alternatively, it could be a clear signal from the Indian government, concerned as it is about its digital sovereignty, that all platforms will need to follow the laws of the land. As Minister Prasad said: 'Social media platforms [are] welcome to do business in India but they need to follow the Constitution and laws of India.'[27] This emphasis on national digital sovereignty and the supremacy of national laws will pose an uphill task for Big Tech firms.

A few clear lessons emerge. One, governments, especially of larger markets like India, will not let Big Tech firms force their hand on these privacy–national security debates. Big Tech firms will need to work closely with governments to work out a fine balance between sovereignty, national security, and the privacy and security of citizens. Two, as much as Big Tech firms might find it inconvenient and troublesome, they will eventually need to adhere to national laws, especially in critical markets such as India. Three, Big Tech firms should expect that, sooner or later, like-minded governments will coordinate their efforts vis-à-vis Big Tech firms. Therefore, the tech firms should be ready for multi-pronged onslaughts from governments.

Russia overpowers Yandex

In December 2019, Yandex's CEO, Arkady Volozh, announced a revamped governance structure for the Russian internet conglomerate. Yandex, the Russian search giant, also offers email services, taxi-hailing, maps, music streaming and cloud storage, and is the equivalent of Google, Uber, AWS and Spotify rolled into one.

But this was no ordinary corporate governance structuring.

In 2014, Russian President Vladimir Putin had described the internet as a 'CIA project' and Yandex as a company that had too much Western influence, causing its share price to plunge. But just five years later, in 2019, Putin spoke warmly about Yandex's executives and praised the scale and scope of its projects, causing its share price to hit a record high.[28] What had transpired in those five years for this turnaround?

Let us back up. In August 2008, Russia fought a short war with neighbouring Georgia, in which cyberattacks and disinformation campaigns played a large role. Yandex News covered articles featuring both the Russian and the Georgian perspectives. This displeased the Kremlin. Later that year, with the support of then-President Dmitry Medvedev, and citing national security grounds, Alisher Usmanov, a Russian commodities oligarch, initiated a hostile takeover of Yandex.

In its efforts to keep Usmanov at bay, in 2009, Yandex ended up giving a 'golden share' to Sberbank, a state lender. This golden share, effectively a veto right, allowed Sberbank to veto any transactions involving more than 25 per cent of Yandex's equity. Over the next several years, this arrangement would largely remain untouched by the Kremlin. But by the mid 2010s, Russia, and particularly Putin, had started to view the internet with even deeper suspicion. In the wake of the Arab Spring protests and social media-enabled mass protests in Russia, Putin had come to view tech platforms as tools used by foreign governments to interfere in Russian domestic affairs.[29] Russia was concerned that with the internet becoming 'a battlefield in its escalating tensions with the West', a national asset like Yandex, with all the data it had accumulated on Russian citizens, could be acquired by foreign firms.[30]

In a press conference in 2014, Putin would raise suspicions about the significant presence of foreigners on Yandex's management and board, including chairman of the Board John Boynton, who was based in Massachusetts. The fact that Yandex was incorporated in the Netherlands didn't help either. This incident would lead to a significant dip in Yandex's share price.[31]

By 2018, the fear of foreign abuse of technology platforms, especially Yandex, was reaching a crescendo in Russia. In October 2018, rumours that Sberbank was acquiring a 30 per cent stake in Yandex caused Yandex shares to plummet more than 10 per cent, losing over $2 billion in market value in two days. Though Yandex CEO Volozh decided not to pursue the deal with Sberbank, negotiations began in earnest with the Kremlin over a new governance structure that might be amenable to the Kremlin.

The Kremlin's onslaught was relentless. In June 2019, a bill proposing to limit foreign ownership to 20 per cent in 'significant information resources' (referring to companies such as Yandex) was introduced by a Russian lawmaker, Anton Gorelkin. With the Kremlin publicly pledging support to Gorelkin's bill, Yandex's stock price continued to bleed in the US share markets. As billions of dollars kept getting wiped off its market value, Yandex seemed to have been pushed on the backfoot by the Kremlin.

Soon Yandex had begun talks with Sergey Kirienko, the domestic policy chief whom Putin had put in charge of controlling the internet in Russia.[32] After essentially thirteen months of gruelling negotiations, in November 2019, Yandex finally announced a new governance structure that seemed to have the blessing of Putin. Sberbank's 'golden share' was being transferred to a newly formed, Kremlin-leaning 'public interest foundation'. It would have the right to veto, among other things, any share consolidations over 10 per cent, and any operational decisions or transactions dealing with intellectual property or transfer of data of the Russian users of Yandex.[33] The board of the new foundation would have eight seats filled with members from prominent business groups and state universities, with only three seats being given to Yandex. Yandex could, most importantly, now be blocked from any agreements with any foreign entities or governments. The control—though indirect—was in place.

The plan was also seemingly a compromise between the systemic liberals within Putin's advisors, such as Audit Chamber head Alexei Kudrin and Sberbank CEO Herman Gref on one side, and the *siloviki* (largely the hawkish (FSB) and Security Council representatives) on the other. The liberals had wanted Yandex to remain private, and managed to get agreement from the hawks on limiting Yandex's management's discretion on strategic matters through the new foundation.[34] As a bonus, soon after Putin personally approved the plan, Gorelkin withdrew his bill. Instead, the Russian Parliament passed a law mandating that Russian tech platforms like Yandex be pre-loaded on devices sold in Russia, boosting Yandex's shares further.[35]

Effectively, Yandex, and possibly the entire Russian tech sector, is now operating with significant supervision from the Kremlin. As Yandex's CEO Volozh wrote in an email to employees, this arrangement allows the company to still control its own daily operations but that 'the public interest now runs through us'. This, according to him, was an optimal solution which would end up balancing three key objectives: 'leaving control of the company in our hands, maintaining the confidence of our international investors in the prospects for Yandex's business and defending the country's interests'.[36]

There are several lessons from the Yandex–Russian tussle as well. The domestic politics and foreign policies of nations will impact Big Tech firms, and therefore, these firms must learn to operate with the constraints that this imposes on them. However, given different stakeholders and ideologies within existing nations, Big Tech firms will need to find allies within the polities of each nation. One might recall how the British East India Company had done the same.

Second, as Bloomberg columnist Leonid Bershidsky has in fact argued, Yandex's delicate dance could be seen as a template for Big Tech firms elsewhere. More concessions might be forthcoming from Big Tech firms as governments, especially the authoritarian ones, move ruthlessly to limit their power. Bershidsky believes that quasi-autonomous structures, such as the public interest foundation established in Russia, could be replicated elsewhere. He, in fact, specifically recommended that Silicon Valley firms also pay close attention to how Yandex evaded stronger Kremlin control by yielding some power to it.[37]

Though Facebook's new independent Oversight Board appointed in May 2020 to help oversee content moderation decisions faced by Facebook does not quite fit the same bill as Yandex's public interest foundation, it is clear that Big Tech companies will need to exercise flexibility—and large doses of creativity—to overcome these waves of attacks from governments.

China makes Alibaba bow (and Jack Ma disappears)

The Alibaba Group, one of China's largest technology conglomerates, owns platforms that see about $1 trillion worth of goods transacted annually. On 10 April 2021, it issued a letter to its customers and the community:

> Today Alibaba Group received the Administrative Penalty Decision issued by the State Administration for Market Regulation (SAMR) of the People's Republic of China. We accept the penalty with sincerity and will ensure our compliance with determination. ... [The penalty] reflects the regulators' thoughtful and normative expectations toward our industry's development. It is an important action to safeguard fair market competition and quality development of Internet platform economies. ... It is not lost on us that today's society has new expectations for platform companies, as we must assume more responsibilities as part of the nation's economic and social development. ... Alibaba would not have achieved our growth without sound government regulation and service, and the critical oversight, tolerance and support from all of our constituencies have

been crucial to our development. For this, we are full of gratitude and respect.[38]

Earlier that day, SAMR had delivered a $2.8 billion penalty on Alibaba. From the statement above, a few things stand out. First, for a letter announcing a multi-billion dollar penalty imposed on the company, Alibaba seems strangely full of gratitude for the government and praise for the regulator. The letter seems to have been drafted by the regulator itself. Second, in the underlying tone, even more than the actual content, the letter demonstrates the emerging dynamic between the Chinese state and its Big Tech firms. Alibaba, a conglomerate that is many times larger than Amazon, seemed to have bowed down in front of the Chinese state.

How did this come about?

For many years, as Jack Ma led the Alibaba group to greater heights, including a $25 billion IPO in New York in 2014, his ambitions dovetailed perfectly with Beijing's focus to help Chinese businesses go abroad. Ma even accompanied Xi on a visit to the US in 2015. But then, things started to change. Alibaba's public clashes on social media with regulators, Xi's confidant Liu He pushing financial regulation in 2017, Ma's derisive statements in public, and the Chinese Communist Party (CCP) snubs followed by even greater snubs by Ma, were all indications that a big clash was brewing between Alibaba and the CCP.

And then came the straw that broke the camel's back. Speaking at the Bund Summit in Shanghai in October 2020, Jack Ma, founder of Alibaba and also chairman of the fintech behemoth the Ant Group, described China's traditional banks as operating with a 'pawnshop mentality'[39] and criticized financial authorities for stifling innovation. In attendance were China's Vice President Wang Qishan, Chinese central bank governor Yi Gang and other senior state-bank executives.

This public criticism of the Chinese authorities was likely planned, as Ma repeatedly referred to his notes at the Shanghai summit. On his mind were probably the recent spate of government regulations and notices that banking regulators were rolling out in recent months to mitigate the risks state banks were assuming by lending to Ant's online customers.[40] Notably, Ant Group's IPO was planned on the Shanghai and Hong Kong bourses just a month later, in November. At $37 billion, it was billed as a miracle, given that 'the biggest IPO in human history' was happening outside of the New York exchanges.[41]

But if Ma's statements were intended to browbeat the regulators, it was not to be. His statement in Shanghai led to a meeting of the Financial Stability and Development Committee headed by Mr Liu, the economics czar for Xi Jinping. The committee decided to 'put all kinds of financial activities under regulation and treat the same businesses in the same way'. This meant that online fintech firms would no longer get any differential treatment vis-à-vis traditional banks. Further, firms such as Ant would now need to finance a minimum of 30 per cent of each loan it provided along with traditional banks.[42]

And then, just days before the planned IPO, the Shanghai and Hong Kong bourses suspended the IPO presumably to protect the interests of Chinese consumers and investors.[43] Ma's personal fortune dipped by $10 billion, just as Alibaba's shares dipped by 10 per cent. Also, as media houses globally noted and highlighted, 'The globetrotting, limelight-addicted Ma simply vanished.'[44]

As Song Qinghui, an economist and regular contributor to Chinese state media, explained, Jack Ma had amassed far too much power and influence, as did Alibaba, and this had gotten to the point where the CCP believed that they had to be cut to size.[45] China watchers believe that this was part of a larger pattern under the leadership of Xi Jinping, who seems intent to show Chinese business leaders that ultimately it is the CCP that controls the destiny of businessmen, and not the other way around.[46] The earlier arrests of Wu Xiaohui (chairman of the Anbang Insurance Group), Wang Jianlin (head of Wanda Dalian) and Xiao Jianhua (head of investment conglomerate Tomorrow Group)— all of whom were at one point considered seemingly unassailable—all fit this alleged pattern.

By later in November 2020, Alibaba's chairman and CEO, Zhang Yong, would toe a completely different line. Speaking at the World

Internet Conference in Wuzhen, Zhang affirmed Alibaba's gratitude to the Chinese government, and said, 'Alibaba is a beneficiary of China's digital economy era, and we are very grateful for this era,'[47] adding that it was the Chinese government's reforms that had paved the way for development and innovation and the subsequent growth of China's internet economy. This deferential, grateful tone, one can assume, is what the higher-ups in the Chinese government expected.

The change in tone by the Alibaba Group's chairman was not going to suffice. In April 2021, the SAMR found that Alibaba had abused its dominant position since 2015 and that its 'choice of two' framework hindered and restricted competition unfairly and ultimately harmed the interests of consumers. Therefore, under the freshly minted Anti-Monopoly Law, SAMR ordered Alibaba to stop these illegal activities and also pay an administrative penalty of 4 per cent of its sales in China in 2019 ($2.8 billion or roughly 18 billion yuan).[48] The fine also came with several rectifications that Alibaba would need to make, including restricting its operations and market share in payments, wealth management, credit and consumer lending businesses, as well as the interlinkages between these businesses.[49]

Further, in a potential first in the tech world, the regulators moved onto Ant's most valuable assets: its data, derived from billions of transactions over the years. This data—and the insights gleaned from it—have been one of the sources of Ant's competitive advantage over traditional banks. With an eye on this rich data, the Chinese Central Bank has required Ant to break its 'information monopoly' on the vast and detailed consumer data on over a billion Chinese people that it has collected.[50]

The lessons for the tech titans in China have been loud and clear. First and foremost, 'loyalty comes first in Xi's China' and that becoming too powerful in a country that only allows a single centre of power can backfire.[51] Second, the Big Tech firms in China will need to toe the line and remain at least publicly 'grateful' to the CCP. The golden era of unrestrained, unregulated growth might indeed be over for China's Big Tech firms, and the Chinese Big Tech firms will need to tread a lot more cautiously, and expect much greater intervention of the regulators.[52] Third, the Chinese example might very well be followed by many other states—especially authoritarian states that look up to China for guidance.

At the same time, as a *Time* article argued, the CCP has to walk a precarious tightrope. Even as it comes down heavily on firms such as Alibaba, it risks casting a pall over investor confidence and also discouraging entrepreneurs whose risk-taking ability and willingness have driven much of China's growth in the tech sector.[53] There might already be some indications that some tech entrepreneurs do not wish to operate in such an environment. More than $600 billion has been wiped off the stock market value of the biggest tech stocks in recent months.[54]

Moreover, other than Jack Ma, who has disappeared from the public eye, a few other prominent entrepreneurs such as Zhang Yiming, the thirty-eight-year-old founder of ByteDance, which owns TikTok, and Colin Huang, the forty-one-year-old chairman of Pinduoduo (PDD), an upstart Alibaba competitor, have stepped down. While neither have made any reference to any policy issues leading to their decisions, some analysts have argued that it is hard to not link their exits to the recent government clampdown.[55]

Furthermore, for all the claims that Big Tech is different from other large sectors that have had their time in the sun, such developments show that from the perspective of the governments, the tech sector is just yet another sector that needs to be tamed. The government, especially in more authoritarian countries, ultimately has many of the tools of control at its disposal, such as the granting (or not!) of licenses, suspending of IPOs, launching of investigations and introducing new legislation, among others. In April 2021, for example, regulators summoned thirty-four of China's largest tech companies (including Tencent, Baidu, Meituan and TikTok) to rectify any anti-competition stances, and specifically warned them not to cross any red lines laid down by the authorities.[56]

Like what happened with Yandex in Russia, most Chinese tech giants will likely revert to cultivating friendly and intimate relations with the government. In any case, many are already part of the Party circles. For example, Tencent founder and CEO Pony Ma and Xiaomi founder and CEO Lei Jun are both members of the National People's Congress (China's parliament), while Baidu founder and CEO Robin Li is a member of the Chinese People's Political Consultative Conference, the country's top political advisory body.[57]

China does not view its clampdown the same way. Rather, it believes—and maybe rightly so—that by acting against monopolistic behaviour so decisively and swiftly (compared to the US, for example), it might actually boost competition in China's tech industry, and boost innovation and lower prices for consumers. The anti-trust action might also help these conglomerates remain focused on specific markets as opposed to mastering them all. Moreover, many Asia-based venture capitalists feel that China is directing its engineering talent towards solving deep tech problems for the country instead of focusing only on consumer-facing entertainment or other utility apps. Not to mention, the cutting to size of the Big Tech firms and the multi-billionaires is intended to create greater equity within society. While Western media has viewed these developments as simply arising out of Beijing's desire to exercise sole control and nip any challenges to its power in the bud, Beijing might still have the last laugh.

Big tech will fight back, strategically

From all the cases discussed above, it might seem that ultimately, when push comes to shove, governments—no matter democratic or authoritarian—will prevail. And that despite the unprecedented massive concentration of power, wealth and influence that the Big Tech firms have accumulated today, the state not will give way to a model of governance and rule where the state does not reign supreme. The recent years have seen the image and perception of Big Tech firms take a beating, and governments have much to do with that.

But it would be foolhardy to think that Big Tech will give up without a fight. Or that this is a one-round battle. This battle will have multiple rounds, and even though it might seem that the governments are winning round one, we can expect that given what's at stake, Big Tech will fight back. The fightback might not be all aggressive and confrontational: along the way, as history has shown, many compromises, co-optation, cooperation and conflict will ensue.

Big Tech has already shown a few of its cards. One, like any large industry, it has realized that it needs to lobby the decision-makers in the policy world and shape public opinion. So, armed as they are with funds, Big Tech firms are likely to continue to increase their spending towards this. This will mean not just lobbying and hiring lobbyists where they can, but also expanding their own internal teams of public policy professionals and experts who can help them navigate this new territory.

Two, Big Tech firms are likely to start to cosy up to governments where they can and, at least publicly, give up their distrust of the state. As Foer points out, the major tech firms are no longer youthful, idealistic start-ups. They are realizing that they can no longer survive in their bubbles and will need to muster up support within government. One way in which they will do so is by making themselves indispensable to governments and politicians alike. The fact is that Big Tech firms do have a lot of skills, talent, networks, users, data, insights and technological capability that governments need.

We have already seen this in action in multiple countries. As Franklin Foer has argued, the recent coronavirus pandemic has come as a golden opportunity for the tech companies to reclaim and embrace 'their old sense of purpose'. As governments around the world have struggled to respond to the crisis, Big Tech firms have tried to present themselves as altruistic partners, 'willing to lend a competent hand'.[58] Satya Nadella, CEO of Microsoft, has even raised the possibilities of a new alliance between business and government to better tackle the unprecedented challenges.[59]

One can expect Big Tech firms to exploit the vulnerabilities of their governments, to find and secure the strategic space for themselves. Zuckerberg's choice of defence against accusations of monopolistic behaviour during one of his testimonies before the Senate was a case in point: his notes revealed that if he had been asked about Facebook's monopolistic behaviour, he planned to play on US fears about China. He would have essentially argued that if Big Tech firms like his are broken up, they would likely cede global technological dominance to China.

There is a major area of cooperation where the governments need the support and cooperation of Big Tech firms: intelligence gathering and cybersecurity. Today, the platforms run by these tech firms are collecting unimaginable amounts of data about users across the world that are incredibly valuable to any government, let alone governments in China and the US, who are in any case engaged in a high level of espionage and intelligence gathering against each other. Chinese tech firms, by many accounts, have already helped the CCP develop advanced surveillance capabilities. Further, tech companies can help governments leverage their data and insights to nudge or alter human behaviour. It is an easy win-win situation for Big Tech firms and the government to cooperate on this front.

The mutual dependence—like for any other large sector—will likely continue. Corporations will remain susceptible to political pressure, but the government will be increasingly dependent on Big Tech firms to fulfil their own data, technology (hardware and software) and surveillance needs. In addition, cybersecurity teams of the Big Tech firms such as Microsoft's Security Response Center (MSRC) and Google's Cybersecurity Action Team—effectively private cybersecurity units—could form a critical support pillar for governments' cybersecurity efforts. And given only a few Big Tech firms will be in a position to help at scale, governments would need to give them concessions in other ways.

Three, Big Tech firms are likely to accept some form of regulation and hope they can get away with a little rap on the knuckles. Learning from the experience of the likes of Microsoft, the Facebooks of the world will eventually soften their stance against regulation. Again, the signs of this evolution are visible already. Mark Zuckerberg, for example, has gone from being a staunch opponent of any governmental interference or regulation to an ardent advocate of 'the right regulation'. Facebook—in light of bipartisan support for anti-trust action against it—has changed its stance and invited government oversight. In fact, it has gone ahead and set up an independent Oversight Board as well, to help it make the strategic content moderation decisions that it often finds itself in trouble for.

Similarly, as Brad Smith of Microsoft has acknowledged, much like Alibaba's letter welcoming the penalty did: 'When your technology changes the world, you bear a responsibility to help address the world that you have helped create.'[60] Smith points out that like in the 1930s, when the banks had become too important economically to be left unregulated, the tech firms have become too significant to be governed by a laissez-faire regime today.[61]

Foer points out that Facebook is not inviting regulation because it suddenly has changed its core beliefs about the role of government. Rather, as Foer argues, it is likely part of a 'grand bargain' under which 'in exchange for government protection of their monopoly, the firms will abide by the dictates of the state'.[62] This is essentially how Yandex or Alibaba have responded to aggressive penalties and harsh action from the state. As we saw in the cases of Yandex and Alibaba, the Big Tech firms in the US will also hope that they can get past this, saying, 'Thank God, it could have been much worse.'

Arising from their intense lobbying efforts, and their openness (albeit forced) to the 'right regulation', Big Tech firms are likely to work hard to shape the set of laws that governments are likely to promulgate in the coming years, in a way that protects their core interests while yielding some ground obviously to governments and public opinion. For them, the right laws that govern their data use (and especially data sharing) will help them deflect any criticism they might come under from their users.

Indeed, smart, savvy and bold governments will have a few more tricks up their sleeve. Governments will look to play the Big Tech firms against each other, the way Australia did. Already, in the US as well, some Big Tech firms find themselves in favour while others find themselves out of favour. Governments could use their leverage to create more such divides among Big Tech firms. However, this would only be possible if serious competitors exist in each of the major sub-sectors of technology. Australia was able to pull off what it did because Bing was waiting on the sidelines. But that is likely to be the exception, not the norm. Such a strategy would depend on whether the Big Tech firms intend to compete, collaborate or collude with each other. Governments could encourage and collaborate more with mid-sized tech firms, and not overly rely on Big Tech firms for their technology requirements. This would further develop more than one meaningful player in different segments.

But if governments are not thoughtful in their approach to this relationship, it could easily move to either extreme: a complete breakdown in the relationship or a deep-rooted alliance. Both these extremes would not be in anyone's interest. A deep-rooted alliance between the two would be the most dangerous from the perspective of citizens. What would be the implications of an emerging alliance between Big Tech firms and governments? The alliance scenario can be damaging for free societies as well. As Foer has argued, 'Without new constraints, this emerging alliance could grow more imperious.' [63] For citizens—whose rights, data, and privacy can be and often are usurped by both—it would be better for the two to actually serve as checks and balances against each other.

Tech firms as an alternative to government and nation states?

Many Big Tech firms, armed with data, technology, cash, influence and high expectations, are starting to acquire powers that have traditionally been the exclusive domains of nation states: assumption of civic duties, shaping foreign policies, launching digital currencies, and building advanced cyberespionage and cyber-military capabilities greater than most governments.[64] This phenomenon of the rise of 'superstar firms' could, as Paul Apostolicas has argued, signal 'a tectonic geopolitical shift in which nation states must devise ways to share influence or fight back against a growing rival center of power'.[65]

Brad Smith has similarly framed technology and Big Tech firms as a potential threat to the four-centuries-old Westphalian system of nation states. Smith has argued that the cross-border nature of technology has raised important questions for the continued relevance of the concepts of sovereignty and the Westphalian type of nation state. He believes that the next decade will shape the balance between the Big Tech firms and nation states.[66]

Since the 1960s and 1970s, the Silicon Valley founders and tech enthusiasts have, in any case, seen technology as a tool to build a 'global village'. Facebook's Mark Zuckerberg at least seems to share parts of that vision. In 2017, for example, Zuckerberg published a long essay called 'Building Global Community'. Talking about the evolution of communities from tribes to cities to nation states, Zuckerberg, according to Max Read, seems to implicitly suggest that Facebook could be 'the next step that should follow the Westphalian order'.[67]

Indeed, tech firms today, through their access and control of vast amounts of data, have a privileged window into our world to an extent that hitherto only states used to have.[68] The social, political, economic, cultural and personal knowledge and understanding that Big Tech firms now have are unprecedented in scale and depth. Many others, too, would like to have a similar window into society—a look into the minds of consumers and voters whose choices their existence depends on.

As Nick Couldry, a professor at the London School of Economics (LSE), pointed out to me, states have, for the first time, become dependent on access to knowledge held by Big Tech firms about the lives of their citizens, reversing a historical trend where knowledge would be transferred from states to corporations. This reversal of the information asymmetry has not just upset states, but also results in many controversial, high-profile battles between states and Big Tech.

Indeed, the 'steady creep' of tech firms and their expanded societal and political role is being aided by the fact that many people across the world believe that governments and democracies today are broken. As Lucie Greene, author of *Silicon States*, explains:

> Among millennials, staggeringly, there is also a unilateral enthusiasm for Silicon Valley to take more of a governmental role. Rightly or wrongly, there is also a loss of faith in government to build our future. Like traditional travel agents surpassed by internet services offering peer-to-peer reviews and cheaper prices, government is at risk of being surpassed by cooler, more efficient tech-savvy companies.[69]

But she warns, and rightly so, that if Silicon Valley were to assume a broader civic role, we must examine what moral framework would accompany that.[70] She highlights the fact that Silicon Valley firms are largely dominated by groups of largely affluent, educated males who are surrounded and advised by people exactly like them.[71] Therefore, she has her doubts about whether Silicon Valley would, in any case, be the right replacement for the state.[72] Even though governments across the world are indeed heavily flawed, and Silicon Valley's promise— really, the promise of many technology start-ups—to fix everything is so compelling and attractive, the question remains: would we be better off being governed by the select few who run Big Tech firms, or by governments that are democratically elected and can be held accountable and removed through free, fair and participative elections?

The basic question pertains to what role do we want the state to play in our lives? This is an age-old question. Many, such as prominent investor and thinker Ray Dalio, have argued that you need the state to help tackle longer-term problems such as climate change as well as challenges such as inequality within society. And as Prof. Arun

Sundararajan at NYU believes, governments should be clearer in their expectations from Big Tech firms. According to him, the rules of the game were indeed set by governments earlier, but when the firms took advantage of those rules, there was a severe backlash against the Big Tech firms. And therefore, it is up to the government to actually set much clearer rules for the road ahead for these firms.

It is clear that the power distribution between markets, private corporations, governments and citizens needs to be brought back into balance. And as Prof. Sundararajan emphasized, the proper management of this relationship will matter the most. Not surprisingly, technology itself might provide some solutions to better manage this relationship. As Don Tapscott has argued in his book, *Blockchain Revolution*, blockchain technology could offer an alternative to the existing powerful intermediaries such as governments and even Big Tech firms that have traditionally established trust and maintained the integrity of transactions between people. But as the limitations of these intermediaries become evident, and the tug of war between them intensifies, blockchain and other emerging technologies could help achieve trust not through intermediaries but 'by cryptography, collaboration, and clever code'.[73]

As my former Wharton professor Prof. Kevin Werbach put it, there has always been this idea of displacing the nation state, but people underestimate the way nation states ultimately exert control. If history is any indication, eventually, blockchain technology, much like the internet, might be co-opted by governments and existing institutions.

As Werbach points out, it's a false dichotomy to say that either nation states or technologies such as blockchain prevail. In some circumstances and countries, blockchain technologies could indeed prove to be a better 'infrastructure of trust' but will need to still be supplemented by other trust-building mechanisms. Yet, when push comes to shove, nation states eventually prevail over any private sector player or technology that threatens to undermine the nation states' legitimacy and overall dominance.

Notes

1. John Perry Barlow, 'A Declaration of the Independence of Cyberspace' (February 1996), https://www.eff.org/cyberspace-independence, accessed on 1 October 2021.

2. Franklin Foer, 'Facebook's War on Free Will', *The Guardian* (September 2017), https://www.theguardian.com/technology/2017/sep/19/facebooks-war-on-free-will, accessed on 1 October 2021.

3. Joel Kotkin, *The New Class Conflict* (Telos Press Publishing, 2014), Kindle.

4. Foroohar, *Don't Be Evil.*

5. Ibid.

6. Steven Johnson, 'The Political Education of Silicon Valley', *Wired* (July 2018), https://www.wired.com/story/political-education-silicon-valley/, accessed on 1 October 2021.

7. Ibid.

8. Franklin Foer, *World Without Mind* (Random House, 2017), Kindle.

9. Ibid.

10. Google, 'Submission to the Australian Senate Standing Committee on Economics' (January 2021), https://www.aph.gov.au/Parliamentary_Business/Committees/Senate/Economics/TLABNewsMedia/Submissions?main_0_content_1_RadGrid1ChangePage=2_20, accessed on 1 October 2021.

11. Tim Berners-Lee, 'Submission to the Australian Senate Standing Committee on Economics' (January 2021), https://www.aph.gov.au/Parliamentary_Business/Committees/Senate/Economics/TLABNewsMedia/Submissions?main_0_content_1_RadGrid1ChangePage=3_20, accessed on 1 October 2021.

12. David Crowe and Lisa Visentin, '"We Will Not Be Intimidated": PM Takes Facebook Fight to India and the World', *Sydney Morning Herald* (February 2021), https://www.smh.com.au/politics/federal/

we-will-not-be-intimidated-pm-takes-facebook-fight-to-india-and-the-world-20210218-p573se.html, accessed on 1 October 2021.

13. Brad Smith, 'Microsoft's Endorsement of Australia's Proposal on Technology and the News', Microsoft blog (February 2021), https://blogs.microsoft.com/on-the-issues/2021/02/11/endorsement-australias-proposal-technology-news/, accessed on 1 October 2021.

14. William Easton, 'Changes to Sharing and Viewing News on Facebook in Australia', Facebook (February 2021), https://about.fb.com/news/2021/02/changes-to-sharing-and-viewing-news-on-facebook-in-australia/, accessed on 1 October 2021.

15. Byron Kaye, 'Australia's Seven West Media Signs Google, Facebook Deals After Media Law Feud', Reuters (May 2021), https://www.reuters.com/technology/australias-seven-west-media-finalises-news-content-deals-with-google-facebook-2021-05-03/, accessed on 1 October 2021.

16. 'UK Supreme Court's Decision on Status of Uber Drivers and Its Significance on Gig Economy', Lexology (April 2021), https://www.lexology.com/library/detail.aspx?g=2d3517f2-ecfe-4de2-b278-827be63c4c50, accessed on 1 October 2021.

17. Ryan Browne, 'Uber Employment Rights Setback Is a "Gut Punch" to Its Prospects in the UK', CNBC (March 2021), https://www.cnbc.com/2021/03/18/uber-is-reclassifying-uk-drivers-as-workers-heres-what-happens-next.html, accessed on 1 October 2021.

18. Ryan Browne, 'Uber Loses a Major Employment Rights Case as the UK's Top Court Rules Its Drivers Are Workers', CNBC (February 2021), https://www.cnbc.com/2021/02/19/uk-supreme-court-rules-uber-drivers-are-workers-not-contractors.html, accessed on 1 October 2021.

19. Ryan Browne, 'Uber Proposes California-Style Gig Work Reforms in Europe', CNBC (February 2021), https://www.cnbc.com/2021/02/15/uber-proposes-california-style-gig-work-reforms-in-europe.html, accessed on 1 October 2021.

20. Dara Khosrowshahi, 'Uber Chief Executive Dara Khosrowshahi Says "We're Turning the Page on Driver Rights"', *Evening Standard* (March 2021), https://www.standard.co.uk/comment/comment/uber-chief-executive-dara-khosrowhahi-drivers-rights-turning-page-b924529. html, accessed on 1 October 2021.

21. 'Uber and GMB Strike Historic Union Deal for 70,000 UK Drivers' (May 2021), https://www.gmb.org.uk/news/uber-and-gmb-strike-historic-union-deal-70000-uk-drivers, accessed on 1 October 2021.

22. Alex Rosenblat, 'Gig Workers Are Here to Stay. It's Time to Give Them Benefits', *Harvard Business Review* (July 2020), https://hbr.org/2020/07/gig-workers-are-here-to-stay-its-time-to-give-them-benefits, accessed on 1 October 2021.

23. 'Government Notifies Information Technology (IntermediaryGuidelines and Digital Media Ethics Code) Rules 2021', Press Release ID: 1700749, Press Information Bureau, Government of India (February 2021), https://pib.gov.in/PressReleseDetailm. aspx?PRID=1700749, accessed on 1 October 2021.

24. Prasid Banerjee, 'Violating Right to Privacy Not Intention with IT Rules: Govt on Whatsapp Case', *Mint* (May 2021), https://www.livemint.com/industry/media/violating-right-to-privacy-not-intention-with-it-rules-govt-on-whatsapp-case-11622036446432. html, accessed on 1 October 2021.

25. Akhilesh Sharma, 'Right to Privacy Not Absolute, Says Government on WhatsApp's Lawsuit', NDTV (May 2021), https://www.ndtv.com/india-news/no-fundamental-right-including-right-to-privacy-is-absolute-government-on-whatsapps-lawsuit-against-new-digital-rules-2449742, accessed on 1 October 2021.

26. 'US, UK and Australia Urge Facebook to Create Backdoor Access to Encrypted Messages', *The Guardian* (October 2019), https://www.theguardian.com/technology/2019/oct/03/facebook-surveillance-us-uk-australia-backdoor-encryption, accessed on 1 October 2021.

27. Government Notifies Information Technology (Intermediary Guidelines and Digital Media Ethics Code) Rules 2021.

28. Max Seddon, 'Inside the Deal Between the Kremlin and Russia's Top Search Engine', *Financial Times* (December 2019), https://www.ft.com/content/dce2e23c-15c5-11ea-8d73-6303645ac406, accessed on 1 October 2021.

29. Evan Gershkovich, 'Yandex's Balancing Act: The Uneasy Coexistence of Russia's Tech Giant with the Kremlin', *MIT Technology Review* 123, no. 5 (September/October 2020), https://wp.technologyreview.com/wp-content/uploads/2020/08/MIT-Technology-Review-2020-09.pdf, accessed on 1 October 2021.

30. Ibid.

31. Ibid.

32. Max Seddon, 'Inside the Deal between the Kremlin and Russia's Top Search Engine', *Financial Times* (December 2019), https://www.ft.com/content/dce2e23c-15c5-11ea-8d73-6303645ac406, accessed on 1 October 2021.

33. Tatyana Stanovaya, 'Yandex Is Safe for Now, but Kremlin Compromise Is Fragile', *Moscow Times* (November 2019), https://www.themoscowtimes.com/2019/11/27/yandex-safe-kremlin-compromise-fragile-a68323, accessed on 1 October 2021.

34. Ibid.

35. Gershkovich, 'Yandex's Balancing Act'.

36. Andrew Roth, 'Russian Internet Giant Grants Veto Powers to Kremlin-Linked Body', *The Guardian* (November 2019), https://www.theguardian.com/world/2019/nov/18/russian-internet-giant-yandex-grants-veto-powers-kremlin-linked-body, accessed on 1 October 2021.

37. Leonid Bershidsky, 'US Big Tech Could Learn from Russia's Yandex', Bloomberg (November 2019), https://www.bloomberg.com/opinion/articles/2019-11-19/silicon-valley-could-learn-from-yandex, accessed on 1 October 2021.

38. 'A Letter to Our Customers and to the Community', Alizila (News from Alibaba) (April 2021), https://www.alizila.com/a-letter-to-our-customers-and-to-the-community/, accessed on 1 October 2021.

39. Jack Ma's speech at the Bund Summit 2020 in Shanghai, Apple Daily (November 2020), https://en.appledaily.com/article/ TRMUNM72DRAQJNCG3ON2JUUF4A/, accessed on 1 October 2021.

40. Jing Yang and Lingling Wei, 'China's President Xi Jinping Personally Scuttled Jack Ma's Ant IPO', *Wall Street Journal* (November 2020), https://www.wsj.com/articles/china-president-xi-jinping-halted-jack-ma-ant-ipo-11605203556, accessed on 1 October 2021.

41. Ryan McMorrow and Sun Yu, 'The Vanishing Billionaire: How Jack Ma Fell Foul of Xi Jinping', *Financial Times* (April 2021), https://www.ft.com/content/1fe0559f-de6d-490e-b312-abba0181da1f, accessed on 1 October 2021.

42. Yang and Wei, 'China's President Xi Jinping Personally Scuttled Jack Ma's Ant IPO'.

43. 'Alibaba Filled with Gratitude, Pledges to Positively Respond to Govt Rules: Chairman', *Global Times* (November 2020), https://www. globaltimes.cn/content/1207723.shtml, accessed on 1 October 2021.

44. McMorrow and Yu, 'The Vanishing Billionaire'.

45. Ibid.

46. Dean Cheng, 'What the Story Behind Xi Jinping, Jack Ma, and the Ant Group IPO Says About China's Economic Future', Heritage Foundation (November 2020), https://www.heritage.org/asia/ commentary/what-the-story-behind-xi-jinping-jack-ma-and-the-ant-group-ipo-says-about-chinas, accessed on 1 October 2021.

47. 'Alibaba filled with gratitude', *Global Times*.

48. The State Administration for Market Supervision has legally challenged Alibaba Group.

'Holdings Limited's online retail platform in China: Administrative Penalties for the Implementation of "Two Election One" Monopolistic Behavior in the Service Market', State Administration for Market Regulation (SAMR), China (April 2021), http://www.samr.gov.cn/ xw/zj/202104/t20210410_327702.html, accessed on 1 October 2021.

49. 'Jack Ma's Double-Whammy Marks End of China Tech's Golden Age', *Bloomberg Quint* (April 2021), https://www.bloombergquint.com/markets/jack-ma-s-double-whammy-marks-the-end-of-china-tech-s-golden-age, accessed on 1 October 2021.

50. 'Ant Group Gives in to Regulators' Pressure; to Restructure as Financial Holding Company', *Business Standard* (April 2021), https://www.businesstoday.in/current/corporate/ant-group-gives-in-to-regulators-pressure-to-restructure-as-financial-holding-company/story/436416.html, accessed on 1 October 2021.

51. McMorrow and Yu, 'The Vanishing Billionaire'.

52. 'Jack Ma's Double-Whammy', *Bloomberg Quint* (April 2021), https://www.bloombergquint.com/markets/jack-ma-s-double-whammy-marks-the-end-of-china-tech-s-golden-age, accessed on 1 October 2021.

53. Sherisse Pham, 'Once China's Richest Man, Wang Jianlin Is Selling Off His Global Empire', *CNN Business* (January 2018), https://money.cnn.com/2018/01/24/investing/wanda-china-wang-jianlin-selling-assets/index.html, accessed on 1 October 2021.

54. Laure He and Jill Disis, 'Can China Still Lead the World in Tech without a New Jack Ma?', *CNN Business* (June 2021), https://edition.cnn.com/2021/06/07/tech/china-tech-crackdown-entrepreneurs-intl-hnk/index.html, accessed on 1 October 2021.

55. Ibid.

56. Zhang Sidong and Martin Choi, 'Chinese Tech Stocks Slump after Beijing Summons 34 Companies in Sign of Heightened Regulatory Oversight', *South China Morning Post* (April 2021), https://www.scmp.com/business/commodities/article/3129369/chinese-tech-stocks-slump-after-beijing-summons-34-companies, accessed on 1 October 2021.

57. He and Disis, 'Can China Still Lead the World'.

58. Franklin Foer, 'What Big Tech Wants Out of the Pandemic', *The Atlantic* (July/August 2020), https://www.theatlantic.com/magazine/

archive/2020/07/big-tech-pandemic-power-grab/612238/, accessed on 1 October 2021.

59. Ibid.

60. Smith and Browne, *Tools and Weapons*.

61. Ibid.

62. Foer, 'What Big Tech Wants'.

63. Ibid.

64. Paul Apostolicas, 'Silicon States: How Tech Titans Are Acquiring State-like Powers', *Harvard International Review* (August 2018), https://blogs.microsoft.com/on-the-issues/2021/02/11/endorsement-australias-proposal-technology-news/, accessed on 1 October 2021.

65. Ibid.

66. Brad Smith and Carol Anne Browne, 'Dawn of a Decade: The Top Ten Tech Policy Issues for the 2020s', LinkedIn (December 2019), https://www.linkedin.com/pulse/dawn-decade-top-ten-tech-policy-issues-2020s-brad-smith/, accessed on 1 October 2021.

67. Max Read, 'Does Even Mark Zuckerberg Know What Facebook Is?' (October 2017), https://nymag.com/intelligencer/2017/10/does-even-mark-zuckerberg-know-what-facebook-is.html, accessed on 1 October 2021.

68. Nick Couldry, and Ulises A. Mejias, *The Costs of Connection (Culture and Economic Life)*, (Stanford University Press, 2019), Kindle.

69. Lucie Greene, *Silicon States: The Power and Politics of Big Tech and What It Means for Our Future* (HarperCollins Publishers India, 2019), Kindle.

70. Ibid.

71. Ibid.

72. Ibid.

73. Don Tapscott and Alex Tapscott, *Blockchain Revolution: How the Technology behind Bitcoin and Other Cryptocurrencies Is Changing the World*, Penguin (2016), Kindle.

11

Digital Empires and Data Colonialism

'If Imperialism may no longer be regarded as a blind inevitable destiny, is it certain that imperial expansion as a deliberately chosen line of public policy can be stopped?'

—John Hobson, *Imperialism: A Study* (1902)

Colonialism is a term that is often bandied about in nations that have been former colonies of European powers. People in these nations have learnt from history that essentially, colonialism was an era of exploitation by 'foreign powers'. Hence, anything that seems 'foreign' and 'exploitative' currently gets termed as 'colonial'. It is a politically explosive term, and a serious accusation. Suddenly, ears get pricked up, because none of the colonized nations wants history to repeat itself. But do today's circumstances resemble European colonialism? Or is the dominance associated with big businesses getting mischaracterized as colonialism?

Is it beginning to look a lot like colonialism?

Several countries—especially those whose digital economies are dominated by foreign Big Tech firms—have raised concerns about 'digital colonialism' as a modern-day avatar of the exploitative colonization of the past.

In using that term, governments or political analysts are referring to a few things. One, certain foreign Big Tech firms, by virtue of their existing large size and disproportionately higher access to capital and technology, are benefiting at the expense (and almost to the exclusion) of domestic tech firms. Michael Kwet has defined digital colonialism as 'the use of digital technology for political, economic and social domination of another nation or territory'.[1]

Within this broader idea of digital colonialism lies the idea of 'data colonialism'. The creation, extraction, monopolization and monetization of data by foreign Big Tech firms for their own benefit is seen as exploitative of a resource technically owned, created and generated by the people of that nation.

In many ways, data-grab is the new form of land-grab. Imagine many centuries ago, when human beings, as they discovered land, laid claim to that land since it was deemed unoccupied (the British-era concept of *terra nullius* essentially referred to this). Or less benignly, imagine certain groups taking an area of land by force, for military or economic reasons. That is what is termed as land-grab, an activity seen as being either unethical or fraudulent and most commonly both.[2]

According to data experts, today's tech firms are currently engaged in the same kind of land-grab. In the absence of strict regulation around 'data-grabbing', they are able to engage in the capturing, tracking and storing of data that is deemed to be theirs for the taking. Further resources such as machine-learning-driven algorithms or targeted recommendation engines or advertising platforms are built upon this data to effectively control the benefits of its use as well. This data-based wealth-grab, or the 'virtual land-grab', is done behind a façade. Just like land-grabs were undertaken to appropriate subsidies, obtain bank loans or speculate on future increases in land values,[3] today's data-grab is following a similar strategy according to critics of Big Tech firms and their data policies.

Data is captured behind a façade of a certain stated purpose (usually, of helping the customer derive some value or convenience), but behind the façade lies an agenda to appropriate the data, obtain large amounts of (venture) capital and speculate on future increases in the value of that data. Most mobile phone applications today, for example, capture more data than they need for the smooth functioning of the application. This additional data capture is driven by nothing but speculation on the future increase in value of that data.

Today, techno-nationalists believe that data is a natural resource of that nation (much like cotton or coal), and the engine of future economic growth. According to them, foreign corporations extracting that data and using it to enrich themselves, and not for powering the economic growth of the host nation is 'digital colonialism'.

This harks back to the European colonial days when the European trading companies were able to establish trading monopolies, and eventually political and economic control in their colonies. Consequently, they were able to extract great amounts of wealth from their colonies, in the form of natural resources, commodities and favourable trade, to transfer back to their home territories.

Others draw an analogy with 'the age of empire', arguing that we are living in a world of tech empires. These tech empires resemble the British empire or the Roman empire. The Big Tech firms today hold massive sway over the rules of the internet and, according to Mark Surman, chairman of the Mozilla Foundation, play both the roles of gatekeepers and rule-makers.[4] This gatekeeper-controlled internet has little in common with the founding vision of an open, decentralized internet. Surman believes the internet is increasingly starting to 'resemble maps from centuries past, when empires ruled vast swaths of land, engulfing independent villages and smaller kingdoms'.[5]

Several academics are starting to study these alleged parallels more rigorously. Prof. Nick Couldry, who has studied colonialism closely, has described the four stages of European colonialism: first, the appropriation of a valuable resource; second, the creation of new social relations to contextualize and make the new situation seem normal;

third, the extreme concentration of wealth arising from that resource appropriation; and fourth, propagation of ideologies and stories to weave a coherent story of what was going on.[6]

Couldry explained to me that the same four stages are true of digital colonialism, though the modes, the intensity and the scale and context of today's colonialism are distinct in their own way.[7] He argued that fundamentally, digital colonialism, like historical colonialism, is looking to acquire large-scale resources from which economic value can be extracted. If European colonists annexed territories, resources and people, data colonialism captures and appropriates the data from the new digital markets, and extracts profit from that data. Just as European colonialism gave rise to the accumulation of capital that drove industrialization, data colonialism is paving the way for the accumulation of data capital by the Big Tech firms.[8]

A similar argument has been made by Shoshana Zuboff, a professor at HBS, in her book, *The Age of Surveillance Capitalism*. Both Zuboff and Couldry essentially have argued that technology and capitalism have combined to enable data about human life to become the source of profits for large firms, leading to large concentrations of wealth. Not just that, the constant monitoring and surveillance of human life, which is essential for continuous extraction of data, degrades human life and makes it a 'direct input to capitalist production'.[9]

During the industrialization era, as I discussed in Chapter 2, the accumulation of capital relied on exploitation of human production through unequal human relations. The accumulated capital, and rapid industrialization, drove an immense rise in economic production. Today, in the technology era, capital is accumulated through the exploitation of data about human life and activities. In this era of technology capitalism or surveillance capitalism, as Zuboff has termed it, human beings have gone from being actors in the production process to raw materials that can be transformed for extracting value in the production process.[10]

Further, during our conversation, Couldry pointed out that this extraction and accumulation of data of persons happen on terms over which the persons are not in control.[11] In some ways, it can therefore be thought of as colonialism of individuals, and not necessarily just nations. The data that Big Tech firms exert their absolute right on as just being 'there for the taking' sounds eerily similar to the colonial-era legal doctrine of *terra nullius*. *Terra nullius* envisioned land such as the territory of Australia that supposedly belonged to no one as being there for the taking as well.[12] Is data the new *terra nullius*?

The other aspect, according to Couldry, that makes the current era look increasingly like colonialism is the concentration of ownership of the data amongst a few. This, he argues, is leading to a likely long-term skewing of the world's economic resource distribution and entrenched power formations, which could eventually lead to a second Great Divergence between nations. This skewed social and economic ordering is a characteristic of colonialism.[13]

For example, the dominant technology powers of this era, including the Big Tech firms, are likely to leverage their ownership of digital infrastructure, technology, data and intellectual property to keep the non-tech powers in a situation of permanent dependency.[14] During the era of industrialization and capitalism, industrialists and capitalists had ensured that labour was in a state of permanent dependence, and now Big Tech firms are likely to do the same. This 'unequal division of labour' is likely to mean that the dependent states will not have the means to catch up, just like the colonies were not able to become industrialized themselves.

Mark Surman, executive director of the Mozilla Foundation, has argued that there is definitely a 'colonial-like trade flow' pattern in the digital economy. Resources, in the form of data, clicks, impressions and payments, are extracted from countries (mostly emerging countries and countries that are dominated by global Big Tech firms), and the rewards from the processing of those resources are largely reaped by the Big Tech firms and their host countries. As Surman explains, 'it's a one-sided flow', with the result that most countries in Asia, Africa and Latin America are net 'importers' in the digital app economy.[15] These markets are extremely dependent on the Big Tech firms for what are increasingly core, essential services such as commerce, payments, transportation and communication.

There are key differences from European colonialism. For example, Couldry points out that data colonialism is not exclusively a Western project this time around. Even other countries with Big Tech firms, such as China, are engaging in a similar form of data colonialism as the Big Tech firms from the West.[16] Regardless of the country of origin, Big Tech firms, therefore, are being seen as having checked off all the four features of European colonialism, as outlined by Couldry. So, his conclusion is clear: we are living in an era of digital and data colonialism.

Another key difference this time around is that the Big Tech firms are not in control of the government of the nation states. As of now, there are no indications of any desire to assume political or overall economic control of dependent nations. In any case, governments around the world are fighting Big Tech firms for control, and often winning as well. Ultimately, if Big Tech firms were to directly or indirectly control most decisions of government, foreign policy, defence and the economy, then we could conclude that we are living in a state of digital colonialism. Otherwise, it might just be another example of big business and its ability to shape the world to its liking.

Colonization of the individual, not the state?

But what about the notion that the digital colonization might not be of nation states, but rather of individuals this time around? Our computers, our phones and our bodies have become trackable devices that are constantly generating and sharing data with others, giving corporations and states access to data that they could hitherto not have imagined getting access to. And it is not just the tracking capability that these devices come with; they can also become the channel to shape, influence and transform behaviour at every point to the extent that it just seems like the natural state to many.[17]

Yuval Harari has similarly described his concern that data being gathered by AI and biotech could help companies and governments 'hack the humans', that is to say, understand humans (their thoughts, their behaviour, their preferences) better than the humans themselves. Algorithms are already deciding what we wear, who we marry, what we eat, where we go to school and how we spend our time, and Harari believes that these data-powered, AI-enabled algorithms could soon be making many more critical decisions for us as well, including who we vote for, and what political, social and economic issues we care about.

Therefore, questions raised by such colonization of the individual become critical for us to think deeply about as a society and race: should humans in the twenty-first century accept a world in which their lives are appropriated through data? And if not, can we, as a society, envision and create a fundamentally differently structured technology ecosystem that does not centralize control of our data?

Is Digital Colonialism Inevitable?

By no means is digital colonialism an inevitable reality. Yes, there might indeed be some similarities between the European colonial era and today, but also some key differences.

Many, though not all, nation states today have a different level of agency, strength, focus on independence and sovereignty, and understanding of history. Nation states are fighting back against the growing influence of Big Tech and do have a wide range of tools at their disposal for their fight. Moreover, both Big Tech firms and nation states still do have the agency and the capability to shape their future destinies and take different, if difficult, decisions on the future structure of the digital economy. As Tim Rühlig, a senior fellow at the German Council on Foreign Relations (DGAP), remarked to me, Europe is increasingly worried that this time around, their economies might get 'colonized' by foreign Big Tech firms. Therefore, the European Commission has taken it upon themselves to use regulation as a strategy to prevent such an outcome.

That might not be within the capability of all countries. Some countries are stronger than others, by virtue of the size of their economy or the strength and capabilities of their governments and other institutions. Weaker, more corrupt countries might very well still be at risk of being dominated by Big Tech firms, directly or indirectly. And that is a risk that we will need to watch out for. The stronger countries are likely to fight the various battles with Big Tech around privacy, data ownership, data localization, content moderation, taxation, monopolistic behaviour, undue influence on elections, etc. The weaker ones, however, might need the umbrella of better global technology governance regimes, as I discuss later in the book.

The roles and strategies of the key nations such as the US and China, as well as prominent Big Tech firms from these nations, will be pivotal in shaping future changes to the technology and data ecosystem. As the beneficiaries of the status quo, they might not want the digital economies of other countries to take root in a way that takes away from the competitiveness and reach of their own companies.

Yet, that view would decidedly be a short-sighted one. In the long term, such vilification and hostility amongst other nation states and their citizens, not to mention their ability to raise digital walls and barriers through regulation, will not serve the US or its companies well. Rather, these companies and countries have the opportunity today to define a future that learns from our past, and is structured to distribute value, wealth and innovation more broadly and fairly for all involved.[18] And they must take up that opportunity.

Big Tech firms and governments have some serious choices to make, and long, deep and frank discussions to have. Big Tech, with so much at stake, will likely be smart and adapt to the challenges being thrown at them by society, governments and citizens. As Maëlle Gavet argues, Silicon Valley firms might indeed start to move away from the micro-targeted approach adopted by the Facebooks and Googles of the world. The long-term acceptability of this model has been contested and questioned, and concerns around privacy violations, data breaches and other issues have risen rapidly. So, a move toward new economic and business models that would be more acceptable to regulators and users might very well make business sense.[19]

Expecting meaningful self-regulation by those who are in the driving seat today and expecting them to refrain from extracting their pound of flesh for being the 'best' in the world would be naïve. Few companies and nations, if any, in the past have had that kind of restraint, discipline and ability, frankly, to withstand the pressures of their own investors and stakeholders. Therefore, governments, society and citizens must play an active role in ensuring fair competition, risk mitigation and protection of the fundamental rights of people.

Greater competition between Big Tech firms might lead to some of these changes. Some firms, for example, might decide that they can gain market share and acceptance amongst users vis-à-vis competitors by actually making the intentional policy and design choices that allow for greater data ownership within user-centred frameworks.[20] In some ways, Apple is trying to assume that positioning vis-à-vis Facebook, as evident from recent updates to its data policy on its iOS app store.

At the same time, greater competition between Big Tech firms might actually push us further in the wrong direction. A 'cold war' between the Big Tech firms is as likely to spark off more formal digital colonialism. Just the fear or paranoia of the other gaining an edge might lead to sub-optimal actions. Obviously, this is not without historical precedent, either. As Walter LaFeber has argued, many countries in the colonial era ended up annexing territories out of a fear that if they didn't do it, the others would.[21] A classic case of prisoner's dilemma.

The role of the employees of Big Tech firms will be critical. The employees—or the internal stakeholders in general, including the shareholders—are like the primary citizens of the new 'net states'. And they increasingly do shape the policy choices of their firms. When Facebook and Apple face off on privacy battles, and the employees of Facebook side with Apple, that shapes Facebook's future policies and strategies. Similarly, when Google employees rise up in protest against Google working for the Pentagon, it restricts the extent to which Big Tech–state collaboration might hurt the rights of common citizens.

The impact of the internal resistance within Big Tech firms, like the internal resistance within colonial empires, could be significant.[22]

As I have argued throughout the book, it is up to us, collectively, to shape the future. Digital or data colonialism is not inevitable. As Prof. Couldry pointed out, there is much greater public awareness of colonial-style relationships and their dangers now than was the case three or four hundred years ago. Moreover, if we look back at European colonialism, a few factors converged for it to finally dissipate around the world. Great power rivalry culminating in the two World Wars led to subsequent weakening of the European economies. Alongside, the socio-political movements such as nationalism gained momentum against the colonial systems.

Similarly, this time around, a combination of factors might work to prevent digital or data colonialism. The rivalry between Big Tech firms could see some firms take up a stronger stance against extractive relationships, which could then become the expectation and norm across the industry. Similarly, socio-political movements that arise to fight against the rising inequality could take up this cause.

Many organizations and governments are already coming together to ensure a more equal relationship between the generators and the users of data. Governments creating better policies and frameworks for data governance could lead the way with development of more open, fairer data protocols. Initiatives by India in this regard are again an interesting example. As Nandan Nilekani has envisioned, India's unique ID-based public data infrastructure and national open digital ecosystems (NODEs) could provide alternative, fairer models of data ownership and usage.

Other emerging technologies such as blockchain, as discussed earlier, could form the backbone of alternate data management structures that do not lend themselves to extractive relationships and more distributed power dynamics. Many scholars have argued against technological determinism, including scholars such as Yuval Harari. Neither in the present nor in the future are the structure, embedded values and ecosystem for technology written in stone. There are indeed alternative ways of leveraging technology to build a better world than we were able to during the previous eras of industrialization, colonization, capitalism, mass agriculture and mercantilist trade.

Notes

1. Michael Kwet, 'Digital Colonialism: The Evolution of US Empire', Long Reads (March 2021), https://longreads.tni.org/digital-colonialism-the-evolution-of-us-empire, accessed on 1 October 2021.

2. *The Global Land Grab: A Primer*, TNI Agrarian Justice Programme (February 2013), https://www.tni.org/files/download/landgrabbingprimer-feb2013.pdf.

3. Ibid.

4. Mark Surman, 'The Rise of Digital Empires Is Creating a Colonial Vision of the Internet—We Have to Stop It', *New Statesman Tech* (September 2016), https://tech.newstatesman.com/guest-opinion/digital-empires, accessed on 1 October 2021.

5. Ibid.

6. Nick Couldry, 'Colonized by Data: The Hollowing Out of Digital Society', Lecture Series at Alexander von Humboldt Institute for Internet and Society, YouTube (November 2019), https://www.youtube.com/watch?v=5tcK-XIMQqE, accessed on 1 October 2021.

7. Ibid.

8. Nick Couldry and Ulises A. Mejias, *The Costs of Connection (Culture and Economic Life)* (Stanford University Press, 2019), Kindle.

9. Ibid.

10. Ibid.

11. Ibid.

12. Ibid.

13. Ibid.

14. Kwet, 'Digital Colonialism'.

15. Mark Surman, 'The Rise of Digital Empires Is Creating a Colonial Vision of the Internet—We Have to Stop It', *New Statesman Tech* (September 2016), https://tech.newstatesman.com/guest-opinion/digital-empires, accessed on 1 October 2021.

16. Couldry and Mejias, *The Costs of Connection*.

17. Ibid.

18. François Candelon and Martin Reeves, 'The New Digital World: Hegemony or Harmony?', BCG Henderon Institute (November 2017), https://www.bcg.com/publications/2017/strategy-globalization-new-digital-world-hegemony-harmony, accessed on 1 October 2021.

19. Maëlle Gavet, 'What's Next for Silicon Valley?', *Harvard Business Review* (September 2020), https://hbr.org/2020/09/whats-next-for-silicon-valley, accessed on 1 October 2021.

20. Coordinating Data Policy and the Public Interest, Geotech Hour, Data Salon Series, The Atlantic Council GeoTech Center, March 2021, https://www.atlanticcouncil.org/blogs/geotech-cues/event-recap-coordinating-data-privacy/, accessed on 1 October 2021.

21. LaFeber, *The New Empire*.

22. Victor Bulmer-Thomas, *Empire in Retreat: The Past, Present, and Future of the United States* (Yale University Press, 2018), Kindle.

12

Reimagining Global Governance

'While the cat's away, the mice will play.'

—Proverb

Sample some of the technology news from around the world in the last few years: the Colonial Pipeline in the US shuts down due to a ransomware attack; an Israeli firm's surveillance software is being used by governments for tracking dissidents; the world's first genetically edited human babies are born in China; central banks ban cryptocurrency but are planning to launch their own digital currencies; the EU initiates anti-trust action against Big Tech firms; India tells WhatsApp not to roll out its new privacy updates; AI threatens to take over jobs performed by humans; fake news and disinformation campaigns might have impacted the outcome of the US elections in 2016; Big Tech firms are paying an effective tax of less than 1 per cent despite billions of dollars in profits. The list goes on.

As fascinated or concerned or bewildered you might be upon reading this news, most of these news stories are essentially about technology-related governance issues. The spread of technology has created global governance issues that span across national borders. Neither are these

366

issues nation-specific, nor can they be addressed by individual nations acting alone.

The nature of the problem is not entirely unprecedented, either. Global issues such as climate change, terrorism, nuclear proliferation and even the spread of earlier technologies such as the telegraph have posed similarly complex global governance challenges before.

There are several issues emerging that are at the heart of global technology governance. We have already in earlier chapters discussed internet infrastructure security and negotiation of standards, global data governance, taxation of global technology firms, and the lack of norms around cybersecurity and cyberwarfare. Other critical issues that require global governance debates include privacy and surveillance technology, the rise of cryptocurrencies and digital currencies, and norms around ethical AI and genetic engineering. Let us examine these in detail first.

Core Technology Governance Issues

Privacy and surveillance technology

As the global availability, affordability and usage of surveillance technology have exploded, privacy and surveillance have increasingly become major global concerns.[1] Personal data today is freely flowing across borders, not just within borders. Yet, there is no universal framework to govern the collection, usage, storage and sharing of personal information or other critical data.[2]

We have already discussed how intelligence agencies conduct mass surveillance of the telecommunications of billions of people around the world, including world leaders and heads of state of many countries. Big Tech firms have more data about you than you can imagine, and most likely understand you better than you do. Governments are increasing the use of AI-enabled facial recognition technologies and surveillance of their own citizens. These surveillance capabilities are transforming the ability of governments to monitor and track individuals like never before. A report of the Carnegie Endowment for International Peace found that over seventy-five countries globally are actively using AI-enabled technologies for surveillance.[3] Chart 12.1 shows the various types of surveillance technology available today.

But what are the rules and guidelines for such surveillance? None, really. Though increasingly, some countries and jurisdictions, such as the European Union, are realizing the urgent need to end this 'free-for-all'.

Many countries are today exporters and drivers of this surveillance worldwide. Prominent among them are China, followed by Japan, the US, Israel, Germany and France. Chinese companies, such as Huawei, Hikvision, Dahua and ZTE, have supplied AI surveillance technology to at least sixty-three of the seventy-six countries that use such technologies.[4] US firms have collectively supplied surveillance technology to at least thirty-two countries. Companies such as Huawei (fifty countries), Japan's NEC Corporation (fourteen), IBM (eleven), Palantir (nine) and Cisco (six) are the major players. The Carnegie Endowment report, while criticizing China's aggressive spread of advanced surveillance technology, also points the blame to countries like the US, Israel, Germany and France for not taking adequate precautions to monitor and control the spread of this technology.

The alleged misuse of Pegasus software, built by Israeli firm NSO, that enabled remote surveillance of mobile phones, if proven true, should serve as a cautionary tale. Pegasus was suspected as having been used, for example, by the Saudi government to spy on the communications of Jamal Khashoggi, a rebel journalist.[5] Pegasus has also allegedly helped the governments of Mexico and UAE to listen in on and track smartphones of dissenters, activists and individuals.[6] NSO has emphatically denied all these allegations.

On the other hand, the NSO Group and its software must also have helped law enforcement agencies around the world apprehend terrorists and paedophiles. But it is hard to monitor the end-use of the software. Neither is NSO alone in this private surveillance industry, much of which is considered to be operating globally in a legal grey area. Some

Chart 12.1 Types of Surveillance Technology

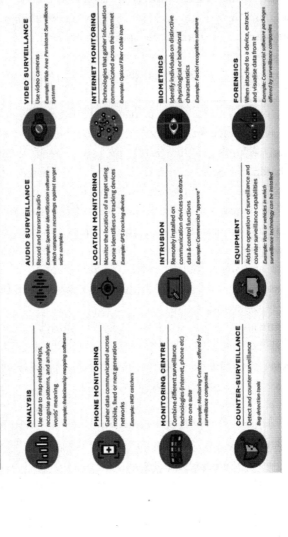

THE TYPES OF SURVEILLANCE TECHNOLOGY

ANALYSIS
Use data to map relationships, recognise patterns, and analyse words' meaning
Example: Relationship mapping software

AUDIO SURVEILLANCE
Record and transmit audio
Example: Speaker Identification software which compares recordings against target voice samples

VIDEO SURVEILLANCE
Use video cameras
Example: Wide Area Persistent Surveillance systems

PHONE MONITORING
Gather data communicated across mobile, fixed or next generation networks
Example: IMSI catchers

LOCATION MONITORING
Monitor the location of a target using phone identifiers or tracking devices
Example: GPS tracking devices

INTERNET MONITORING
Technologies that gather information communicated across the internet
Example: Optical/Fiber Cable taps

MONITORING CENTRE
Combine different surveillance technologies (internet, phone etc) into one suite
Example: Monitoring Centres offered by surveillance companies

INTRUSION
Remotely installed on communication devices to extract data & control functions
Example: Commercial "spyware"

BIOMETRICS
Identify individuals on distinctive physiological or behavioral characteristics
Example: Facial recognition software

COUNTER-SURVEILLANCE
Detect and counter surveillance
Bug detection tools

EQUIPMENT
Aids the operation of surveillance and counter surveillance capabilities
Example: Vans or vehicles in which surveillance technology can be installed

FORENSICS
When attached to a device, extract and visualise data from it
Example: Commercial software packages offered by surveillance companies

Source: 'The Global Surveillance Industry', Transparency International, https://privacyinternational.org/explainer/1632/global-surveillance-industry, accessed on 30 June 2021.

of the other prominent firms include German firm FinFisher, Italian firm Hacking Team and the Spanish firm Mollitiam.[7]

Surveillance can be conducted broadly along all parts of the telecommunications sector, and involve internet service providers (ISPs), submarine cable providers, telcos, network equipment manufacturers, in addition to surveillance companies, contractors and distributors. Given the wide spectrum of companies and actors that could be involved, the question of whether there are sufficient global controls in place to prevent the abuse of such powerful software becomes critical.

Most governments are not incentivized to create export controls or other restrictions on such cyber weapons. The use of stronger encryption technologies like E2EE by private tech companies has made it harder for governments to 'listen in'. The services of firms like NSO, Mollitiam and FinFisher have therefore become much more valuable.[8] Moreover, today, the private surveillance firms sell the most sophisticated commercial spyware on the international market, which can be bought by anyone, not just governments. This implies that all scrupulous and unscrupulous, state and non-state actors today can have access to some of the most sophisticated surveillance tools, cyber weapons, in the world.

Unfortunately, the impact of weak export controls globally has had major political and social implications. As UN Special Rapporteur David Kaye noted in his report to the UN Human Rights Council, surveillance of individuals, often activists, journalists, opposition leaders or critics, has thrived amid the lack of governance or oversight over the sale, use or export of such technologies to governments and other organizations.[9] As a result, these surveillance tools have made it easier to interfere and undermine key human rights such as privacy, freedom of speech and expression, religious freedom and peaceful protest. The operations of the private surveillance industry and its close collaboration with government agencies, he argued, were currently 'a free-for-all'.[10]

Before leaving his position in 2020, Kaye urged that the world treat the sale and use of dangerous spyware much like other dual-use technology systems or even nuclear weapons. The strictest level of oversight and safeguards must be adopted, he argued, to prevent unlawful surveillance.[11] Much like nuclear technology, these tools need an international watchdog that can not only control their spread, monitor their end-users, but also have the ability to penalize countries and blacklist companies that fail to adhere to internationally established guidelines and laws. Else, surveillance technology can end up having extremely serious consequences for the world.

The 5G cybersecurity threat to critical infrastructure

With 5G, the internet is moving from being largely a communications and information system to a control system that communicates with, connects and controls the operations of a wide variety of devices.[12] From a security standpoint, more than losing access to communications and online financial transactions systems, the shut-down of critical infrastructures such as oil pipelines, power plants, transportation and nuclear weapon systems is becoming the primary concern.

Several incidents illustrate the severity of the risks. In 2007, the cardiologist of then US Vice President Dick Cheney, Dr Jonathan Reiner, had expressed concern that the wireless capability on Cheney's implanted defibrillator could be hacked and the device could be used by terrorists to shock him into cardiac arrest.[13] Then, in 2010, the Stuxnet worm, a cyberweapon, infiltrated and sabotaged the control systems for Iranian nuclear centrifuges, impairing the Iranian nuclear weapons programme.[14] More recently, in May 2021, the US-based Colonial Pipeline Company became a victim of a ransomware attack, throwing large parts of the US East Coast into chaos.[15]

Following the SolarWinds and Colonial Pipeline attacks, President Biden signed an executive order focused on prevention of such attacks on federal government networks and other critical infrastructure.[16] In line with this strategy to 'prevent' these attacks, Biden, at the Biden–

Putin Summit in Geneva in June 2021, stressed upon President Putin that 'certain critical infrastructure should be off-limits to attack—period—by cyber or any other means.'[17]

While no agreement was reached at the Summit, the two leaders did agree to constitute a task force of experts to identify mutual specific agreements about what's off-limits.[18] Biden publicly threatened to respond with American cyber capabilities if the Russians ran afoul of this understanding.[19] Many analysts and Russia-watchers believe that the outcomes of such taskforces or statements will be no better than the agreement that President Obama struck with Chinese President Xi Jinping in 2015 to not conduct or support cyberespionage and theft of intellectual property for commercial gain.[20]

Still, some analysts have argued that 'the meeting represented a watershed moment for the prominence of cybersecurity on the global agenda'.[21] Indeed, this issue will need global technology governance regimes, and not just wishful thinking. Past agreements or conventions, such as the Geneva War Conventions, can serve as benchmarks for the creation of similar conventions that can protect the basic lives and dignity of citizens that are threatened by such cyberattacks on critical infrastructure.

Cryptocurrency and digital currencies

Cryptocurrencies are being used widely, yet, like many other emerging technologies, have managed to evade global governance norms and oversight.

Unlike the traditional currencies such as the US dollar, the euro, or the renminbi, cryptocurrencies such as bitcoin or ethereum are not issued or backed by sovereign nation states or central banks. There is no role envisaged for any intermediary, let alone a government, in the use of these currencies by people or entities wishing to transact with each other. Much like the internet, blockchain technology envisages a much smaller role of governments, if any at all, and challenges the historical control of various arms of the state. These technologies have been recognized as shifting 'power and the locus of authority away from the state'[22] and contributing to the 'decentralization of political power within societies'.[23]

But as with other dimensions of the battle of state versus Big Tech, the governments are not caving in to this challenge, either. Countries are responding in one of three ways: one, regulate cryptocurrencies; two, outright ban cryptocurrencies and declare them illegal; or three, launch a central bank digital currency (CBDC).

Countries such as the UK, the US, Singapore, Canada, the Philippines, Switzerland, Germany, Thailand, Indonesia and South Korea are regulating (or planning to regulate) cryptocurrency. Note the big overlap this list has with the emerging winners in the tech era. On the other hand, countries such as China, Bangladesh, Algeria, Saudi Arabia and Qatar have banned trading in cryptocurrencies, made initial coin offerings illegal, and in some cases (though not all), prohibited the purchase, sale, use and possession of cryptocurrency. Similarly, albeit late to the game, India is bringing its own bill to ban private cryptocurrencies. As an Indian commentator, Manu Joseph, put it, 'A Bohemian idea that defies state control can easily gain popularity but cannot escape regulation.'[24]

The final category of countries, including some from the first two categories, such as India, China, the US and Europe, have understood the potential benefits of digital currencies, yet they do not want to give up control of the currency domain. These countries are therefore floating the idea of a central bank digital currency (CBDC). These digital currencies would be based on blockchain technology (like bitcoin), but with two key differences. One, they would not be encrypted (they would be designed for tracking, not anonymity like bitcoin), and two, most importantly, they would be issued by the existing power-brokers of currency: central banks.

As Prof. Werbach explained to me, the view of central bankers on this issue is informed by over 500 years of history. CBDCs are definitely the future, Werbach believes, but that CBDCs are likely to coexist with other crypto-currencies (such as Stablecoin). Eventually,

Werbach surmised, different countries will end up on different parts of the spectrum on this issue.

Global financial and geopolitical implications of CBDCs

We might be at a critical inflection point last seen by the world economy when it moved from coins to paper currencies, or even from gold-backed currency to just central bank-backed currencies. As Eswar Prasad has argued, 'the era of cash is drawing to an end and that of central bank digital currencies has begun'.[25] CBDCs will, no doubt, have major implications for the world's financial systems and structures, and by extension, the economic destinies of nations.

CBDCs would transform the ability of nations to understand economic trends and money flows within their nations much better. CBDCs would help countries develop new tools for collecting and leveraging real-time data that could help them make intelligent decisions about the economy.[26] Digital currencies could lead to novel types of monetary policy, such as a digital currency that loses value over time, so users are encouraged to spend it quickly.[27]

In the case of China, inspired by the rich data captured by WeChat Pay and Alipay,[28] the Chinese government might use CBDCs to track detailed transaction-level data for its citizens. Already, China is ahead of all other major powers in piloting its homegrown digital yuan in cities such as Shenzhen, Shanghai and Beijing. State-owned banks and tech firms are developing digital distribution systems for it.[29,30] Moreover, China's decision to launch its own CBDC could threaten the dominance of the US dollar as the world's pre-eminent currency by boosting the renminbi's adoption.[31]

Though some, like Paul Krugman, disagree,[32] the dominance of the US dollar is believed to be a big driver of the US's continued control of the world's trading and financial institutions. With the rise of China's CBDC, as well as others, the ability of the US to continue to exercise the same level of influence over the world's financial and trading transactions will suffer greatly.[33] For example, the US currently wields great influence over the SWIFT platform for international transfers, but the digital yuan and other CBDCs could sidestep the SWIFT platform entirely.

The US, recognizing this threat to their dominance of financial systems, is starting to adopt a more sophisticated (allow, but regulate and prepare) approach to cryptocurrencies. The US Federal Reserve (the Fed) and its chair Jerome Powell have been categorical in saying, 'It will tread very carefully into the digital currency space, given the important role the US dollar plays in the global economy.'[34] At the same time, the Fed has expedited its consideration of CBDCs, with Powell stating that the Fed will take the lead in the evolution of international standards for CBDCs.[35]

Moreover, if the still-nascent CBDCs do end up becoming the future currencies of our times, then cryptocurrencies may indeed face a more rapid decline than we anticipate. As Eric Rosengren, president of the Federal Reserve of Boston, has argued, he 'could not see a long-lived use case for Bitcoin in a world where central banks were likely to offer their own alternatives eventually'.[36] The state strikes back, again. No surprises there. Looking back into the arc of history, however, Prasad points out that just a century ago, private currencies actually competed with each other and with government-issued currencies. The recent developments, according to him, imply 'a return from the dominance of official currencies to renewed competition between private and fiat currencies'.[37]

But even as the geopolitical competition over digital currencies plays out, key questions of governance will need to be thoughtfully addressed for this once-in-a-era technological development: Who will regulate, monitor and resolve issues surrounding these currencies and cross-border payments at the global level? What would be the international standards for such currencies, and who would set those standards? What, how and where exactly are decisions made about blockchain-based activities and disputes? How would the countries work together to prevent the misuse of these technologies for illicit uses? How would these digital currencies coexist with, and relate to, existing currencies? What role would private sector firms play versus central banks in this ecosystem? What privacy frameworks would be needed to secure the data related to these currencies and their flows? Is a blockchain-based currency desirable for all actors and participants of the global economy?

Various international organizations have recently started examining issues related to cryptocurrencies, crypto-assets, and CBDCs. In October 2020, the G7 central banks and Bureau of International Settlements (BIS) had, under the chairmanship of ECB president Christine Lagarde, published a report assessing the feasibility of CBDCs and laying down the core principles of a CBDC.[38] Subsequently, after a meeting in May and June 2021 of the G7 finance ministers, central bankers and the heads of the IMF, World Bank, and OECD, the G7 stated that they would work towards common principles and international standards for CBDCs and publish their conclusions by end-2021. One can expect that this grouping, following the lead of the US, will adopt a much more cautious approach than the challenger, China.

Norms for ethical AI

The future evolution of AI-based technologies poses as much a global governance challenge as a source of geopolitical and technological competition.

The US National Security Commission on Artificial Intelligence has explicitly linked the future of AI to the geopolitical contest between democratic and authoritarian regimes in general, and the US and China in particular.[39] The US worries that it will lose leadership in a key emerging technology. But it is concerned that the Chinese— and other like-minded authoritarian regimes—will push the use of AI-enabled surveillance and biometrics as tools of surveillance and political oversight. Therefore, the US wants adequate transparency, oversight and accountability built into global AI governance regimes to prevent its misuse for illiberal purposes by authoritarian regimes.

However, from the Chinese perspective, they are more concerned about leveraging AI technologies to leapfrog the US in technological leadership by 2050, than with setting the rules and norms for the use of AI. For China, it is less a political debate and more about the economic gap that China seeks to narrow. This is not unlike the debate on climate change, where the incumbent powers (that is, the developed nations) emphasize values, norms and ethics while developing countries focus on minimizing any constraints such global governance regimes might place on their quest for economic convergence with developed nations.

Several issues and debates, many of them representing differences in underlying values, are at the core of the quest for ethical uses of AI. One, AI-based systems are inherently laid with the biases of their makers, and can further concentrate power and influence in the hands of those designing them, while concealing responsibility and liability behind the façade of complex black box algorithms.[40] Predictive policing algorithms (PredPol), for example, have been found to be implicitly biased against certain communities. These AI-enabled algorithms can further entrench and propagate past racist practices that might have skewed the criminal justice system against certain communities.[41]

Two, AI-based tools can be misused in quite a wide variety of ways. For example, such tools are enabling massive disinformation campaigns that manipulate public opinion, mislead people and deliberately spread false narratives. Similarly, the alleged use of AI-enabled facial recognition technologies by China and other countries for identifying and racially profiling its citizens has come under heavy criticism. Text-generating AI technology could power thousands of articles and social media posts that could purposely drown out other views and perspectives.[42]

Such technological capabilities are getting better by the day, as evidenced by Alphabet's May 2021 demonstration of LaMDA's natural conversation capabilities. (LaMDA is an AI-enabled language model and application that can synthesize various concepts from training data that it has been fed, and then hold a conversation about any topic.)[43] Now, imagine the ability for LaMDA to generate synthetic text, fake emails or social media posts. If LaMDA has been fed past email conversations between you and your spouse, for example, a future email from LaMDA, pretending to be your spouse might sound exactly like your spouse, with all their attendant language and punctuation quirks.

AI literacy, let alone a deep and sophisticated understanding of its scope and implications, remains very poor amongst policymakers and citizens alike. Much like all start-ups today claim to be leveraging AI, governments are increasingly mentioning AI in their strategy documents, without understanding much about it.

Chart 12.2 categorizes the broad, high-level governance gaps expected in the case of AI, categorized by near-, middle- and long-term scenarios. We are currently dealing with the short-term governance gaps, but the medium- and long-term gaps (titled 'Near' and 'Next' respectively) are of sufficient significance that they need to be prepared for immediately as well. Autonomous AI-enabled weapons systems being leveraged by militaries and even non-state cyber-attackers could escalate into fatal conflict, even when it could actually have been avoidable. These scenarios—even if they might seem outlandish today—do need to be seriously discussed, debated, deliberated and acted upon today, both within and amongst nations.

Much like with other global governance problems of great import, global deliberations on AI technology need to be prioritized. Indeed, national and international institutions have begun developing some nascent frameworks for AI governance. For example, the EU has published 'Ethics Guidelines for Trustworthy Artificial Intelligence', while the Vatican has issued its 'Rome Call for AI Ethics'.[44]

Innovative governance frameworks could serve as templates for future discussions. Canada's Directive on Automated Decision-Making, for example, includes requirements such as explicit detailing and explanations of decisions both pre- and post-facto, especially when algorithms or AI technology has been leveraged for decision-making. Private AI players, such as Google, have acknowledged the magnitude of the problems, and have accordingly focused on minimizing or eliminating well-known risks in their AI models, such as biases, mirroring hateful speech, or propagating misleading information.[45]

Chart 12.2 Summary of the Short-, Medium- and Long-Term AI Governance Gaps

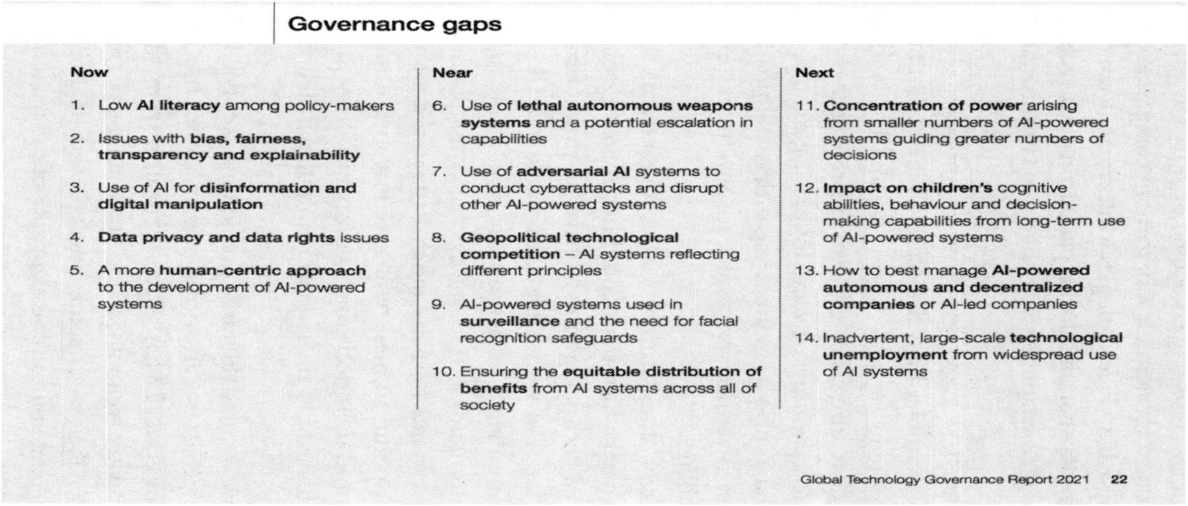

Governance gaps

Now

1. Low **AI literacy** among policy-makers

2. Issues with **bias, fairness, transparency and explainability**

3. Use of AI for **disinformation and digital manipulation**

4. **Data privacy and data rights** issues

5. A more **human-centric approach** to the development of AI-powered systems

Near

6. Use of **lethal autonomous weapons systems** and a potential escalation in capabilities

7. Use of **adversarial AI** systems to conduct cyberattacks and disrupt other AI-powered systems

8. **Geopolitical technological competition** – AI systems reflecting different principles

9. AI-powered systems used in **surveillance** and the need for facial recognition safeguards

10. Ensuring the **equitable distribution of benefits** from AI systems across all of society

Next

11. **Concentration of power** arising from smaller numbers of AI-powered systems guiding greater numbers of decisions

12. **Impact on children's** cognitive abilities, behaviour and decision-making capabilities from long-term use of AI-powered systems

13. How to best manage **AI-powered autonomous and decentralized companies** or AI-led companies

14. Inadvertent, large-scale **technological unemployment** from widespread use of AI systems

Global Technology Governance Report 2021 **22**

Source: 'Global Technology Governance Report 2021', WEF In Collaboration with Deloitte, Insight Report (December 2020), http://www3.weforum.org/docs/WEF_Global_Technology_Governance_2020.pdf, accessed on 1 October 2021.

That said, the acrimonious exits from Google of Timnit Gebru and Margaret Mitchell, two researchers focused on ethics in AI, draw focus to the contradictions sometimes inherent in companies seeking to profit from cutting-edge AI technologies while trying to conduct ethical research on the limits that should be placed on such technologies.[46] Such dilemmas and contradictions are likely to continue and, in fact, likely get worse.

Many countries have moved to limit the negative consequences of AI. China, for example, has criminalized fake news that has been created with AI systems or bots.[47] New Zealand has worked closely with an independent university ethicist to pre-emptively develop a framework for incorporating privacy, human rights and ethics into the process of designing government algorithms. Similarly, the UK has outlined a set of ethical principles to govern the use of facial recognition technology.[48]

Given its likely long-lasting and consequential impact on humanity, philosophers, historians and thinkers are engaging with the complex impact AI technology might have on the human race. For example, Yuval Harari, a world-respected thinker and historian, has observed that 'we are already becoming tiny chips inside a giant system that nobody understands'.[49] He warns that 'this all-encompassing system could understand humans much better than we understand ourselves'. At that point, humans will have lost their authority, their own mindfulness and their decision-making capabilities to algorithms and technology that would make (and manipulate) their choices and decisions.[50]

AI experts have refuted Harari's predictions. Fei-Fei Li, another AI expert, argues that we are decades away from the technology becoming that powerful. Li has drawn optimism from the fact that society has dealt with technology and its incumbent challenges to humanity before. Albeit with some missteps and detours, she avers that humans have come out on the right side of the technology versus humanity debate.

Ultimately, several cross-disciplinary discussions amongst a wide range of stakeholders will be needed globally on the strategic, sometimes existential questions posed by the rise of AI technologies.[51] Accordingly, as Li recommends, AI experts must come together with humanists, historians, artists, neuroscientists, governments, businesses, philosophers, social critics and a wide variety of people from various disciplines to shape the future of AI and how it evolves and how it is used.[52]

A New Global Governance Regime

Unfortunately, few existing formal institutional frameworks are designed to enable these kinds of debates and deliberations on technology governance. Moreover, the rapid pace of development of the internet and its adoption has not afforded the world 'the luxury of a carefully planned global governance framework'.[53]

Current structure of tech governance

The current institutional structure, given its organic evolution, looks like institutional patchwork. Chart 12.3 broadly summarizes the architecture of the institutional internet governance framework today. Various layers or aspects of technology governance are being governed either by institutions such as the UN or the WTO and their arms, or by technology-specific institutions such as ICANN.

Some, like ICANN Board member Danko Jevtović, believe that despite the current system being organic, complex, and sometimes inefficient, it works. Yet, several problems exist with today's tech governance structures. One, the current set of global institutions primarily reflect the global power dynamics of post-world war era. Unless these global institutions adapt to the changed power equations in the world, parallel institutional frameworks might start to assume greater significance.

Chart 12.3 An Architectural Depiction of the Current Internet Governance Ecosystem

Internet governance ecosystem

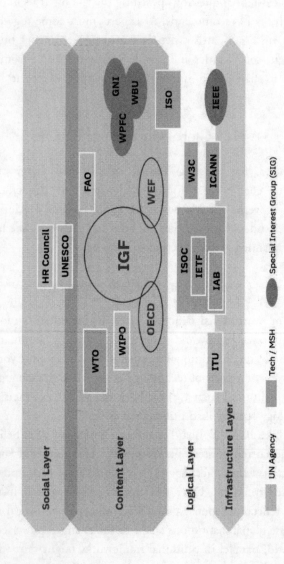

Source: Matthias C. Kettemann, Wolfgang Kleinwächter, Max Senges, 'Implementing Sustainable Digital Cooperation: Towards a #NextGenerationInternetGovernance for the 2020s'. https://www.hiig.de/wp-content/uploads/2019/11/Kleinwa%CC%88chter-Kettemann-Senges-eds.-Global-Framework-for-Cyber-Peace-2019.pdf, accessed on 1 October 2021.

Moreover, these existing institutions were all born in the pre-digital age. Instead of thinking about technology issues afresh, existing global institutions often try to rely on and simply reinterpret existing charters, agreements and conventions. This is often either inadequate or, worse, mischaracterizes the problems completely by applying industrial-era frameworks to modern-day technology-era issues.

Broad-based institutions taking on technology policy issues

Digital-age governance questions often do not fit within the frameworks outlined in the UN Charter and other international conventions. For example, do hacking or cyber-offence attacks constitute a 'use of force' forbidden by Article 2.4 of the UN Charter? And if so, would such an attack trigger Article 51, which allows for the right of self-defence, and in this case, a counter-cyberattack? Should there be a moratorium or a ban on lethal autonomous weapon systems and digital mass surveillance technologies?[54]

To consider all these 'digital-age' governance questions, the First Committee of the UN General Assembly has set up two subgroups, the twenty-five-member Group of Governmental Experts (GGE) and the Open-Ended Working Group (OEWG). These groups are sometimes handicapped by their inability to engage in completely fresh, grounds-up thinking about technology governance. On other occasions, they become entangled in the rivalry between major powers as UN bodies are often liable to. For example, Russia, with Chinese support, had pushed for the creation of the OEWG as a way to get all the 193 member states to participate in technology governance, as opposed to the selective twenty-five-member GGE that was considered more aligned to US views.

Since their inception in 2004, the GGEs have had moderate success. They have focused on the application of international law to cyberspace, and the importance of safeguarding critical infrastructure from state- and non-state-led cyberattacks.[55] The GGE has relied on specific UN Human Rights Council and General Assembly resolutions to push for protection of human rights on the internet, including the right to privacy in the digital age.[56] The OEWG's March 2021 report on cybersecurity and stability has failed to address the root causes of global cyber instability today. Generally, the UN has struggled to ensure the stability and security of cyberspace, let alone deal with broader technology governance issues.[57]

Several international institutions are working on other aspects of digital governance as well. The WTO, OECD and BRI are focused on digital trade and taxation, and the UN Human Rights Council on human rights such as privacy and freedom of speech and expression in the digital age. The International Labour Organization (ILO) has deliberated on the future of work in the digital age, while several others such as United Nations Educational, Scientific and Cultural Organization (UNESCO), World Intellectual Property Organization (WIPO), Organization for Security and Co-operation in Europe (OSCE), OECD, International Telecommunications Union (ITU), and the Council of Europe have started to develop frameworks for the ethical development and regulation of Artificial Intelligence.[58]

Technology-specific institutions

The initial internet governance institutions were based on familiarity, trust, and expertise in technology. But this is changing fast, as technology governance has become a broader, multifaceted issue.[59]

Historically, internet governance was overseen by institutions such as the Internet Corporation for Assigned Names and Numbers (ICANN, founded in 1998), and standard-setting organizations (SSOs) such as the International Telecommunications Union (ITU, founded in 1865 as the International Telegraph Union), and the International Standards Organization (ISO, founded in 1946). In addition, different global organizations focus on developing standards for different aspects of the telecommunications infrastructure, such as the internet (IETF, the Internet Engineering Task Force, 1986), the Web (W3C, the World Wide Web Consortium, 1994), and mobile broadband standards (3rd

Generation Partnership Project, 3GPP, 1998). The 3GPP, for example, is a significant player in the ongoing battle for 5G standards.[60]

In addition, multi-stakeholder-oriented expert groups have been formed outside of the framework of the existing set of multilateral institutions. Launched at the 2017 Munich Security Conference, the Global Commission on the Stability of Cyberspace (GCSC), for example, comprises twenty-six prominent independent commissioners, representing an extremely diverse set of geographies as well as the private, government and civil society sectors.[61]

There are several private-sector or industry coalitions, though these are currently largely US-leaning coalitions. For example, the Cybersecurity Tech Accord (CTA) has 151 technology member companies such as NEC, Facebook, FireEye, GitHub, HP, Microsoft, Cisco and Cloudflare, but seemingly no Chinese or Russian companies.[62] The CTA reports, relying on the US Cyberspace Solarium Commission's findings, view China, Russia, Iran and North Korea as 'the top perpetrators of nation-state attacks', and therefore it is not surprising that no Chinese or Russias companies are members of the CTA.[63] Similarly, a multi-stakeholder collective like the Paris Call for Trust and Security in Cyberspace (PCTSC) brings together almost eighty states, thirty-five local governments, nearly 400 civil society organizations and 700 private sector companies, but, like the CTA, has no representation from countries like China or Russia.[64]

Divergent Approaches to Internet Governance

The Chinese approach to internet governance

China is advancing its own vision for internet governance in these forums while attempting to create a parallel set of internet governance forums. For the last several years, it has carefully worked towards establishing leadership in existing international technical institutions, such as the ITU. It is now attempting to use that to push forward its vision, technology and standards.

The Chinese vision of creating 'a community of shared future in cyberspace' was first outlined during the World Internet Conference (WIC) held at Wuzhen in China in 2014. The vision document, entitled 'Jointly Building a Community with a Shared Future in Cyberspace' (known as the 'Wuzhen Plan'), proposed a multilateral approach, keeping nations as the dominant decision-makers but being open to inputs from other non-state stakeholders. The Chinese want to re-architect the internet's underlying protocols and architecture in a way that would allow countries to control and monitor the internet a lot more.[65] This has been reflected in the new IP plan that they put forth for consideration at the ITU.

Beijing has launched the Global Data Security Initiative (GDSI). Under the GDSI, China seeks to develop a set of international norms and rules on data security that, it argues, take into account the interests of all countries, not a select few.[66] Speaking at the China Internet Governance Forum in 2020, Wang described GDSI as having eight key objectives: first, maintaining open, secure and stable global data and technology supply chains; second, non-use of technology to damage critical infrastructure or steal critical data belonging to other countries; third, prevent the use of information technology to conduct large-scale surveillance of other countries; fourth, avoid requiring domestic companies to store data generated or collected outside, in your own country; fifth, respect the cyber-sovereignty of all countries; sixth, retrieval of cross-border data to help fight crime must be done through proper judicial and other channels (rather than espionage); seventh, avoid setting up backdoors in technology products and services; and eighth, avoid using user's dependence on the tech products for seeking illegitimate gains.[67]

Many of these are oblique criticisms of the model they believe is being followed on the ground by the US government and Big Tech firms. These objectives and principles do indicate several potential areas of common ground with the US (for example, avoiding damage to critical infrastructure), yet some key thorny differences remain. The Chinese vision does not, for example, emphasize the protection of human rights, freedom of expression or privacy. Similarly, China, unlike the US, the UK, Australia and others, wants to avoid setting up backdoors in technology products. And though the GDSI does mention the need to prevent the use of large-scale surveillance of other countries, it is silent on the issue of mass domestic surveillance.

The US-led internet governance approach

The US approach towards internet governance differs from the Chinese in substantial ways on three key dimensions: the Chinese preference for multilateral (focused on nation states) instead of multi-stakeholder forums (that include private actors as well); the Chinese emphasis on a shared future but not shared values such as human rights, privacy or freedom of expression; and the Chinese predilection for top-down internet governance and control versus more decentralized development and control of the internet.[68]

The US has focused on pushing existing institutions that they control or have influence over to take up and shape the internet governance agenda. This includes institutions such as the G7, G20 and technical institutions such as ICANN. Unfortunately, the US had for many years ignored technical standards organizations such as the ITU and IEC. As a result, it lost significant ground to the Chinese, who gradually assumed various leadership roles in these organizations. But now, under the Biden administration, the US is starting to exert its influence and leverage its alliances and partnerships with other countries to gain back control of these institutions.

The G20 is relying on the internet governance approaches put forth by European and American dominated organizations such as the OECD. The G20, for example, has pushed for a human-centred approach to AI, as recommended by OECD guidelines as well. Similarly, in pushing for the worldwide implementation of the G20/ OECD Base Erosion and Profit Shifting (BEPS) package, the G20 has sought to largely follow the work of other specialized West-dominated institutions on the various aspects of internet governance.[69]

The debate over multilateral or multi-stakeholder technology governance

One of the key debates in technology governance has been on whether it should be multilateral or multi-stakeholder governance. Multilateral governance emphasizes the primacy of the role of nation states, while multi-stakeholder governance would allow for the active involvement of non-state stakeholders.

The two major geopolitical rivals and tech powers, the US and China, fall very clearly in different camps on this debate, as do the respective global organizations they support. China and others such as Russia, actually support a multilateral model of technology governance because they are able to secure the support of several developing nations from Central Asia, Africa, Southern and Eastern Europe, and Latin America. Many of these nations support China at these forums in return for significant economic or trade benefits.

On the other hand, the US and its allies support the multi-stakeholder model primarily because that allows them to bring in a wide number of US-leaning private technology firms and technology associations to the table. Moreover, issues of internet or technology governance, such as cybersecurity, cannot be addressed without engaging non-state stakeholders. The reality is that those who build and manage the internet infrastructure and products, and those who conduct and respond to cyberattacks, are as likely to be non-state actors as governments.

The UN, despite being a multilateral institution, has attempted to accommodate other stakeholders in newly formed forums. For example, in 2005–06, the UN secretary-general set up the Internet Governance Forum (IGF) as a 'multilateral, multi-stakeholder, democratic and transparent platform for discussions on internet governance issues'.[70] Since then, IGF summits have been held every year, at varied locations across the world, such as Kenya, Azerbaijan, India, Brazil, France and Germany. The IGF has tried to balance both the approaches by recognizing a 'leading role' for governments in cybersecurity, with the private sector taking the lead in day-to-day technological operational matters.

The geopolitics of institutions: ICANN vs ITU

Technology-specific institutions have historically focused on managing critical internet infrastructure, technology protocols and setting of standards. But in recent years, they have become the battlegrounds for geopolitical conflicts. Two prominent technology-specific institutions—the ITU and ICANN—are currently battling it out for becoming the pre-eminent organization for technology governance in the world.

ITU and ICANN have emerged as proxies for a much wider geopolitical dispute over control of cyberspace between the US and China.[71] ICANN, headquartered in California, was originally set up by the US to oversee the assignment and allocations of domain names and IP addresses. For many years, ICANN operated under the oversight of the US government. In October 2016, ICANN became a completely independent body.[72] This transition of control was welcomed by other countries and seen as a significant step towards multi-stakeholder control of the internet's core infrastructure.

On the other hand, the ITU is an inter-governmental organization that was formed in 1865 and has seen the evolution of telecommunications from the telegraph, telephony to pre-internet telecommunications. ITU has traditionally represented the interests of nation states only and is now a specialized agency of the UN. The ITU has been termed as 'the most important UN agency you have never heard of'.[73] Others see the ITU as 'an anachronistic relic of an earlier era' that has been completely out of touch with the modern internet communications sector and, as a result, is incapable of adapting itself to the needs of the modern era.[74]

The former, more positive view of the ITU is held by China, Russia and others, while the latter, less positive view, has been dominant in the US. The US tech companies see the ITU as a symbol of the highly regulated model of telecom and not representative of the new model of industry-led deregulated communications services.[75] In fact, the US had set up ICANN in the 1990s primarily for this reason. ICANN has indeed not placed government interests at the centre, but instead focused on building a competitive, largely re-regulated, international communications sector in line with industry requirements.[76] But ICANN has been criticized by other countries for attempting to impose US values to the internet infrastructure (even though the US Congress has criticized it for 'pursuing paths that were at odds with American interests'.[77])

The ITU and ICANN have clashed openly as well, with the support of their respective backers. For example, in 2012, the Dubai Summit of the ITU pitted 'revenue-seeking developing countries and authoritarian regimes that want more control over internet content against US policymakers and private net companies that prefer the status quo'.[78] Many of the ITU member countries were eager to have the UN-affiliated ITU govern the internet instead of ICANN. Some, like Russia, pushed for the sovereign right of nation states to regulate the internet within national boundaries.

But almost eighty countries, such as the US, UK, Canada and Australia, dissented, refusing to back these proposals on the grounds that greater government control over the internet could be abused to overly restrict internet content and flows.[79] The US/ICANN camp framed it as the defence of the open internet.[80] But in essence, it did not want countries led by China and Russia to shape internet governance under the UN/ITU banner in ways that were not amenable to US interests.

Still, China and Russia have persisted in their attempts to make the ITU more powerful and reduce the importance of ICANN and other US-controlled organizations in the technology governance space. Along with China and Russia, other nations that value cyber sovereignty, such as the Arab states, support the ITU.

In April 2020, former Russian President Dmitry Medvedev had explicitly stated Russia's opposition to US control of the Domain

Name System (DNS): 'At this time the US fully controls the Domain Name System used to resolve IP-addresses. That's how it happened historically, but simply and bluntly put, it shouldn't be this way.'[81]

Notably, the chairman of the ITU, Zhao Houlin, is Chinese-born. According to some analysts in the US, Zhao has enabled the Chinese influence in the ITU to grow significantly over the last few years, while at the same time actively attempting to undermine the influence of ICANN. As evidence of his open backing of China, US analysts have pointed to Zhao's statements that categorized US security concerns about Huawei's 5G mobile networks as being driven by politics and trade considerations rather than any evidence of actual security lapses.[82] Zhao has urged the international community to give Huawei an equal and fair opportunity.[83]

China, which now sends the largest delegations to ITU meetings, has attempted to use its influence in the ITU to push forth new IP standards. While the Chinese 'New IP' proposal could be seen as promoting an alternative form of top-down, centrally-controlled internet, Huawei has defended it, arguing that the new IP solutions are intended to support future applications such as Internet of Everything (IoE), holographic communications, and telemedicine.[84]

According to Niels ten Oever, a former Dutch delegate at the ITU, while the Western fear of China's vision of a top-down architecture might have some basis, the fact is that internet governance is by and large dysfunctional. There is indeed 'room for an alternative' that could be filled by China's vision, he argues, unless countered by a more compelling US or democratic alternative.[85]

The Americans, especially under the Biden administration, seem to have realized the gravity of the challenge being posed to them by the potential Chinese–Russian dominance of these international technology organizations.[86] For example, if the Chinese and Russians are able to get the new Chinese IP standards accepted, the new internet network could replace the US-designed technological architecture that has underpinned the Web for many decades. This new alternate form of the internet would have a top-down design, and allow greater control, oversight and monitoring of all devices connected to the networks. In such a scenario, some believe that states could choose to implement a Western internet or a Chinese one, raising fears of a 'splinternet'.[87]

The US Secretary of State Antony Blinken has therefore emphasized the importance of the upcoming race to replace ITU Secretary-General Zhao when his term ends in 2022:

> There are relatively few items that are ultimately going to have a greater impact on the lives of people around the world than the ITU post. It may seem dry and esoteric, but it's anything but. And so, we're very, very actively engaged on this front.[88]

On the other hand, Russia's gameplan was outlined by Ernest Chernukhin, the foreign ministry's special coordinator for information and communications technology:

> The optimal option … would be transferring internet management prerogatives specifically to the ITU, as it is a specialized UN body, which has the needed expertise on these issues. This strategic objective may be achieved by electing or promoting the Russian candidate to the position of the ITU Secretary-General in the 2022 elections … and by holding the 2025 anniversary UN Internet Governance Forum in Russia.[89]

Not surprisingly, both the US and Russia have put forth strong candidates for the race. The American candidate, Doreen Bogdan-Martin, is currently serving as the director of the ITU's development bureau. In endorsing her candidacy, Blinken emphasized how 'leadership of the ITU is vital to the US telecommunications industry, as well as US defence, intelligence and aeronautics agencies'.[90]

The US has only held this post at ITU once in its history, from 1960 to 1965. It is, however, campaigning aggressively for support from African, European and Latin American countries. The Russian candidate, Rashid Ismailov, a former deputy minister of telecom and mass communications for Russia, has held senior executive-level positions at Ericsson, Huawei and Nokia. Besides China, he is expected to command significant support from various nations, including the Scandinavian nations.[91]

The future?

Wolfgang Kleinwächter, a former member of the ICANN board and a member of the GCSC, believes the 'senseless' battle between multi-stakeholderism and multilateralism, and the tug of war between ICANN and the ITU has actually 'created unfriendly confrontation and undermined traditional trust'.[92] Unless the major internet nations find ways to work together within these institutions, the agenda of the internet will not move forward. A deeper split in the global institutional framework could further increase the likelihood of a 'splinternet'. ICANN Board member Danko Jevtović worries that in case of such fragmentation, the larger countries might still find their way around it given the scale of their domestic markets, but the innovation ecosystems of smaller countries, like his native country, Serbia, would suffer greatly.

Though the COVID pandemic should have reinforced the need for greater global cooperation, 2020 and 2021 have unfortunately seen most countries adopt a 'My country first' approach, Kleinwächter says. He describes the developments during these last two years thus: 'The global cyberspace was filled with building new barriers, widening old gaps, growing mistrust, nasty cyberattacks, more cybercrime and the first Internet-based drone-war in the Caucasian mountains.'[93]

Still, hope can be derived from the fact the early 2020s have at least seen issues related to the internet, digital economy and cyberspace become the top priority on the agenda of world politics.[94] Major reports and roadmaps, such as the Final Report of the UN Secretary-General's High-level Panel on Digital Cooperation in 2019 and the UN Secretary-General's Roadmap on Digital Cooperation in 2020, as well as major summits like the Munich Security Conference and the Biden-Putin Summit in 2021, have all built the momentum that was required for internet governance to reach centre stage in global governance bodies.

The complexity of internet governance, more than other complex global policy issues, will require a holistic, multi-stakeholder approach. Yet as some governance experts have suggested, bringing all the complex issues related to technology governance into one large 'negotiation package' might not lead to any productive outcome. Neither the UN Convention on the Law of the Sea or the Paris Climate Agreement would be good models for the global negotiation framework for digital issues.[95] Much like the US is bringing out its Big Tech anti-trust bills as five bills instead of an omnibus bill, global internet governance proposals might be easier to pass if proposed in bite-sized forms rather than omnibus forms. Moreover, regional bilateral or multilateral agreements should be worked upon at a regional level, as those might be easier to achieve and can ultimately serve as the basis for large, global agreements.

Internet governance, it would be sufficiently clear by now, is no longer merely about the technical infrastructure or architecture, but has much greater economic, political and strategic implications for our world. As DeNardis has argued, a much more expansive lens of inquiry than even offered by domains such as technology, political science or economics is therefore necessary. The cultural, political, societal and, I would argue, historical context in which these contemporary internet policy issues are arising, necessitate a broad, cross-disciplinary approach to internet governance.[96]

Johanna Weaver, formerly the lead cyber negotiator for Australia at the United Nations and now director of the Tech Policy Design Centre at the Australian National University, concurs. As Weaver explained to me, the current governance structures are broadly doing fine when it comes to strictly technical governance of the internet. But much more work is needed on the tech policy governance front, given the incredibly broad range of issues. Different specialized agencies or groups might be needed for the major issues, such as digital trade, cybersecurity, the data economy, currencies, and emerging technologies such as AI. As Weaver and I envisioned what this would look like, it seemed a village of inter-connected houses, and not one single mansion, was the appropriate analogy.

Serious challenges for cooperation and alignment remain

In some ways, we are in the nascent stages of working out the tech governance models and frameworks. We have some emerging norms, but those norms need to start evolving into institutions. Yet, serious challenges for global digital cooperation and alignment exist, and cannot be wished away.

One, the low barriers to developing and using cyber capabilities means that it is hard to ensure cooperation, compliance and monitoring of such a wide range of state, private and proxy actors. As we saw with the Colonial Pipeline attack or the SolarWinds attack, there are multiple layers of actors involved in these attacks. The hacker groups form and disband at such frequency that it becomes hard to establish norms that would be adhered to widely. This is one key way in which cyberattacks differ from nuclear warfare, where the world has largely dealt with a finite set of known actors.

The anonymous hacker groups see their anonymity and lack of requirements to adhere to any norms or rules set by nation states as their comparative advantage. For them, hacking or ransomware attacks are often more about economic gains than geopolitical ones. Like drug cartels or terrorist cells that generally remain underground, we can expect anonymous hacker groups to continue to act outside the domain of international norms, rules and agreements. The global institutional framework will need to acknowledge and recognize this, and make the necessary provisions for their actions and behaviour. Lessons from the ways the world has tackled the illicit arms and drugs trade, as well as terrorism, would be instructive.

Two, there is 'a dearth of great power cooperation' on this issue, because the incentives are currently not aligned.[97] The Chinese and Russians, given the asymmetric US conventional military superiority, see cyberattacks as a form of 'guerrilla warfare' against the US. In particular, the Chinese see cyberespionage as a way to neutralize the US's likely superior traditional espionage capabilities as well.

On the one hand, there are multiple international cybersecurity platforms where the Chinese and Russians are not members, and feel the US has stacked the odds against them; on the other, China and Russia are increasingly using their influence in the UN to try and shape the new cyber world order in their favour.[98] For example, in December 2019, despite vocal US opposition, Russia managed to win (by seventy-nine votes to sixty) the approval of the UN General Assembly to start drafting a new global agreement to replace the 2001 Budapest Convention on Cybercrime. (Russia and China had not ratified the Budapest Convention as they considered it too intrusive for their model of internet governance.)

Moreover, states often remain opaque about their own defensive and offensive cyber-capabilities, as these often lie with defence or intelligence agencies. That means it is hard to measure adherence to norms anyway, given their activities are clouded in secrecy.

Here, lessons from how agreements such as the Nuclear Non-Proliferation Treaty were reached would be helpful. Then, like today, the great power rivalry was intense, yet the major powers of the time did eventually come together to tackle the core issue. A similar realization of common goals, and achievement of common ground, amongst the major cyber powers is needed. Understandably, elimination of this threat is unlikely. We will have to live with it for a long time to come. But as Kleinwächter has urged, the world needs to 'understand more, fear less'.[99]

Key Conclusions

Behind most of these technology governance issues I have discussed are underlying differences in values that need to be much more widely understood and publicly debated: privacy versus security; law enforcement and data collection objectives; unrestrained competition and warfare versus a basic respect for human life and dignity; widespread access to technology versus strict enforcement of intellectual property rights; freedom of expression and media versus national security; individual privacy versus data-collection-driven business models of internet firms; authoritarian values of preserving absolute control and surveillance versus the democratic values of openness and freedom; and the trade-off between continuous focus on efficiency versus a human-centred focus on providing everyone with fair access and opportunity.[100,101]

Even though the decisions around these competing values impact the daily lives of every connected being on the planet, today, these governance decisions often get taken behind closed doors. Control over many of these technology policy issues lies as much with private tech firms and global institutions as it does with the offices of bureaucrats and parliaments.[102] But there is hardly enough public discussion or debate about the underlying competing values and how they might shape our lives. That needs to change, immediately.

Though it does not seem prepared or ready, the world needs to urgently develop both the intellectual underpinnings and an appropriate institutional framework to address these global governance challenges. The institutional frameworks and mechanisms we set up to address the conflicts over technology governance will determine the outcome of some of the most important public policy issues of our time. As former Indian foreign secretary Vijay Gokhale pointed out to me, 'wars will be fought in rule making' because rule-making powers and capabilities will be critical in deriving commercial and economic advantage from the new technologies.

More importantly, they will shape the evolution and the use of technology in the twenty-first century, and hence our collective economic, political and societal destinies. As internet governance expert Laura DeNardis has argued, how these global competing values get negotiated and resolved will have a significant impact on global connectivity, innovation, security and, really, our societies and the world order.[103] And, quite possibly, the destiny of nations and humans.

Notes

1. Katja Franko Aas, '"Crimmigrant" Bodies and Bona Fide Travelers: Surveillance, Citizenship and Global Governance', *Theoretical Criminology* 15 (2011): 331, https://iow.eui.eu/wp-content/uploads/sites/18/2013/04/04-Rijpma-Background1-Crimmigrant-Bodies.pdf, accessed on 1 October 2021.

2. C.D. Raab, 'The Governance of Global Issues: Protecting Privacy in Personal Information', *New Modes of Governance in the Global System*, International Political Economy Series, Koenig-Archibugi M., Zürn M., eds (London: Palgrave Macmillan, 2006), https://doi.org/10.1057/9780230372887_6.

3. Steven Feldstein, 'The Global Expansion of AI Surveillance', Carnegie Endowment for International Peace (September 2019), https://carnegieendowment.org/2019/09/17/global-expansion-of-ai-surveillance-pub-79847, accessed on 1 October 2021.

4. Ibid.

5. Stephanie Kirchgaessner, 'Saudis Behind NSO Spyware Attack on Jamal Khashoggi's Family, Leak Suggests', *The Guardian* (July 2021), https://www.theguardian.com/world/2021/jul/18/nso-spyware-used-to-target-family-of-jamal-khashoggi-leaked-data-shows-saudis-pegasus, accessed on 4 October 2021.

6. David D. Kirkpatrick, 'Israeli Software Helped Saudis Spy on Khashoggi, Lawsuit Says', *The New York Times* (December 2018), https://www.nytimes.com/2018/12/02/world/middleeast/saudi-khashoggi-spyware-israel.html, accessed on 1 October 2021.

7. Samuel Woodhams, 'This Secretive Firm Has Powerful New Hacking Tools', *Wired* (June 2021), https://www.wired.co.uk/article/phone-hacking-mollitiam-industries, accessed on 1 October 2021.

8. Nicole Perlroth, 'How Spy Tech Firms Let Governments See Everything on a Smartphone', *The New York Times* (September 2016), https://www.nytimes.com/2016/09/03/technology/nso-group-how-

spy-tech-firms-let-governments-see-everything-on-a-smartphone. html, accessed on 1 October 2021.

9. 'Surveillance and Human Rights—Report of the Special Rapporteur on the Promotion and Protection of the Right to Freedom of Opinion and Expression', UN Human Rights Council (May 2019), https:// documents-dds-ny.un.org/doc/UNDOC/GEN/G19/148/76/PDF/ G1914876.pdf?OpenElement, accessed on 1 October 2021.

10. 'UN Expert Calls for Immediate Moratorium on the Sale, Transfer and Use of Surveillance Tools' (June 2019), https://www.ohchr.org/EN/ NewsEvents/Pages/DisplayNews.aspx?NewsID=24736&LangID=E, accessed on 1 October 2021.

11. Ibid.

12. Laura DeNardis, *The Internet in Everything* (Yale University Press, 2020), Kindle.

13. Dana Ford, 'Cheney's Defibrillator Was Modified to Prevent Hacking', CNN (October 2013), https://edition.cnn.com/2013/10/20/us/ dick-cheney-gupta-interview/index.html, accessed on 1 October 2021.

14. DeNardis, *The Internet in Everything*.

15. Sara Morrison, 'How a Major Oil Pipeline Got Held for Ransom', Vox Recode (June 2021), https://www.vox.com/recode/22428774/ ransomware-pipeline-colonial-darkside-gas-prices, accessed on 1 October 2021.

16. 'President Signs Executive Order Charting New Course to Improve the Nation's Cybersecurity and Protect Federal Government Networks', The White House, Washington DC (May 2021), https://www. whitehouse.gov/briefing-room/statements-releases/2021/05/12/ fact-sheet-president-signs-executive-order-charting-new-course-to-improve-the-nations-cybersecurity-and-protect-federal-government-networks/, accessed on 1 October 2021.

17. 'Remarks by President Biden in Press Conference', The White House (June 2021), https://www.whitehouse.gov/briefing-room/

speeches-remarks/2021/06/16/remarks-by-president-biden-in-press-conference-4/, accessed on 1 October 2021.

18. Ibid.

19. Joe Walsh, 'Biden Vows Retaliation on Any Future Russian Hacks on Critical Infrastructure', *Forbes* (June 2021), https://www.forbes.com/sites/joewalsh/2021/06/16/biden-vows-retaliation-on-any-future-russian-cyberattacks-on-critical-infrastructure/?sh=73c6303e1fab, accessed on 1 October 2021.

20. Adam Segal, 'The US–China Cyber Espionage Deal One Year Later', Council on Foreign Relations (September 2016), https://www.cfr.org/blog/us-china-cyber-espionage-deal-one-year-later, accessed on 1 October 2021.

21. Georges De Moura and Tal Goldstein, 'What the Biden-Putin Summit Reveals about Future of Cyber Attacks—And How to Increase Cybersecurity', World Economic Forum (June 2021), https://www.weforum.org/agenda/2021/06/joe-biden-vladimir-putin-summit-cybersecurity/, accessed on 1 October 2021.

22. J.P. Singh and J. Rosenau, eds., *Information Technologies and Global Politics: The Changing Scope of Power and Governance* (SUNY Press, 2002), 2.

23. E. Skolnikoff, *The Elusive Transformation: Science, Technology, and the Evolution of International Politics* (Princeton University Press, 1993), 240.

24. Manu Joseph, 'Governments Will Eventually Defeat Cryptocurrencies', *Mint* (February 2021), https://www.livemint.com/opinion/columns/governments-will-eventually-defeat-cryptocurrencies-11613317872625.html, accessed on 1 October 2021.

25. Eswar Prasad, *The Future of Money: How the Digital Revolution Is Transforming Currencies and Finance* (Belknap Press, 2021), 354

26. Yaya J. Fanusie and Emily Jin, 'China's Digital Currency, Center for New American Security' (January 2021), https://www.cnas.org/

publications/reports/chinas-digital-currency, accessed on 1 October 2021.

27. Mohammad Davoodalhosseini, Francisco Rivadeneyra and Yu Zhu, 'CBDC and Monetary Policy', Bank of Canada, Staff Analytical Note 2020-4 (February 2020), https://www.bankofcanada.ca/2020/02/staff-analytical-note-2020-4/, accessed on 1 October 2021.

28. Raymond Zhong, 'China's Cryptocurrency Plan Has a Powerful Partner: Big Brother', *The New York Times* (October 2019), https://www.nytimes.com/2019/10/18/technology/china-cryptocurrency-facebook-libra.html, accessed on 1 October 2021.

29. Nathaniel Popper **and** Cao Li, 'China Charges Ahead With a National Digital Currency', *The New York Times* (March 2021), https://www.nytimes.com/2021/03/01/technology/china-national-digital-currency.html, accessed on 1 October 2021.

30. Fanusie and Jin, 'China's Digital Currency'.

31. Michael Hasenstab, 'China's Digital Currency Is a Threat to Dollar Dominance', *Financial Times* (April 2021), https://www.ft.com/content/3fe905e7-8b9b-4782-bf2d-fc4f45496915, accessed on 1 October 2021.

32. Paul Krugman, 'The Greenback Rules. So What?', *The New York Times* (May 2021), https://www.nytimes.com/2021/05/28/opinion/us-dollars-currency.html, accessed on 1 October 2021.

33. Michael Hasenstab, 'China's Digital Currency Is a Threat to Dollar Dominance', *Financial Times* (April 2021), https://www.ft.com/content/3fe905e7-8b9b-4782-bf2d-fc4f45496915, accessed on 1 October 2021.

34. Jeanna Smialek and Neil Irwin, 'A Fed President Predicts the Bitcoin Boom Won't Last', *The New York Times* (February 2021), https://www.nytimes.com/2021/02/19/business/rosengren-bitcoin.html, accessed on 1 October 2021.

35. Colby Smith, 'Powell Advances Fed Work on Possible "Digital Dollar"', *Financial Times* (May 2021), https://www.ft.com/content/

ca4875dc-b7ed-463c-aa3f-941694d5f284, accessed on 1 October 2021.

36. Smialek and Irwin, 'A Fed President Predicts the Bitcoin Boom Won't Last'.

37. Eswar Prasad, *The Future of Money*, 355.

38. 'Central Banks and BIS Publish First Central Bank Digital Currency (CBDC) Report Laying out Key Requirements', Press Release, Bank for International Settlements (October 2020), https://www.bis.org/press/p201009.htm, accessed on 1 October 2021.

39. 'Final Report, US National Security Commission on Artificial Intelligence' (March 2021), https://www.nscai.gov/wp-content/uploads/2021/03/Full-Report-Digital-1.pdf, accessed on 1 October 2021.

40. Alex Hanna and Meredith Whitaker, 'Timnit Gebru's Exit From Google Exposes a Crisis in AI', *Wired* (December 2020), https://www.wired.com/story/timnit-gebru-exit-google-exposes-crisis-in-ai/, accessed on 1 October 2021.

41. Will Douglas Heaven, 'Predictive Policing Algorithms Are Racist. They Need to Be Dismantled', *MIT Technology Review* (July 2020), https://www.technologyreview.com/2020/07/17/1005396/predictive-policing-algorithms-racist-dismantled-machine-learning-bias-criminal-justice/, accessed on 1 October 2021.

42. Hannah Murphy, 'The New AI Tools Spreading Fake News in Politics and Business', *Financial Times* (May 2020), https://www.ft.com/content/55a39e92-8357-11ea-b872-8db45d5f6714, accessed on 1 October 2021.

43. Eli Collins and Zoubin Ghahramani, 'LaMDA: Our Breakthrough Conversation Technology', Google Blog (May 2021), https://blog.google/technology/ai/lamda/, accessed on 1 October 2021.

44. 'Global Technology Governance Report 2021: Harnessing Fourth Industrial Revolution Technologies in a COVID-19 World', WEF In Collaboration with Deloitte, Insight Report (December 2020),

http://www3.weforum.org/docs/WEF_Global_Technology_
Governance_2020.pdf, accessed on 1 October 2021.

45. Collins and Ghahramani, 'LaMDA'.

46. Tom Simonite, 'A Second AI Researcher Says She Was Fired by
Google', *Wired* (February 2021), https://www.wired.com/story/
second-ai-researcher-says-fired-google/, accessed on 1 October 2021.

47. 'China Criminalises "Fake News" Created with AI, Bots', Al Jazeera
(November 2019), https://www.aljazeera.com/news/2019/11/30/
china-criminalises-fake-news-created-with-ai-bots, accessed on 1
October 2021.

48. 'Global Technology Governance Report 2021', WEF In Collaboration
with Deloitte.

49. Yuval Noah Harari, 'Yuval Noah Harari on Big Data, Google and
the End of Free Will', *Financial Times* (August 2016), https://www.
ft.com/content/50bb4830-6a4c-11e6-ae5b-a7cc5dd5a28c, accessed
on 1 October 2021.

50. Ibid.

51. Eleonore Pauwels and James Cockayne, 'Artificial Intelligence
and Global Governance: A Thought Leadership and Engagement
Platform', UN University (October 2018), https://ourworld.unu.
edu/en/artificial-intelligence-and-global-governance-a-thought-
leadership-and-engagement-platform, accessed on 1 October 2021.

52. Yuval Noah Harari, YouTube video at Stanford on 'The Upcoming
AI Upheaval', https://www.youtube.com/watch?v=d4rBh6DBHyw,
accessed on 1 October 2021.

53. Laura DeNardis, *The Global War for Internet Governance* (Oxford
University Press USA, 2014), Kindle.

54. Wolfgang Kleinwächter, 'International Law and Cyberspace: It's the
"How", Stupid', CircleID (December 2020), https://www.circleid.
com/posts/20201210-international-law-and-cyberspace-its-the-how-
stupid/, accessed on 1 October 2021.

55. 'Fact Sheet: Developments in the Field of Information and Telecommunications in the Context of International Security', United Nations Office for Disarmament Affairs (July 2019), https://unoda-web.s3.amazonaws.com/wp-content/uploads/2019/07/Information-Security-Fact-Sheet-July-2019.pdf, accessed on 1 October 2021.

56. 'Advancing Cyberstability', Global Commission on the Stability of Cyberspace (November 2019), https://cyberstability.org/report/#appendix-a-norms-adopted-by-the-un-gge-54see-united-nations-general-assembly--report-of-the-group-of-governmental-experts-on-developments-in-the-field-of-information-and-telecommunications-in-the-context-of-inter, accessed on 1 October 2021.

57. Arindrajit Basu, Irene Poetranto and Justin Lau, 'The UN Struggles to Make Progress on Securing Cyberspace', Carnegie Endowment for International Peace (May 2021), https://carnegieendowment.org/2021/05/19/un-struggles-to-make-progress-on-securing-cyberspace-pub-84491, accessed on 1 October 2021.

58. Wolfgang Kleinwächter, 'Internet Governance Outlook 2021: Digital Cacaphony in a Splintering Cyberspace', CircleID (January 2021), https://www.circleid.com/posts/20210108-internet-governance-outlook-2021-digital-cacaphony/, accessed on 1 October 2021.

59. DeNardis, *The Global War for Internet Governance*.

60. Jonathan Coopersmith, JoAnne Yates and Craig N. Murphy, 'Let's Thwart This Terrible Idea for Standards Setting', IEEE Spectrum (March 2021), https://spectrum.ieee.org/tech-talk/geek-life/history/lets-thwart-this-terrible-idea-for-standards-setting, accessed on 1 October 2021.

61. Global Commission on the Security of Cyberspace Website, https://cyberstability.org/, accessed on 1 October 2021.

62. 'Cybersecurity Tech Accord Celebrates over 150 Signatories', Tech Accord (April 2021), https://cybertechaccord.org/cybersecurity-tech-accord-celebrates-over-150-signatories/, accessed on 1 October 2021.

63. The Economist Intelligence Unit, 'Securing a Shifting Landscape: Corporate Perceptions of Nation-State Cyber-Threats', Report of Cybersecurity Tech Accord (February 2021), https://cybertechaccord. org/uploads/prod/2021/02/eiu-cybersecurity-tech-accord-report. pdf, accessed on 1 October 2021.

64. 'Paris Call for Trust and Security in Cyberspace', https://pariscall. international/en/, accessed on 1 October 2021.

65. Murgia and Gross, 'Inside China's Controversial Mission'.

66. Chun Han Wong, 'China Launches Initiative to Set Global Data-Security Rules', *The Wall Street Journal* (September 2020), https:// www.wsj.com/articles/china-to-launch-initiative-to-set-global-data-security-rules-11599502974, accessed on 1 October 2021.

67. 'Global Initiative on Data Security', Ministry of Foreign Affairs of the People's Republic of China (September 2020), https://www. fmprc.gov.cn/mfa_eng/zxxx_662805/t1812951.shtml, accessed on 1 October 2021.

68. Kleinwächter, 'Internet Governance Outlook 2021'.

69. 'G20 Osaka Leaders' Declaration', Japanese Ministry of Foreign Affairs website (June 2019), https://www.mofa.go.jp/policy/ economy/g20_summit/osaka19/en/documents/final_g20_osaka_ leaders_declaration.html, accessed on 1 October 2021.

70. 'Internet Governance Forum, Brochure', http://www.intgovforum. org/multilingual/index.php?q=filedepot_download/4099/481, accessed on 1 October 2021.

71. Phillip Hallam-Baker, 'The Geo-Politics of ICANN vs ITU', CircleID (July 2010), https://www.circleid.com/posts/the_geo_politics_of_ icann_vs_itu/, accessed on 1 October 2021.

72. Craig Timberg, 'Contract Expiration to End US Authority over Internet IP Addresses', *The Washington Post* (September 2016), https://www. washingtonpost.com/business/economy/contract-expiration-to-end-us-authority-over-internet-ip-addresses/2016/09/30/4610adbb-c039-4b92-8637-ebd15874cf12_story.html, accessed on 1 October 2021.

73. Kristen Cordell, 'The International Telecommunications Union: The Most Important UN Agency You Have Never Heard Of', Center for Strategic and International Studies (December 2020), https://www. csis.org/analysis/international-telecommunications-union-most-important-un-agency-you-have-never-heard, accessed on 1 October 2021.

74. Geoff Huston, 'ICANN, the ITU and WSIS and Internet Governance—Part I', APNIC (October 2004), https://www.apnic. net/community/ecosystem/igf/articles/icann-wsis-part-i/, accessed on 1 October 2021.

75. Ibid.

76. Ibid.

77. Jonathan Koppell, 'You Got a Better Idea?', *Slate* (28 November 2012).

78. 'Bitter Struggle over Internet Regulation to Dominate Global Summit', NBC News (November 2012), https://www.nbcnews. com/technology/technolog/bitter-struggle-over-internet-regulation-dominate-global-summit-1C7276578, accessed on 1 October 2021.

79. Lee, 'Has the US Just Given Away the Internet?'.

80. Ackerman, 'The U.N. Fought the Internet'.

81. Ignatius, 'Russia Is Trying to Set the Rules for the Internet'.

82. Miles, 'Huawei Allegations Driven by Politics'.

83. Ibid.

84. Murgia and Gross, 'Inside China's Controversial Mission'.

85. Ibid.

86. Kristen Cordell, 'How to Win at the International Telecommunications Union', Center for Strategic and International Studies (May 2021), https://www.csis.org/analysis/how-win-international-telecommunications-union, accessed on 1 October 2021.

87. Murgia and Gross, 'Inside China's Controversial Mission'.

88. David Ignatius, 'Russia's Plot to Control the Internet Is No Longer a Secret', *The Washington Post* (May 2021), https://www.washingtonpost.com/opinions/2021/05/04/russias-plot-control-internet-is-no-longer-secret/, accessed on 1 October 2021.

89. Ibid.

90. Antony Blinken, 'US Support for ITU Secretary-General Candidacy of Doreen Bogdan-Martin', US State Department, March 2021, https://www.state.gov/u-s-support-for-itu-secretary-general-candidacy-of-doreen-bogdan-martin/, accessed on 1 October 2021.

91. Cordell, 'How to Win at the International Telecommunications Union'.

92. Wolfgang Kleinwächter, 'Framing the Internet Governance Debate: The Long Road to WSIS+20 (2025)', CircleID (March 2021), https://www.circleid.com/posts/20210304-framing-the-internet-governance-debate-long-road-to-wsis-2025/, accessed on 1 October 2021.

93. Kleinwächter, 'Internet Governance Outlook 2021'.

94. Kleinwächter, 'Framing the Internet Governance Debate'.

95. Ibid.

96. DeNardis, *The Global War for Internet Governance*.

97. Christian Ruhl et al., 'Cyberspace and Geopolitics: Assessing Global Cybersecurity Norm Processes at a Crossroads', Carnegie Endowment for International Peace (February 2020), https://carnegieendowment.org/2020/02/26/cyberspace-and-geopolitics-assessing-global-cybersecurity-norm-processes-at-crossroads-pub-81110, accessed on 1 October 2021.

98. Brett D. Schaefer, Dean Cheng and Klon Kitchen, 'Chinese Leadership Corrupts Another U.N. Organization', The Heritage Foundation (May 2020), https://www.heritage.org/global-politics/commentary/chinese-leadership-corrupts-another-un-organization, accessed on 1 October 2021.

99. Wolfgang Kleinwächter, 'Understand More, Fear Less: How the Future of the Internet Can Be Designed with a Human Face', Internet Society (April 2017), https://www.internetsociety.org/blog/2017/04/understand-more-fear-less-how-the-future-of-the-internet-can-be-designed-with a human-face/, accessed on 1 October 2021.

100. DeNardis, *The Global War for Internet Governance*.

101. 'Global Technology Governance Report 2021: Harnessing Fourth Industrial Revolution Technologies in a COVID-19 World', WEF in Collaboration with Deloitte, Insight Report (December 2020), http://www3.weforum.org/docs/WEF_Global_Technology_Governance_2020.pdf, accessed on 1 October 2021.

102. DeNardis, *The Global War for Internet Governance*.

103. Ibid.

PART FIVE

~

THE CHANGING FACE OF SOCIETY AND HUMANITY

'After industrialisation, the shift from the farm to the factory was rapid and painful. With computerisation the new shift from the factory to something new will be still more rapid and in consequence, still more painful.'

—Isaac Asimov, *Asimov's New World* (1983)

'Ultimately, what the tech industry really cares about is ushering in the future, but it conflates technological progress with societal progress.'

—Jenna Wortham, *New York Times Magazine* (2016)[1]

'A technological and economic development which does not leave in its wake a better world and an integrally higher quality of life cannot be considered progress.'

—Pope Francis, *Laudato Si'* (2015)[2]

13

Equality, and I Will Be Free

Technology, Inequality and Society

but I keep on marching forward,
and you keep on coming last.

Equality, and I will be free.
Equality, and I will be free.

—Maya Angelou, *Equality: A Poem* (1990)

Nobel Prize winner Angus Deaton has argued that 'inequality is often a consequence of progress'.[3] Winners try to prevent others from following their lead, removing the ladders behind them, so to speak. Inequality, and often long-term inequality, results. The Industrial Revolution was obviously a time of progress, but mostly for the industrializing nations. The rest of the world didn't get to climb the ladder until much later.

As Erik Brynjolfsson and Andrew McAfee have argued in *Race Against the Machine,* we are again entering a phase of world economic history where, given such rapid technological progress, many might get left behind.[4] The winners might again remove the ladders behind them. The current technological revolution will mean that fewer workers are necessary for the production of the essential goods and services for the world's population. Millions are becoming unemployed or unemployable across various sectors of the economy. This structural displacement—not unlike the one we saw during the industrialization era—will become the single most significant, and divisive, issue in the twenty-first century.[5]

Moreover, the significance of human-led work in the production process will continue to be subsumed by technology. If the mechanical power unleashed by industrialization had replaced humans' performance of physical tasks, the computing power unleashed by the technology era is replacing our exercise of mental or thinking power.[6] Algorithms are already increasingly making the decisions for us. As Nobel Prize winner Wassily Leontief has argued, the role of humans as the most important factor of production will diminish in just the same way tractors and cars eliminated the role of horses and other animals during the Industrial Revolution.[7]

If this era of rapid technological progress, like the Industrial Revolution, comes to be seen as propagating inequality, growing structural unemployment, disproportionately distributing the productivity gains, and de-emphasizing human worth, then social and political movements such as the ones we saw in the aftermath of industrialization will be inevitable. Such an outcome, with rising nationalism and identity politics, populism, and contempt for democratic institutions, might lead to global upheaval.

Part of what this will boil down to is whether the number of jobs destroyed or made irrelevant exceeds the number of new jobs created, and whether those who lose their jobs are able to make the transition to the new economy jobs. This is not dissimilar to the industrial era, when the rural unemployed thronged to industrial towns and cities to find jobs. The estimates and projections for the new economy jobs (and destruction of the old jobs) varies. As a WEF report on Future of Work estimates, eighty-five million jobs may be displaced by a shift in labour from humans to machines, while ninety-seven million new jobs may be created in that transition.[8]

The rise of the new tech elites: The oligarchic moment of the twenty-first century?

As we saw in Part 1 of the book, each structural economic transition has led to the emergence of new elite groups. During the agriculture era, we had seen how engineers that were able to bring groups of people together to work on irrigation or other such projects would rise in stature. And as geopolitics would emerge with the rise in trade and dependency, warriors would be the ones that history would highlight. There is a reason why history remembers emperors and warriors such as Alexander the Great. The rise of global trade started to shift power to the merchants and trading houses (think, the Medicis of Italy), and the feudal lords would slowly begin to fade in importance. The Glorious Revolution of 1688 in Britain, in some ways, would mark that transition as well. Subsequently, it was the industrialists such as Rockefeller and Carnegie that would emerge as the elite class, followed by the capitalists and financiers such as JP Morgan and the Rothschild family.

Technology, today, is leading to the creation of the 'new tech elites'. On the one hand, there is increasing concentration of wealth. I have already discussed the growing astronomical riches of Big Tech firms, and their investors, founders and employees. Rana Foroohar describes the 'incredible economic bifurcation' unleashed by tech, relying on a 2016 report by the Economic Innovation Group that showed that just 75 of America's over 3000 counties constitute over 50 per cent of all new job growth. These counties are the ones that house the large tech firms in cities such as San Francisco, Palo Alto and Austin.[10] That, again, is unlikely to be an isolated phenomenon if we were to look at similar metrics in other countries.

The winner-take-all economics of many new tech products and platforms is a cause of worry from the perspective of rising inequality. It tends to concentrate profits and foster a virtuous (or vicious, depending on your perspective) cycle where the products of the winners—with their monopoly over data—keep getting better. As a result, they get more users and hence more data, and the cycle continues. And therefore, as Kai-Fu Lee predicts, we are likely to 'see greater and greater concentration of these astronomical sums in the hands of a few, all while unemployment lines grow longer'.[11]

Joel Kotkin has described this as the 'oligarchic moment' of the twenty-first century.[12] Kotkin argues that at critical economic transition points, oligarchs tend to rise. The US's transition from a largely agrarian economy to an industrialized power in the nineteenth and early twentieth centuries had witnessed the rise of the John Rockefeller, Henry Ford, Andrew Carnegie and J.P. Morgan. These industrial-era moguls, with 'riches beyond the dreams of Midas', had soon replaced the older mercantile and agricultural elites of pre-industrial America, and wealth had started to accumulate in the cities of America such as New York. The foundations of investment firms such as Goldman Sachs, J.P. Morgan and Lehman Brothers, the largest consumer firms such as Unilever and P&G, publishing and news giants such as Hearst and Reuters, were laid at that time. And soon, many of these industrial leaders would enter politics and become members of the political class.[13]

Kotkin argues that much like the Rockefellers of the previous century, the tech titans of today are enjoying their oligarchic moment. They have taken advantage of the paradigm economic shift in the world to garner and accumulate wealth and power. The emergence of the digital economy is allowing the tech giants to set up the foundations for what are likely to be the economic giants of the next century across various sectors of the economy, including media and entertainment, advertising, trade and commerce, financial services and others.[14]

The new tech laggards: The fear of becoming irrelevant in the twenty-first century

If we peek back into history, we realize that these structural transitions have made some groups irrelevant to the core engines of the economy. For example, Sidney Willhelm pointed out in his book *Who Needs the Negro?* that the automation unleashed by the Industrial Revolution and the subsequent tech era during the twentieth century moved the average African-American 'out of his historical state of oppression into one of uselessness'. Willhelm argues that while African-Americans had remained passively dependent on the white-dominated power structures in previous centuries, this state of uselessness made them 'forgotten', and they would eventually vent their frustration and anger through urban protests in the 1960s.[15] He concludes that the impact of the technological revolution and its ability to transform socio-economic relations, including race relations, will be immense.[16] Rifkin affirms Willhelm's predictions, arguing that today, millions of 'un-skilled and un-needed' African-Americans are 'trapped in a permanent under-class'.[17]

As Isabel Wilkerson has so eloquently put it in *Caste*:

> The hierarchy of caste is not about feelings or morality. It is about power—which groups have it and which do not. It is about resources—which caste is seen as worthy of them and which are not, who gets to acquire and control them and who does not. It is about respect, authority, and assumptions of competence—who is accorded these and who is not.[18]

This will, by no means, be an isolated example in the world. Countries around the world are likely to witness such socio-economic consequences for large communities of people being left behind, and worse, rendered useless in the new economy. One can only imagine that even a country like India—that often might seem like it is one of the beneficiaries of the tech era—might actually witness an immense amount of socio-economic upheaval amongst various groups in the coming decades if this structural transition is not managed well.

The promise of absorption of the rural worker class in the manufacturing and service sectors is being challenged today, as these newer-economy sectors are themselves undergoing their own technology revolution and shedding millions of jobs.[19] As Brynjolfsson and McAfee argue, the industrial-era workers 'want to work, to offer their labour to the economy, but their capacity as workers doesn't match the new environment'.[20] Much of this workforce in the remainder of their lifetimes will be unable to cross over to the new digital economy.

Some groups that have been marginalized in previous eras might continue to remain so. Technology—and specifically the access and exposure through mobile phones and internet—holds promise for hitherto marginalized groups like women. Yet, the promise is not translating into reality. As Reshma Saujani, founder of Girls Who Code, highlighted to me, women still make for a disproportionately small share of STEM-related fields in education at all levels as well as the tech workforce, though there is significant variation amongst countries.[21] Movements such as Girls Who Code are trying to remedy this situation, but Saujani acknowledged that structurally they are facing an uphill battle.

In fact, research by Accenture and Girls Who Code showed that women's share of the US computing workforce is less than 25 per cent, and is actually declining.[22] In 1995, 37 per cent of computer scientists were women; now, it is 24 per cent. Moreover, almost 50 per cent of the women in tech drop out by the age of thirty-five.[23] Not surprisingly, few women are in the top positions at technology firms, and none of the 'top richest' lists includes women. According to an IMF study, women face over a 70 per cent chance of their existing jobs getting automated in the next two decades.[24]

Another technology-driven structural change in the economy and the workforce seems to be the decline of the middle-wage workers. As Susskind has pointed out, since the 1980s, new technologies that have emerged seem to have helped low-skilled workers as well as high-skilled workers, but not so much the middle-skilled workers. The pay and share of jobs for the two ends of the job spectrum have risen much more than for the middle. This phenomenon is known as 'polarization' or 'hollowing out'.

For many countries, the middle is where the majority of jobs used to be. This was the middle class of people with well-paid jobs as secretaries, salespeople, production workers and administrative officers.

But now, a greater share of overall employment in many countries has been assumed by the higher-paid professionals and managers on one end, and low-paid workers such as cleaners, delivery executives, drivers and waiters on the other end. [25]

Is the backlash inevitable?

As historian Niall Ferguson has pointed out, such great disruptions in the past were accompanied by events such as the religious wars of the sixteenth and seventeenth century, as the printing press and the Age of Enlightenment upset the societal orders in ways not dissimilar to how the digital economy is doing today.[26]

As Carl Frey argues in his book, *The Technology Trap*, as a result of the likely social upheaval, many of these technologies run the risk of being blocked. If those who stand to gain from these technologies end up (directly or indirectly) holding political power, then these technologies will spread, else they might face major hurdles in adoption. Frey points to the Industrial Revolution, when for the first time in Britain, political power and influence was with the merchants and the new industrial class. These groups happened to stand to gain the most from mechanization. This confluence meant that the Luddites were unable to stop the juggernaut of industrialization technologies. And Britain avoided what Frey calls the technology trap in which labour-replacing technologies are vigorously resisted for fear of their destabilizing or transformative force.[27]

It is not that the government or political power was consistently on the side of the industrial class. During the Industrial Revolution, there were times when the state, troubled as it was by the growing discontent of resentful workers, stepped in to slow down, if not stop, the spread of some of the inventive technologies.[28] We have discussed the modern-day analogue of this tug of war at length in the chapter on Big Tech versus the state.

Daniel Susskind, in his recent book, *A World Without Work,* has argued that in the past, technological progress has not always led to mass unemployment because machines have not always substituted people. Often, they have complemented their skills so that demand for machine-enabled people has risen. 'Throughout history,' Susskind has argued, 'there have always been two distinct forces at play: the substituting force, which harmed workers, but also the helpful complementing force, which did the opposite.'[29] Frey argues that the Industrial Revolution created as many productivity-enhancing and hence wages-enhancing technologies as it did labour-replacing technologies. Therefore, the proportion of people who were adversely impacted by the labour-replacing technologies was smaller than those who benefited from the other technologies.

But, with the coming AI revolution, the picture may be much more dismal. As Kai-Fu Lee predicts, it will make irrelevant millions of jobs across the spectrum, including accountants, line workers, paralegals, radiologists and the like.[30] This transition will happen much faster— two to three decades at best—than earlier transitions that the world has witnessed. Therefore, the labour-replacing automation technologies being unleashed by AI could cause a worse populist backlash than the one during the Industrial Revolution.

Recall our discussion about the relative importance of the factors of production. If technology and capital help make labour more productive, that will be a good outcome for all. But if technology ends up replacing labour as a factor of production, then countries or groups within countries that are rich in labour are likely to fight back, as the Marxists and Soviets did against capitalism.

The coming socio-political and economic movements

When labour at the bottom end of the spectrum was displaced during the Industrial Revolution, we saw the rise of socio-political movements as well as political parties that focused on defending the rights of the labour class. As Tim Wu has pointed out in his book, *The Curse of Bigness*, industrialized nations at one point seemed to have learnt the lesson after suffering communist and fascist revolutions. After two world wars and a Great Depression, these nations had changed their approach to the economic distribution of gains. They had rejected several economic models such as the laissez-faire's rule of the wealthy, the dictatorial communism of the working class, and fascism's state-led capitalism.

Instead, these nations had then embarked on what Wu calls 'the re-democratization of economic policy and the politics of wealth redistribution'.[31] This path led to the creation of large, well-off middle classes who enjoyed a great stretch of prosperity and reduced the gap between the rich and poor. Through the rising prosperity of the middle class, these countries seemed to have beaten out the communist, socialist and fascist ideologies that had often emphasized the glaring inequalities incumbent in a state of unfettered capitalism.

But as Tim Wu argues, 'that was then, and yet here we are again, as if trapped in a bad movie sequel'. Many of the gains made in the 1960s and 1970s in countries such as the US and UK seem to have been lost. As in the 1910s, there is an increasing re-emergence of a large divide between the rich and the poor. The world's richest now own over 45 per cent of the world's wealth, and the wealth of the world's ten richest billionaires, as we saw, exceeds the GDP of many nations.

Wu argues that the return to concentrated economies, where certain industries and a few companies dominate, is reminiscent of the early twentieth century. This concentration is today obvious—and we discussed this in the context of the Big Tech firms. The growth and scale of the Big Tech firms have much to do with this increasing concentration of our economies.

There are stark similarities of our global economy today to that of the early twentieth century. Therefore, Wu argues, it is not surprising that our politics today seems to be matching the politics of that time. Economic distress experienced by large sections of society—and the widespread anger and demand for something fairer—had led to the communist revolutions in the then-Soviet Union and China and fascist revolutions in countries such as Italy, Spain, Germany and Japan.

Today, similar economic grievances and demands for something fairer are leading to the angry rise of populism and nationalism again. As historian Daniel Headrick pointed out to me, we are witnessing more polarized polities and economies, amid rising criticisms of democracy. It would not be surprising to see the rise of social, economic and political movements, as well as political parties, that focus on preserving the relevance and importance of the middle class. In China, the CCP's recent crackdowns on Big Tech firms are partly a response to the growing economic disparities and resultant grievances amongst certain sections of society.

With rising technological displacement of the middle, as we have seen in the past, we are likely to see the further rise and deepening of the 'welfare state' as well. [32] There will be increasing disagreements and differing views on how to manage and share the economic gains arising from technological progress, how to constrain the rising political and economic power of Big Tech, and finally, how to provide continued meaning and purpose through their work to people.[33] Many of the groups that fear their growing irrelevance in the new socio-economic order might band together, just as proponents of nationalism and Marxism often did across the developing world.

Prof. Mauro Guillen, author of *2030: How Today's Biggest Trends will Collide,* pointed out to me the likelihood of an inter-generational conflict as well, given population trends across the world. The values of the younger generation are inherently different in various dimensions, as Prof. Headrick points out. Managing this structural transition will therefore also become a massive policy challenge for governments and societies.

The way forward: technological or societal progress?

Around the world, a fundamentally transformative, and historically significant, transition is underway, but we have often failed to grasp the potential consequences.

Preventing the consolidation of economic wealth and power is likely to become increasingly important for many nations that do not want a repeat of the early twentieth-century history of communist and fascist movements, ultra-nationalism and wars. But the second half of the twentieth century offers many lessons in how blunting the impact of this economic disparity for the disadvantaged can actually work. Policymakers must learn from these historical analogues.

That is easier said than done, as the economic and political power of the rich and wealthy often blocks attempts of the governments to address such rising inequality. In many nations, these firms and sectors—especially Big Tech firms and the technology sector—are in fact driving rapid economic growth, employment and dynamism in the economy. Attempting to limit the growth of the very companies and sectors that are driving a big chunk of economic growth will be a tough challenge for governments.

To the extent that technology can be designed keeping social equities in mind in the first place, the jobs of policymakers might become slightly easier. MIT economist Daron Acemoglu has called for a re-think on technology that primarily leads to automation and job substitution. Instead, Acemoglu argues, companies and governments should incentivize research on technologies that boost productivity but not necessarily lead to job substitution through automation.[34]

This path towards only automation-driving technologies is not pre-ordained. Countries, Acemoglu argues, should not be taxing labour more heavily than capital either.[35] He offers two key recommendations to course-correct. One, governments must provide incentives to shift innovation's focus towards human-friendly technologies that not just lead to increases in productivity but also generate broad-based good employment and shared economic prosperity. AI and digital technologies, for example, can be used to improve teacher training and promote student-centred and personalized education. Similarly, in healthcare, these technologies can empower nurses, technicians and doctors to provide better services to much broader swathes of people, even in remote areas. Essentially, the mobile phone, and apps such as Zoom, can be considered in this category as well.[36]

While it might seem like hara-kiri to many that Acemoglu is asking government to shape the future development of technology, the reality, Acemoglu argues, is that this is nothing new, either. Governments have always influenced and shaped the evolution of technology and its adoption via tax policies and incentives, support for research in universities and as a buyer of technology. The foundation of the internet due to government-funded research in the US is just one of many examples.[37]

But it is not just the government's role to shape the societal outcomes of technology. Technology, I believe, is not deterministic. Rather, as Philosopher-Professor Philip Brey emphasizes, 'technology, which is itself shaped by society, actively shapes society' as well. It does so 'by influencing the way in which people behave, the way in which social roles, relations and institutions are constructed, and the manner in which culture manifests itself.' I wholeheartedly subscribe to this view of the mutual, two-way relationship between technology on the one hand, and a society and its culture and values on the other.

It becomes imperative, therefore, for societies and cultures to think deeply about the values that they hold dear. Leveraging research in the disciplines of science and technology studies (STS) and the philosophy of technology, Brey pushes for assessing the societal impact of technology by evaluating whether it is contributing to—or detracting from—the realization of the core values that societies hold dear. This assessment and, deeper conversations around this question, is one of the things I hope to spark with this book.

Given the truly global reach of technology today, as Prof. Debora Spar of HBS pointed out to me, we must realize that different societies and cultures will often hold dear a different set of values. It is not surprising then that much of the global conflict over technology today is driven by differences in values among cultures and societies. Essentially, as clichéd as it might sound, values matter.

Regardless, we must remember not to conflate technological progress with societal progress. Societal progress would imply that the technology era would prop up segments of the population such as women, minorities and other disadvantaged groups that have traditionally been economically and socially marginalized. Societal progress would imply less of a narrow-at-the-top pyramid structure, and a system that allows for upward mobility for all, regardless of their starting points. And societal progress would imply a system where technology makes our world sustainable for all.

Notes

1. Jenna Wortham, 'Can Silicon Valley Really Do Anything to Stop Police Violence?', *The New York Times Magazine* (July 2016), https://www.nytimes.com/2016/07/24/magazine/can-silicon-valley-really-do-anything-to-stop-police-violence.html, accessed on 1 October 2021.

2. Pope Francis, *Encyclical Letter Laudato Si' of the Holy Father Francis on Care for Our Common Home*, The Vatican (May 2015), https://www.vatican.va/content/francesco/en/encyclicals/documents/papa-francesco_20150524_enciclica-laudato-si.html#_ftnref92, accessed on 1 October 2021.

3. Angus Deaton, *The Great Escape* (Princeton University Press, 2013), Kindle.

4. Brynjolfsson and McAfee, *Race Against the Machine*.

5. Jeremy Rifkin, *The End of Work*, 2004, quoted in *Race Against the Machine*, Brynjolfsson and McAfee.

6. Quoted in *Race Against the Machine*, Brynjolfsson and Andrew McAfee.

7. Wassily Leontief, 'Technological Advance, Economic Growth, and the Distribution of Income', *Population and Development Review* 9, no. 3 (September 1983): 403–410, https://www.jstor.org/stable/1973315, accessed on 1 October 2021.

8. 'The Future of Jobs Report 2020', WEF (October 2020), http://www3.weforum.org/docs/WEF_Future_of_Jobs_2020.pdf, accessed on 1 October 2021.

9. Foroohar, *Don't Be Evil*.

10. Lee, *AI Superpowers: China, Silicon Valley*.

11. Kotkin, The New Class Conflict.

12. Kotkin, The New Class Conflict.

13. Kotkin, The New Class Conflict.

14. Rifkin, *The End of Work*, p. 79.

15. Rifkin, *The End of Work*, p. 80.

16. Ibid.

17. Isabel Wilkerson, *Caste* (Penguin Books, 2020), Kindle.

18. Rifkin, *The End of Work*.

19. Brynjolfsson and McAfee, *The Second Machine Age*.

20. 'A Complex Formula: Girls and Women in Science, Technology, Engineering and Mathematics in Asia', UNESCO, Document TH/EPR/14/037-200 (2015), https://unesdoc.unesco.org/ark:/48223/pf0000231519, accessed on 1 October 2021.

21. 'Cracking the Gender Code', Joint Report by Accenture and Girls Who Code (2016), https://www.accenture.com/_acnmedia/PDF-150/Accenture-Cracking-The-Gender-Code-Report.pdf#zoom=50, accessed on 1 October 2021.

22. 'Resetting Tech Culture', Joint Report by Accenture and Girls Who Code (2019), https://www.accenture.com/_acnmedia/PDF-134/Accenture-A4-GWC-Report-Final1.pdf, accessed on 1 October 2021.

23. 'Gender, Technology, and the Future of Work', International Monetary Fund, Staff Discussion Notes No. 18/07 (Oct 2018), https://www.imf.org/en/Publications/Staff-Discussion-Notes/Issues/2018/10/09/Gender-Technology-and-the-Future-of-Work-46236, accessed on 1 October 2021.

24. Susskind, *A World Without Work*.

25. Jonathan A. Knee, 'Review: Even on the Internet, What's Old Is New Again', book review of *The Square and the Tower: Networks and Power from the Freemasons to Facebook* by Niall Ferguson, in *The New York Times* (January 2018), https://www.nytimes.com/2018/01/11/business/dealbook/niall-ferguson-book-review.html, accessed on 1 October 2021.

26. Carl Benedikt Frey, in his preface to *The Technology Trap: Capital, Labour and Power*.

27. Susskind, *A World Without Work*.

28. Ibid.

29. Lee, *AI Superpowers*.

30. Tim Wu, *The Curse of Bigness: How Corporate Giants Came to Rule the World* (Atlantic Books, 2020), Kindle.

31. Susskind, *A World Without Work*.

32. Ibid.

33. Daron Acemoglu, 'Re-Making the Post-Covid World', Finance and Development (March 2021), https://www.imf.org/external/pubs/ft/fandd/2021/03/COVID-inequality-and-automation-acemoglu.htm, accessed on 4 October 2021.

34. Ibid.

35. Ibid.

36. Ibid.

14

Technology, Climate and the Future of Our Planet

Even as I was writing this book, early in 2021, Bill Gates launched his new book, *How to Avoid a Climate Disaster*. It was not a pure coincidence that the founder of one of the Big Tech firms had chosen to write a book about the perils of climate change, instead of the perils of the digital age.

Anyone following the news in 2021 has probably seen the headlines be dominated globally by at least two things: COVID-19 and climate. Partly due to the havoc unleashed on our lives by the virus, we have started to take climate change and the urgency for action more seriously. Leadership changes at the helm of the United States might have played a role, as might have the latest assessment report published by the United Nations Intergovernmental Panel on Climate Change (IPCC) in August 2021.[1] Or it might have been the incessant forest fires, floods, droughts, and hurricanes that different parts of the world, from California to Australia, were experiencing.

At the same time as Gates' book was launched, Silicon Valley was abuzz with a new obsession: climate tech. Venture capitalists like Chris Sacca, who had made their fortunes investing in internet technology start-ups and the likes of Twitter were suddenly launching climate tech funds. My partner, Nihal Mehta and I both agree that climate tech seems at a stage not dissimilar to where internet tech was when we started ENIAC Ventures and India Internet Fund over a decade ago. Tech, within the course of the last decade, had gone from being the exciting, new thing to being seen as the new 'Wall Street'. And Mehta rightly pointed out to me that unless in the coming decade, tech was used for good, the criticisms coming from those who had not ridden the wave of the internet would very well be justified.

And so it seemed quite appropriate to me that Gates was writing about climate change, and the Valley was bearing witness to climate tech funds. It is clear that climate will shape tech, and tech will shape climate. As I lay out in this chapter, climate change could very well be the next force of history that would indelibly shape the economic, political, geopolitical, ecological and societal systems of the world.

Importantly, technology today has the potential to contribute to the good of human society. And the goal, in the words of Gates, is clear: how to avoid a climate disaster. Otherwise, the Great Tech Game could very well be derailed, and the very existence of humanity endangered.

～

Just as we face the social strains associated with emerging technologies, we will also be obliged to reorganize our energy economy to ensure that the planet on which all our efforts are founded remains habitable. This will require that we reckon with the consequences of choices made in previous economic revolutions. The industrial era gave humans the ability to harness the energy of coal, steam, and oil and replace human labour with mechanical power. Access to and control of these sources of energy, especially oil, therefore shaped the geopolitics of our world. Over the last two to three centuries, we have lived through and accepted a fossil-fuel-driven economy that has pursued scale and cost-efficiency with little regard for sustainability, our ecology, and in many instances, quality of life.

Today, the scant regard paid to environmental impacts during and since the Industrial Revolution has reached unsustainable levels. Fortunately, contemporary technology offers us alternative energy solutions that might both enable a more sustainable economy and make the century-old geopolitics of oil irrelevant. As in other areas of the current tech revolution, this once-in-an-era energy transition presents both an opportunity, and an urgent need: the choices we make and implement in the coming decades will shape our ecological, economic, political and societal destiny.

The impact of ecological (im)balance on economic growth and our lives

The urgency of this energy revolution is clear: the climate and ecological balance of our planet govern our lives. Natural disasters can wreak havoc, destroy crops, spark civil wars and disputes, and influence migration patterns.[2] If current carbon emissions continue on the existing patterns, millions of people will see displacement, and their living conditions deteriorate sharply by 2050.

Climate change also directly impacts economic growth. Estimates suggest that the world will be poorer by $20 trillion if we do not manage to limit the average global temperature rise to 1.5 degrees Celsius instead of 2 degrees. If we continue on our current emissions trajectory (which will entail a 4-degree rise by 2100), we stand to destroy any chance of economic growth in the world.[3]

More importantly, as climate activist Naomi Klein has pointed out, a temperature increase exceeding 2 degrees might trigger significant adverse climate events such as the disintegration of the Antarctic ice sheet and the submerging of coastal population centres from the Maldives and Netherlands to Mumbai, Shanghai and New York. Similarly, brutal heat waves, droughts, hurricanes, wildfires and other unpredictable climate events can destroy crops, reduce yields (Indian wheat and US corn could plummet by 60 per cent), and disrupt societies and communities.[4]

Even in advance of some of these most drastic effects, high levels of pollution in cities such as Delhi and Beijing have already negatively impacted not just the health of the local residents but also their levels of happiness and their freedom to live as they please. Children in these cities often develop long term lung or breathing problems—an ongoing crisis linked to the density and energy intensity of carbon-dependent cities. Cities, as per a WEF report, contribute 70 per cent of all carbon emissions, and consume 78 per cent of the world's primary energy, despite only covering 3 per cent of the earth's land surface. And currently, the portion of the world's population living in cities is estimated to grow from 54 per cent to 68 per cent by 2050, which will likely exacerbate the problem, unless the pattern of growing energy consumption and carbon emissions is broken.

Economic competitive advantage driven by clean tech

Clean energy technologies are increasingly critical for countries seeking to decarbonize or transition to green economies. The value of the clean energy supply chains is, therefore, at an all-time high.[5] Most global automobile manufacturers have committed to phase out fossil-fuel-based cars within the next decade, and replace them with cleaner options such as electric vehicles (EVs). As in other elements of the tech revolution, various industries can benefit from the shifts occurring as clean tech replaces the fossil-fuel power that drives many manufacturing units. Clean tech offers the advantage of not just being cheaper, but also less volatile in its pricing because of more reliable supplies. And given the decentralized nature of clean energy production in many cases, clean tech could potentially also support the decentralization of our heavily dense urban centres.

Clean tech, as an industry, is, therefore, expected to grow rapidly, and drive an economic competitive advantage for nations. Denmark, for example, is now considered a clean-tech hotspot. It leads the world in wind power, with wind power fuelling 30 per cent of its electricity consumption. Even more impressively, 50 per cent of its total energy produced comes from renewable sources. Denmark has facilitated an attractive ecosystem for innovative clean-tech companies to set up base in Denmark, with Vestas, Siemens Wind Power, Novozymes, Danisco and Haldor Topsøe all having set up R&D centres in Denmark.[6]

In addition to technologies such as EVs, the coming 5G and AI revolutions are going to have a particularly strong impact on the energy technology transition. 5G- and AI-enabled smarter cities, power grids, transport and energy appliances will facilitate a significant reduction in energy usage and improved distribution efficiency. These are all examples of a broader trend, where energy technology is intersecting with information technology. As Thomas Friedman suggested in his book, *Hot, Flat and Crowded,* this combination of energy technology with information technology might offer potential solutions for the massive energy crisis that the world is faced with -and might suggest possible strategies for nations to situate themselves in the new economy.[7]

Energy poverty, tech poverty and the geo-economic disadvantage

Just as the world's superpowers address energy concerns with enormous strategic investments, many of its poorest citizens face energy concerns of their own in the form of energy poverty. Energy poverty, as Friedman terms it, refers to those who don't have access to electricity, and as a result, do not have access to the internet and other tools that have led to the 'flattening' of the world.[8] Energy poverty, most prevalent in Africa and South Asia, then creates what I call 'tech poverty'. This tech poverty—a lack of access to technology or knowledge of that technology—will therefore lead to an immense geo-economic disadvantage for many nations and regions of the world.

If the energy poverty is not alleviated, large swathes of South Asia and Africa will remain disconnected from the trade networks, technology supply chains, education and healthcare opportunities, communication networks, and all the other benefits with which the technology-haves will continue to climb further on the economic ladder. In fact, the double whammy of energy and technology poverty will widen the economic gap, irreversibly.

Addressing energy and tech poverty, then, are crucial social, humanitarian and geopolitical goals. But this urgency must be managed with an awareness of the massive energy and carbon costs of the internet. As discussed earlier, the basic infrastructure underlying the internet are the deep undersea cables, and the mammoth data centres that tech firms are increasingly building across the world. These data centres, in turn, require large amounts of energy to power them, and then power both servers and cooling mechanisms. (This was one of the reasons why Big Tech firms have built their data centres in Ireland and other parts of Northern Europe that have cooler climates).

For this reason, expanding the digital economy stands to dramatically increase global energy consumption. For instance, with 23 per cent of global data centres, Chinese data centres' energy consumption is expected to alone contribute 160 million tons of CO2 emissions by 2023, which is the equivalent of the annual emissions of the UK's passenger cars.[9] In addition to data centres, new emerging technologies such as AI and bitcoin are guzzlers of energy. Training AI models requires energy-hungry computer processing power, while mining bitcoins is similarly energy-intensive. At the same time, e-commerce has its own increasingly large carbon footprint. E-commerce has made convenience the game, but its reliance on one-at-a-time delivery networks and disposable packaging pose substantial carbon and ecological risks.

If increasing economic reliance on digital technology, then, is not coupled with more sustainable energy systems, it will create catastrophic carbon outcomes—the digital and energy revolutions must occur together. Fortunately, countries like Denmark are leading the move towards low-carbon or carbon-free data centres. Not just Facebook, but many other tech majors are setting up data centres worth billions of dollars in Denmark, due to top-of-the-line Danish clean-energy infrastructure facilities.[10]

These new technologies—and the applications and businesses that they spawn—are entailing energy choices and decisions that will have a long-lasting impact. While we are still early enough in the internet revolution, we—especially Big Tech firms and governments—must ensure that more responsible and sustainable energy choices are made in this economic revolution than in the previous.

From brown to green: The changing geopolitics of the twenty-first century

Climate change has for several years now been a major global governance challenge for the world, a source of geopolitical tension, and a national security threat. Climate cooperation between developed and developing nations has been difficult to achieve, despite various authoritative reports such as the first '1.5°C Report' of the UN's Intergovernmental Panel on Climate Change (IPCC) in 2018, highlighting the enormity of the risk.[11] David Wallace-Wells, in his book, *The Uninhabitable Earth,* has estimated that damages from climate-change-driven incidents could exceed $600 trillion—more than twice the existing global wealth. He has argued that with the rising incidence of such events, conflict and warfare could double.[12]

Most analysts agree that the fossil fuel industry is slowly being phased out. Oil demand is expected to have peaked already, and the clean tech industry is growing rapidly. Previous International Energy Agency (IEA) analysis had predicted the flattening of oil demand around 2030, but factors such as the COVID pandemic, rapidly falling costs of renewable sources, continuous oil price volatility, and rise of technologies such as EVs has expedited the change.[13]

Our current global energy economy, then, is undergoing a once-in-an-era transition from brown hydrocarbon-based fossil fuels to green renewables. Previous energy transitions—for example, the US's shift from wood to coal in the late nineteenth century—were similarly driven by technological advancement.

This transition away from oil will have massive geopolitical and geo-economic implications—and not just for oil exporters and importers. For over a century, nations possessing oil and gas reserves had power and influence in the world. Major wars and conflicts were driven by the need to secure access to oil.[14] But in the coming transition, oil exporters that have failed to diversify their economy will become extremely vulnerable and domestic instability might erupt. In contrast, renewables are more widely produced than oil, and are not dependent on strategic transit routes. Therefore, the traditional geopolitics of oil (overdependence on dominant fuel suppliers or the threat of disruption of strategic transit routes) will gradually fade away.[15]

Yet, geopolitics of energy will not go away. Its colour might change though: from brown to green. Climate change has already become an arena of great power politics. The great US–China decoupling and the open conflict brewing between the two countries have put climate change collaboration at risk. When the US (the second-largest source of emissions) under President Trump withdrew from the Paris Accord, it made it easier for even China (the largest source of emissions) to withdraw to the sidelines.

The US has been increasingly ceding ground in the clean technology sector to China. China is already home to over 50 per cent of the world's EVs, 60 per cent of solar panels, and 90 per cent of the world's critical minerals. China is currently dominating the global supply chains for solar photovoltaics (solar PV), wind turbines, lithium-ion batteries and EV technologies, and its exports to the European Union, the United States, Japan and other OECD nations have surged in recent years.[16]

As former foreign secretary of India Ranjan Mathai has pointed out, the geographical concentration of these transformative minerals could be even worse than oil, not to mention the volatility of price and supply. He has surmised, therefore, that geopolitical competition driven by nations' quest for energy independence will continue. Matt Tilleard, partner at Crossboundary Africa, shared an alternative view with me. According to him, the future of energy geopolitics will depend on what type of battery wins out in clean tech, which in turn will shape the demand for minerals. There is a likelihood, he argues, that some of the rare earths that today seem critical might not be as valuable if different battery technologies emerge.

In any case, US attempts at decoupling might or might not be effective when it comes to progress in the clean-tech space. Chinese firms are so firmly entrenched in the global supply chain for clean tech that any decoupling or attempts to exclude China from the global clean-tech sector would result in major roadblocks in the global clean-tech journey.

The US Congress, driven in part by a desire to beat China in clean-tech innovation, are making a green funding push; for example, $20 billion for semiconductor research and manufacturing in the US, and $110 billion over ten years into energy technology, AI, and materials science, among other areas. Such bills and serious investments have been tagged as 'Made in America 2025', with clear parallels to China's 'Made in China 2025' plan.[17]

It is critical for the world's two climate superpowers to find ways to simultaneously compete yet collaborate.[18] Indeed, some analysts have wondered whether this conflict might have a silver lining for climate change. Much like the Cold War led both sides to compete aggressively on technological innovation and yielded technology breakthroughs such as Lasik eye surgery, LED lighting and early solar cells, the current stand-off between the US and China could also, according to some, help 'foster a race to the top' in energy and clean-tech innovation.[19]

How Can Climate Tech Help?

Fortunately, the pace of innovation in energy technology is also high, and many emerging technologies have the potential to transform the energy sector, making it cleaner and renewables-focused. This transformation will become a critical driver of competitive advantage for nations, economically and geopolitically. If we follow the money, we get several clues for how and where technology may play a role. Climate tech funds today are investing in certain broad themes: renewable energy generation and access; low-carbon transport and mobility; energy-efficient buildings, cities and industries; better forest and land use; waste management and resource conservation; greenhouse gas (GHG) capture and storage; health, food and water security; and climate and earth data generation and analysis.

These efforts will rely both on leveraging existing technologies, and the development of new ones. AI algorithms and a 5G-networked economy can significantly optimize grid performance and efficiency through improved supply and demand forecasting.[20] Specifically, AI-based predictions could help optimize combinations of renewable and traditional energy planning, and result in significant cost-savings and optimized consumption.[21]

Technological innovation can hopefully combat the very threats to biodiversity that it in many ways has helped create during the industrial era. John O'Brien has explained, technology can help reverse the biodiversity destruction caused by the quest of humans for higher standards of living for a rapidly growing human population.[22] According to experts, the more biodiversity a nation has preserved, the greater the resilience of its population and environment to emerging biological, ecological and health threats. This is especially critical for countries such as Indonesia and Brazil, whose territories contain some of the richest biodiversity hotspots in the world.

Real-time data—acquired through technologies such as hyperspectral imagery of landscapes, cameras, aerial and aquatic drones, remote sensing and rapid alert systems—on the health and vibrancy of habitats and the biological processes going on in biodiverse habitats could help. Future advancements, such as brain mapping of species or use of robots in sensitive environments, and even genetic technologies such as CRISPR, could help protect vulnerable species.[23]

On the other hand, new technologies such as green hydrogen could play a critical role. Experts consider the possibility of converting renewable energy into hydrogen as a potential game-changer. Hydrogen energy storage has much longer discharge times than existing batteries. Governments and corporates globally are setting ambitious goals for reducing emissions and making such technological shifts. In September 2021, Mukesh Ambani, chairman of the Indian oil-to-telecom conglomerate, Reliance Industries, reiterated his commitment to invest INR 75,000 crore (approximately US$ 100 billion) in green energy facilities as part of the company's shift towards renewables. India could meet its 1–1–1 target for green hydrogen, he claimed, meaning that India could become the first country to achieve a cost of $1 per kilogram of green hydrogen in one decade.

Transitions to these new energy technologies will become a critical driver of competitive advantage for nations, economically and geo-politically. At the same time, hopefully, as start-ups and entrepreneurs look at solving what is being considered as the most pressing challenge facing humans today, one expects, and hopes, that technology can help fasten the reversal of the damage we have done over the last few centuries.

The New Space Frontier: Looking beyond our planet

Just a few months after Bill Gates launched his book on climate, Amazon founder Jeff Bezos travelled to space and back aboard his rocket ship, *New Shepard*. As I showed my daughters the footage of Bezos landing back on Earth, it felt like a historic moment. Amid all the criticism of such wasteful 'joy rides', Bezos outlined his vision: 'We need to take all heavy industry, all polluting industry and move it into space, and keep Earth as this beautiful gem of a planet that it is.'[24] Both Bezos and Gates, it seems, were coming at the same issue, from different angles.

Other intersections of technology, resource usage, and existential species-scale questions will be encountered as we continue our exploration of space. Since 1967, outer space had been governed by the 1967 Outer Space Treaty (OST), which was signed by 132 countries, including the United States, Russia and China. This treaty foresaw the dangers of outer space becoming the next frontier for colonization and resource extraction. Remarkably agreed upon at the height of the Cold

War, OST designated outer space as common heritage and permitted only its peaceful exploration. No claims of sovereignty could be made by any country.

In 2015, though, President Obama signed into law the 2015 SPACE Act, which, along with an April 2020 Executive Order (EO) signed by President Trump, started to change this understanding. Outer space is no longer being viewed by the US as the global commons. Instead, the US has begun to promote public and private sector mining of the Moon and other planets, effectively supporting the recovery and use of resources from outer space.[25] The EO paved the way for private commercial exploration of outer space, an endeavour that has for many years obsessed entrepreneurs such as Jeff Bezos, Elon Musk and Richard Branson. In December 2019, notably, the US established a Space Operations Command as the sixth independent branch of the US armed forces.[26]

The week prior to the release of the EO, NASA had released its own plan for sustained lunar exploration as part of the Artemis Program, in which in situ resource utilization was envisioned as a key enabling factor. That is to say, that the utilization of space resources to further grow the commercial space economy.[27] The Artemis Program sees the Moon as the gateway to the rest of the solar system and envisions a 'sustained long-term presence on the lunar surface'. It can serve as a source for ground-breaking discoveries itself, but also serve as the testing ground for deep-space systems and as a pit stop for the human mission to Mars.[28]

These statements and plans, reminiscent as they are of the early days of the colonial era, demonstrate the US's keenness to actively partner with private players such as SpaceX and Boeing, and establish a first-mover advantage in space—possibly as a way to one-up China, which is building its own lunar and outer space exploration capabilities.[29] While the appropriation of or claims of sovereignty over the Moon are still unlikely, leading nations are increasingly considering the Moon as a space to advance their own interests. In the absence of global regimes, certain countries such as Luxembourg have followed the US lead and already put in place national regulatory frameworks that make ownership of space resources possible, and provide legal protection to investors, explorers and miners.[30]

Commercially and geopolitically, these interests might be substantial. As Sheetz points out, the resources on the lunar surface, such as water ice and rare-earth metals such as yttrium and neodymium, are valuable for enabling deeper space explorations and for other applications such as laser technologies and other emerging technologies. They are estimated to be valued at tens of trillions of dollars.[31] According to a WEF White Paper, this renewed race to capture lunar and outer space resources creates a potential for new space resource wars.[32]

These resource considerations and tensions will, of course, interact with similar terrestrial concerns. The US's interest in the Moon's reserve of rare earths, for example, may be linked to its desire not to depend on China for any critical pieces in its own global supply chain. As Ramin Skibba points out, platinum-group metals in space may end up being the new oil, and lead to geopolitical and astropolitical conflicts.[33]

Key Conclusions

Today, we are at the beginning of the end of the fossil-fuel era, and technology is playing a major role in that transition. The ongoing shift to a cleaner, greener economy is as massive a shift as the one we saw during the industrial era. As our planet descends into the Anthropocene Epoch, climate change, biodiversity, the environment and our ecology—effectively, the state of our planet—and our choice of energy sources will greatly shape the future of our world.

We continue to suffer from the choices the world's industrializing nations made during the industrial era, and the accompanying emphasis on mindless consumption, convenience and unsustainable growth. The energy and technological choices the leading economies of the technology era make today will shape the climate and our ecology for a long time. Technology must be leveraged fully to fix the mistakes we have made in the previous era. But most importantly, our lifestyle,

values and consumption choices—and not just our energy sources—
must reflect this renewed emphasis on a more consciously sustainable
economic model. We must no longer take the ecology, the climate and
biodiversity for granted.

Notes

1. 'AR6 Climate Change 2021: The Physical Science Basis',
   Intergovernmental Panel on Climate Change (August 2021), https://
   www.ipcc.ch/report/ar6/wg1/#FullReport, accessed on 1 October
   2021.

2. David Wallace-Wells, *The Uninhabitable Earth* (Penguin Books Ltd,
   2019), Kindle.

3. Ibid.

4. Naomi Klein, *This Changes Everything* (Penguin Books Ltd, 2014),
   Kindle.

5. Sarah Ladislaw et al., 'Industrial Policy, Trade, and Clean Energy
   Supply Chains', CSIS–Bloomberg NEF Report (February
   2021), https://csis-website-prod.s3.amazonaws.com/s3fs-public/
   publication/210224_Ladislaw_Industrial_Policy.pdf?DRja.
   V6axwyBE_PV6Chmdi5k2VqOq33n, accessed on 1 October 2021.

6. 'Denmark—The CleanTech Hotspot in Europe, A Factsheet', https://
   investindk.com/publications/danish-cleantech-industry, accessed on
   1 October 2021.

7. Thomas Friedman, *Hot, Flat and Crowded: Why We Need a Green
   Revolution—and How It Can Renew America*, (Farrar, Straus and
   Giroux, 2008).

8. Ibid.

9. Anna Holzmann and Nis Grünberg, '"Greening" China: An Analysis
   of Beijing's Sustainable Development Strategies', *Meris China
   Monitor* (January 2021), https://merics.org/en/report/greening-
   china-analysis-beijings-sustainable-development-strategies, accessed
   on 1 October 2021.

10. 'Google Joined Other Big Tech Giants with a 4.5-Billion-Dollar Data Centre in Denmark', Invest in Denmark, Ministry of Foreign Affairs of Denmark, https://investindk.com/cases/google-joined-other-big-tech-giants-with-a-4-5-billion-dollar-data-centre-in-denmark, accessed on 1 October 2021.

11. Todd Stern, 'Can the United States and China Reboot Their Climate Cooperation?', Brookings (September 2020), https://www.brookings.edu/articles/can-the-united-states-and-china-reboot-their-climate-cooperation/, accessed on 1 October 2021.

12. Wallace-Wells, *The Uninhabitable Earth*.

13. Edoardo Campanella, 'After Decades of Wrong Predictions, Oil May Finally Be Peaking', ForeignPolicy (July 2020), https://foreignpolicy.com/2020/07/13/peak-oil-pandemic-predictions/, accessed on 1 October 2021.

14. James Londale, 'What Will the End of Oil Dependence Mean for Geopolitics?', BBC News (January 2020), https://www.bbc.com/news/world-50974609, accessed on 1 October 2021.

15. Paul Stevens, 'The Geopolitical Implications of Future Oil Demand', Chatham House (August 2019), https://www.chathamhouse.org/sites/default/files/2019-08-14-FutureOilDemand.pdf, accessed on 1 October 2021.

16. Sarah Ladislaw et al., 'Industrial Policy'.

17. Scott Tong, 'Harvesting Ill Will: Can the US and China Turn a Budding Cold War into a Clean Energy Space Race?', Wilson Center Insight & Analysis (September 2020), https://www.wilsoncenter.org/article/harvesting-ill-will-can-us-and-china-turn-budding-cold-war-clean-energy-space-race, accessed on 1 October 2021.

18. Ibid.

19. Sarah Ladislaw and Nikos Tsafos, 'Race to the Bottom: The Case for a New US International Energy Policy', Center for Strategic and International Studies, https://csis-website-prod.s3.amazonaws.com/s3fs-public/publication/200706_SRF_RacetotheTop_WEB_v2FINAL.pdf, accessed on 1 October 2021.

20. Ben Warren and Arnaud de Giovanni, 'If Green Energy Is the Future, How Can Technology Lead the Way?', EY Report (November 2020), https://www.ey.com/en_us/power-utilities/if-green-energy-is-the-future-how-can-technology-lead-the-way, accessed on 1 October 2021.

21. Thierry Mortier, 'Why Artificial Intelligence Is a Game-Changer for Renewable Energy' (November 2020), https://www.ey.com/en_us/power-utilities/why-artificial-intelligence-is-a-game-changer-for-renewable-energy, accessed on 1 October 2021.

22. John O'Brien, 'Technologies for Conserving Biodiversity in the Anthropocene', *Issues in Science and Technology* XXXII, no. 1 (Fall 2015), https://issues.org/perspective-technologies-for-conserving-anthropocene-biodiversity/, accessed on 1 October 2021.

23. Ibid.

24. Paul Rincon, 'Jeff Bezos Launches to Space Aboard New Shepard Rocket Ship', *BBC News* (July 2021), https://www.bbc.com/news/science-environment-57849364, accessed on 1 October 2021.

25. Encouraging International Support for the Recovery and Use of Space Resources, Executive Order 13914 of April 6, 2020, Federal Register Vol. 85, No. 70 Friday, April 10, 2020, https://www.govinfo.gov/content/pkg/FR-2020-04-10/pdf/2020-07800.pdf, accessed on 1 October 2021.

26. United States Space Force, official website, https://www.spaceforce.mil/About-Us/About-Space-Force/Mission/, accessed on 1 October 2021.

27. Ian A. Christensen and Christopher D. Johnson, 'Putting the White House Executive Order on Space Resources in an International Context', *The Space Review* (April 2020), https://www.thespacereview.com/article/3932/1, accessed on 1 October 2021.

28. 'NASA's Plan for Sustained Lunar Exploration and Development', a report, https://www.nasa.gov/sites/default/files/atoms/files/a_sustained_lunar_presence_nspc_report4220final.pdf, accessed on 1 October 2021.

29. Michael Sheetz, 'NASA Chief Bridenstine Talks SpaceX and Boeing, Returning to the Moon and Life on Mars', CNBC (February 2019), https://www.cnbc.com/2019/02/14/nasas-bridenstine-on-spacex-and-boeing-the-moon-and-life-on-mars.html, accessed on 1 October 2021.

30. 'Luxembourg, a Rising Star in the Space Industry', Deloitte, https://www2.deloitte.com/lu/en/pages/technology/articles/luxembourg-space-industry-companies.html, accessed on 1 October 2021.

31. Michael Sheetz, 'NASA Chief Bridenstine Talks SpaceX and Boeing'.

32. 'Navigating the Geopolitical Landscape A Mining and Metals Sector Perspective', WEF White Paper (July 2016), http://www3.weforum.org/docs/WEF_WP_Navigating_the_Geopolitical_Landscape.pdf, accessed on 1 October 2021.

33. Ramin Skibba, 'Mining in Space Could Lead to Conflicts on Earth', Nautilius (May 2018), https://nautil.us/blog/-mining-in-space-could-lead-to-conflicts-on-earth, accessed on 1 October 2021.

15

Bio-Technology, Genetic Engineering and the Future of Humanity

The summer of 2019 saw the IPO of tech companies such as Lyft and Zoom. Accompanying them was the stock market debut of a company called Beyond Meat. Beyond Meat, a Los Angeles–based producer of plant-based meat substitutes, was founded in 2009 with the mission of combating—wait for it—climate change. Backed by a slew of celebrities and top-tier venture capital firms, Beyond was valued at $3.8 billion on the day of its IPO; by June 2021, its market cap had almost tripled.

Just a few months after Beyond's IPO, a friend, an investor at a Singapore-based investment firm, sent me an image of a plant-based veggie burger made by a company called Impossible Foods. He was raring to get Impossible to come to India. By April 2021, news reports were suggesting that Impossible, Beyond's competitor, was preparing to go public through an IPO that would value it at roughly $10 billion.[1]

Both Beyond Meat and Impossible Foods have been riding high on the trend towards plant-based protein. Their products are now available at over 18,000—20,000 stores each, including prominent chains such as White Castle and Burger King that now sells Impossible Whoppers.

They are part of what is now being called the bio-economy.

~

Biotechnology is not as much talked about, maybe, as information technology in today's world. Yet, just as information technology is drastically changing our world, biotech is actually transforming fields ranging from medicine to military power to agriculture. If the great advances in the nineteenth century resulted from a mastery of chemistry and electricity, and in the twentieth century from a mastery of physics, then advances in biology could, according to some, hold the same promise and transformational potential in the twenty-first century. The Great Tech Game, so to say, could very well become the Great Bio-Tech Game.

Bio-tech—or more specifically, research and innovation in the life sciences and biotechnology enabled by advances in engineering and computing—is driving the evolution of what has been termed the bio-economy. These advances have medical, agriculture and industrial applications. As the US National Academy of Sciences, in a 2020 report, states, the US bio-economy is today shaping Americans' everyday lives 'in terms of the food they eat; the health care they receive; the quality of their environment; and the fuels, materials, and products they consume'.[2]

The report estimated the US bio-economy in 2016 at about $1 trillion,[3] putting it at roughly half of the size of the current US digital economy. A broader definition would put the number at $1.4 trillion, or roughly 7.5 per cent of the entire US GDP. Examples of products generated by the bio-economy would include GM crops like salmon, drugs, medical devices, biofuels and bio-based plastics.

Synthetic biology (or 'synbio'), in particular, has been compared with the internet: if the internet was about bits, synbio is about atoms. Synbio, considered as an enabling technology, could yield products such as lab-grown bacon, plant-based meat (think Beyond or

Impossible burgers), biosynthetic fabric-based clothes, and biofuels for cars. The disruption, as a McKinsey report put it, 'extends well beyond healthcare' into food, agriculture, energy and consumer products.[4]

The parallels with the digital economy don't end there. Bio-tech capabilities, much like software engineering and data science, are increasingly being seen as a source of economic competitive advantage as they drive a whole new mode of production. Much like digital technologies, the powerful technologies driving the bioeconomy today also lead to national security and economic risks and complexities. Consequently, the technology's rapid progress has raised important economic, geopolitical, social, ethical and regulatory considerations, and demonstrated an urgent need for its global governance.

Ethics of genetic engineering

One of the most prominent and widely debated components within bio-tech has been genetic engineering. With modern genetic technology, a new powerful, transformative prospect has cropped up: genetic editing of human genes. The CRISPR technology has allowed human beings to now do genetic editing (inserting, deleting and replacing pieces of DNA) much more precisely, simply, efficiently and cheaply.[5] However, like many other emerging technologies, gene editing prompts deep concerns even as it promises great rewards. On the one hand, it has the potential to transform various sectors, including healthcare, energy and agriculture.[6] It can help treat various genetic disorders, especially those that are caused by mutations in single genes.

But profound ethical issues start to arise when these genetic modifications are made to germ-line cells such as sperm, eggs and embryos. These germline modifications could be passed on to future generations, meaning that genetic modification technology offers the ability to make permanent modifications to human DNA and to select the traits we want – an immense change to the essence, and future, of humanity.[7]

Moreover, genetic editing technology is increasingly being utilized to develop modern, deadly bioweapons. The COVID-19 virus, whether lab-made or not, has shown us a preview of the havoc pathogens can wreak on our world. Dr Jennifer Doudna, winner of the Nobel Prize in 2020 for her work on CRISPR,[8] has expressed concerns about the slippery slope journey from disease-focused applications of the technology to 'less compelling or even troubling implications'.[9] The ease, simplicity, efficiency, versatility and wide availability of gene-editing technology, she has pointed out, leads to the possibility of multiple potential misuses. Ultimately, like AI or other emerging technologies, genetic engineering will require careful consideration and oversight.[10]

As chart 15.1 illustrates, two dimensions are key in analysing the ethics of the uses of genetic engineering: purpose of editing (therapy vs enhancement), and level of editing (somatic is non-inheritable editing while germline is inheritable editing).

Somatic therapy is largely considered acceptable, whereas germline enhancement is not. While somatic therapy can help treat diseases such as leukaemia, germline enhancement fills no nameable medical need. In fact, germline enhancement—changes to inheritable genes designed to increase physical or cognitive capacities—could generate new, and deep, forms of inequality as certain groups of humans might get profound power and change our society in unpredictable ways. The other two quadrants—somatic enhancement and germline therapy— pose less drastic ethical and practical problems of their own.

At present, human genetic trait selection is generally supported only if it helps a couple avoid passing a serious genetic defect-based illness to their child, but not for social or non-medical purposes such as having a baby of a particular sex.[12] Enhancement violates many fundamental core beliefs of many societies and is therefore often considered unacceptable, but genetic editing to create healthy babies/ humans is.[13]

Chart 15.1: Framework to understand Human Genetic Modification: Purpose and Level (or Impact) of Application

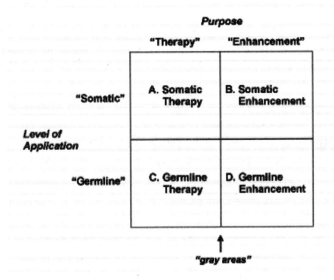

Source: Richard Hayes, 'Genetics and Other Human Modification Technologies: Sensible International Regulation or a New Kind of Arms Race?', Testimony before the Committee on Foreign Affairs, US House of Representatives (June 2008), https://fas.org/irp/congress/2008_hr/genetics. pdf, accessed on 30 June 2021.[11]

The complex debate around human germline editing was brought into focus in 2015 when Chinese researchers attempted to modify the gene responsible for β-thalassaemia, a potentially fatal blood disorder in humans, using CRISPR/Cas9 technology. The scientists involved made it a point to use 'non-viable' embryos (that is, those which could not result in a live birth) obtained from local fertility clinics.[14] But news of the Chinese scientists having genetically modified human embryos for the first time sparked off a broad debate on the ethics and morality of human germline editing. *Were we ready?* the world asked.

The work was considered by many to be 'very controversial', with some warning that it was a short and slippery slope from this kind of editing to designer babies.[15] Many questioned the certainty of the non-viability of the embryos and expressed concern about such research spreading to viable embryos in the future.[16]

Since then, the controversy and disputes around the norms and rules around such research have continued. A few years later, a Chinese scientist, He Jiankui, recruited couples whose husbands were living with HIV infections. During the IVF procedure, before insemination, He recommended using CRISPR to alter the gene to cripple the CCR5 protein that HIV uses to infect a person.[17] This would spare the child the risk of ever becoming infected.

Soon thereafter, He Jiankui's announcement in 2018 of the world's first genetically modified infants was 'decried by many in the scientific community as irresponsible and dangerous'.[18] Chinese scientists felt that their research had been sullied by the whole incident.[19] The Chinese government and the international scientific community alike painted He as a rogue scientist.[20] (As per some accounts, however, quite a few other people knew about the experiment prior to the announcement, but did not anticipate the severe backlash it would eventually face.)

Such cases have put the international genetics research community on high alert for potential breaches of genetic-engineering norms. These concerns are amplified by the fact that genetic trait selection is problematic not just ethically or morally, but also because our understanding of genes still remains limited. Contrary to popular perception, there isn't one universal 'best' genome. Different DNA sequences may be desirable in one environment, but not in others. For example, the CCR5 gene can make certain people resistant to infection by HIV, but it also makes people more susceptible to the West Nile virus. And since we don't know which environments we'll be exposed to in our lives, it is hard to identify the perfect genome for all situations. As Porteus says, with all humility, the scientific community is just embarking on their quest for understanding these interactions.[21]

The geo-economic competition around genetic engineering: Another opportunity for countries to leapfrog?

A notable feature of the present genetic-engineering conversation is that it is not at present defined by technological scarcity. Researchers worldwide have been able to take the CRISPR-Cas9 system and build various applications. Access to the technology has therefore not been the limiting or constraining factor here. But countries have different regulatory regimes and philosophies around gene editing, which are shaping the evolution of the field in their respective nations.

China, for example, has been continuing its research into the safety and feasibility of CRISPR editing, specifically for diseases most prevalent in China. Along with agriculture and food, Chinese researchers have taken a lead when it comes to CRISPR-based research on animals with the goal of achieving higher-quality meats, disease-resistant livestock, and new medical treatments and organs for human transplantation.[22] Even though the He Jiankui incident made China's advancements in CRISPR research infamous, many researchers feel that China is taking the lead on CRISPR-related research, especially in agriculture and GM-modified organisms. As Jon Cohen and Nirja Desai point out, the number of patent applications from China has risen rapidly in recent years, with China dominating the agricultural and industrial realms of CRISPR-related research.[23]

Around 2015–16, the US and Europe were leading, for example, in the number of research papers around CRISPR, followed by China and Japan. Other countries such as India, Brazil and Russia were very behind.[24] But by 2018–19, the picture had changed quite dramatically. As chart 15.2 shows, China has caught up in the number of CRISPR-related papers, though the quality of the papers still doesn't necessarily match the quality of the papers coming out of the US.

Chart 15.2 Country-wise split of CRISPR-related papers, 2012–2018

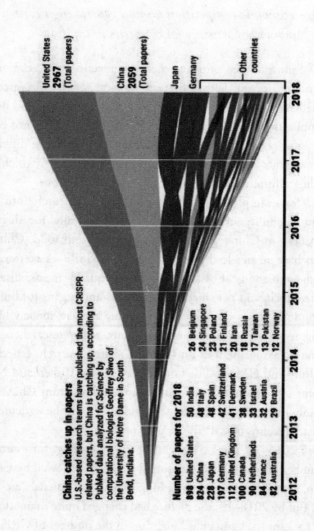

China catches up in papers
U.S.-based research teams have published the most CRISPR related papers, but China is catching up, according to PubMed data analyzed for Science by computational biologist Geoffrey Siwo of the University of Notre Dame in South Bend, Indiana.

Number of papers for 2018

898	United States	50	India
824	China	48	Italy
228	Japan	48	Spain
197	Germany	42	Switzerland
112	United Kingdom	41	Denmark
100	Canada	38	Sweden
90	Netherlands	33	Israel
84	France	32	Austria
82	Australia	29	Brazil
26	Belgium		
24	Singapore		
23	Poland		
21	Finland		
20	Iran		
18	Russia		
17	Taiwan		
13	Pakistan		
12	Norway		

United States 2967 (Total papers)

China 2059 (Total papers)

Japan
Germany

Other countries

2012　2013　2014　2015　2016　2017　2018

Source: Jon Cohen and Nirja Desai, With its CRISPR revolution, China becomes a world leader in genome editing, *Science* (Aug 2019), https://www.science.org/news/2019/08/its-crispr-revolution-china-becomes-world-leader-genome-editing, accessed on 1 October 2021.

Experts by and large agree that the US is still keeping ahead of China by leaps and bounds in the field of biotechnology. As Scott Moore argues, the US might be losing its lead over China and others in other critical emerging technologies, but that is not the case in biotechnology. The US, he points out, accounts for almost half of all biotech patents filed in the world between 1999 and 2013—still a dominant position in research, development and commercialization in the biotech sector.[25]

But the Chinese government seems determined to close the gap and is actively investing in biotechnology. Chinese venture capital and private equity firms invested $45 billion in the sector between 2015 and 2017. Chinese life sciences researchers recruited under the Thousand Talents programme account for almost 20 per cent of the total recruited talent pool to come back to China from abroad.[26] China has also been an early mover in the space of applying CRISPR technology to agriculture and crop-related improvements,[27] application areas that are considered less risky, with fewer ethical dilemmas.[28] This is not just because it doesn't involve human embryos, but also because humans have been successfully 'playing God' with crops for thousands of years now. More importantly, it can solve real food security and productivity issues faced by the large population of Chinese engaged in the agricultural sector.

The Chinese government is betting that CRISPR can actually transform the country's supply of food. According to Li Jiayang, former Chinese vice minister of agriculture, getting the highest-yield supervarieties requires that the Chinese find the right genes and work with them.[29] Not surprisingly, there are several researchers in China now attempting to use CRISPR to modify crop genes. In 2017, China's state-owned company ChemChina announced it was acquiring Syngenta—amongst the world's four largest agribusinesses with a large R&D team working on CRISPR—for $43 billion.

These R&D investments are beginning to reach market viability. Chinese CRISPR-edited tomatoes and corn may soon reach markets— and may address long-standing issues in China's agricultural economy. Per-hectare corn yields in China are presently only 60 per cent of US yields, partly because of damage done to the crop by corn earworms. This is a notable competitive disadvantage relative to the US, where 82 per cent of corn crops have been engineered for earworm resistance. China has therefore been obliged to import corn. CRISPR-edited crops could help China become less dependent on importing certain foods.

These and other similar Chinese investments in genetic editing represent an interesting economic opportunity. For China, genetic engineering technologies (like AI technologies) present another opportunity to catch up and maybe even overtake US dominance in sectors where the US has long led.

Challenges still remain. For example, the CRISPR editors can sometimes make unintended 'off-target' mutations. And scientists still must know how to identify the right genes to edit; a much more difficult ask that is that much more difficult when there are multiple genes to be changed. As per geneticist Catherine Feuillet, while changing a single gene has been the bread and butter of biotech, high-value adaptations that might affect yield or drought tolerance often require coordinated edits to multiple genes.[30]

Some researchers have argued that the precision of CRISPR editing—and especially the ability to edit genes without introducing any foreign DNA—could bring new efficiency to the aeons-old process of livestock breeding and selection of livestock.[31] They acknowledge that much more research is still needed to solve for 'off-target effects' and other potential risks to animal genomes before such gene editing would become widely acceptable to the public and governments.[32]

Whither India?

Contrast China's approach to biotechnology and GM crops with India. India has not taken a technology-progressive approach to genetic engineering, whether in medicine and public health or in areas such as agriculture.

There are serious, significant concerns in India about adoption of GM crops. While GM crops may require less pesticide sprays or deliver cheaper products to consumers, farmers hold sincere concerns about global agritech or food companies making Indian farmers dependent on patented technologies and about the possible negative ecological impacts of GM crops in the long-term.[33]

It has been argued that India's policy indecisiveness on biotechnology risks creating a bleak future for biotech in India.[34] Policy ambivalence of this kind hurts India's ability to compete globally in the field of biotechnology. Bhagirath Choudhary, director at the Delhi-based South Asia Biotechnology Centre, argues that India risks missing out on opportunities to significantly improve crop yields, shelf lives and disease resistance.[35] Others like geneticist and former Vice Chancellor of Delhi University Deepak Pental, have pushed for a stronger vision for national adoption of agri-technology.[36]

A bright spot, as India's principal scientific advisor to the Prime Minister, K. VijayRaghavan, pointed out to me, has been the pioneering work done by the Biotechnology Industry Research Assistance Council (BIRAC). Set up by India's Department of Biotechnology (DBT), BIRAC undertakes strategic research and innovation in biotech. BIRAC has been nurturing the nascent biotech start-up sector in India, and has the stated aim of serving as a catalyst for India to achieve a $150 billion bio-economy by 2025.[37] According to BIRAC's India Bioeconomy Report, the value of India's bio-economy in 2020 stood at $70.2 billion.[38] Contrast this with the US bio-economy, which at roughly $1 trillion, is currently fourteen times bigger.

Recall our discussion from earlier chapters: adoption and penetration of technology, knowledge and skills are essential for laggards to catch up with economic leaders. Not doing so leads to an increasing economic divergence, and catching up becomes almost impossible. While ethical and monopolistic dominance concerns remain, these concerns should not lead to banning or discouragement of biotech research and innovation in India. Rather, these concerns should be addressed and tackled through a greater emphasis on cutting-edge research in this field, promotion of competition, and specific regulation to tackle potential monopolistic dominance.

COVID-19, incidentally, highlighted the role bio-tech capabilities could play, especially in the field of public health. India was understandably proud of having developed its own indigenous vaccine (Bharat Biotech's Covaxin), which in turn allowed it to partake in the global vaccine diplomacy. But indirectly, it highlighted how advancements in biotechnology – such as gene sequencing and editing, synthetic biology (synbio) and genomics—can help not just diagnose, prevent and treat infectious diseases but also help develop diagnostic tests, vaccines and drugs.[39]

Several gaps—funding for research, skilled scientific talent pools, predictable regulation, market access—need to be filled, and could be complemented by the foundational work being done to build India's digital health infrastructure ecosystem. But as discussed in the taxonomy of strategies, digital challengers like India must have a laser focus on emerging technologies and position themselves competitively early in the game, and not when established incumbents have already emerged.

The geopolitical implications of biotech

Biotech has another application, with significant geopolitical ramifications: deadly bioweapons. Biotechnology, and in particular genetic editing, has become increasingly connected with national security considerations.[40] The threat of biological warfare, or the use of biochemical weapons, is by no means new. Even during the Cold War, both the US and the Soviet Union are believed to have worked on offensive biological weapons programmes involving non-contagious, contagious and often lethal bacteria and viruses such as the plague, smallpox and anthrax.[41] As genetic engineering technology developed further in the 1970s, these countries began to consider developing new, lethal pathogens that could resist known therapies as the next-generation bioweapons.

The risk posed by these historic bioweapons, however deadly, was tempered by the fact that only a few large states with deep investments in the global order possessed the means to edit and develop bioweapons. However, the latest advancements in genetic editing have changed that, dramatically increasing the risk of biological warfare in the process. The new genetic editing technology is by most accounts as easy to use as software like Microsoft Word or WordPress. In 2016, James Clapper, the then-director of National Intelligence of the US, therefore warned that genetic editing by countries with different regulatory and ethical standards has substantially increased the risk of the development and use of deadly biological agents or bioweapons.

The US obviously worries the most about the Chinese in this context, but the concern is mutual. US academics have pointed to the increasing prevalence of the concept of *zhishengquan* or biological dominance in the Chinese military's writings on future warfare. But the Chinese are equally, if not more, concerned about American and international advancements in biotech-driven warfare, given their long head start.

In the US, biotechnology is the site of significant national security investment. The US's Defense Advanced Research Projects Agency (DARPA)—onetime inventors of the internet, launched a Biological Technologies Office in 2014 to 'merge biology, engineering, and computer science to harness the power of natural systems for national security'.[42] Much of the agency's biological research—such as the development of powered exoskeletons for soldiers or brain-stimulation technology to heal wounded soldiers—has wide applicability for combat and war.[43] Several other countries, not just the US or China, have considered using genetic or bioweapons in future wars.[44]

This discussion obviously finds even greater relevance in light of the COVID pandemic. As Vivek Wadhwa said, 'The genetic engineering genie is out of the bottle.' Whether COVID-19 originated in a lab or not, the next pandemic could very well be bioengineered in a garage, given the cheap, widely available and easily usable technology.[45] This means that the threat posed by genetically engineered diseases may

THE GREAT TECH GAME

not be limited to the activities of states. Much like cyber-hackers, bio-hackers or bio-terrorists acting with or without state backing could attempt to wreak havoc on the world.

Towards a Responsible Framework for Regulation and Governance

We are on the threshold of a dangerous era of not just designer babies, but also designer bugs.[46] As with AI, we need to develop responsible frameworks as well as global and national institutions for regulation and oversight of genetic technologies.

Nobel Laureate Jennifer Doudna has argued that governments, especially the US, can play an active role in this effort, specifically in three ways. First, they should provide information and recommendations to the broader scientific community about the emerging risks and benefits of genetic engineering. Second, they must bring together international consortia of scientists and researchers to start drafting guidelines for regulation, monitoring and oversight of worldwide research and applications of genetic engineering technology. Third, greater public awareness of the benefits and risks of genome editing must be emphasized so that the necessary public debates can commence.[47]

Existing institutional frameworks and mechanisms, such as institutional biosafety committees and stem cell research oversight committees, could help as well.[48] A consortia of research institutes and scientific societies, such as the US National Academy of Science, the Royal Society in London and the Chinese Academy of Science, might play an important role in the development and implementation of norms.[49]

Given the wide range of applications (much like in the context of AI), experts have recommended the inclusion of not just scientists, but ethicists, philosophers, lawyers, physicians and even potential patients in these global discussions. Much as we discussed in questions of technology governance earlier, a multi-stakeholder approach might be necessary for the governance of genetic editing.

That is effectively what the International Commission on the Clinical Use of Human Germline Genome Editing (ICCUHGGE) has attempted in recent years. ICCUHGGE, comprising eighteen members from ten countries, has consulted experts from diverse fields such as science, medicine, law, ethics, genetics, psychology and patient advocacy groups. The commission created a six-tiered hierarchy of the potential uses of human germline editing, ranging from most to least compelling rationales, given the risks.[50] For example, genetic editing intended for enhancement (that is, to make children taller, smarter or better) was at the bottom of the hierarchy.[51]

Earlier, we discussed the ongoing battle for internet governance control between the UN-affiliated ITU and ICANN. Similarly, the US and UK scientist-dominated ICCUHGGE's foray into biotech governance matters has been criticized by some as stepping on the remit of the UN-affiliated WHO, which has taken up deliberations on governance of genome editing as well.[52] Regardless of the politics of such institutional frameworks, universally agreed and accepted guidelines and norms for technologies such as CRISPR must be developed urgently.

The reality is that given the simplicity and easy availability of the technology, it will be extremely difficult to put regulations in place for the applications of CRISPR.[53] Already, worries abound that 'the genie is out of the bottle'. DNA fragments available online can be used to reconstruct the smallpox virus for as little as $200,000. And such capabilities, in the hands of rogue actors, could be a nightmare for humanity.

Nations often dither in submitting to international norms and treaties for emerging technologies, as in the case of cyberwarfare as well. Similarly, in the absence of binding international consensus on genetic editing, it is fair to assume that certain states—especially those considered rogue by parts of the international community, or those who feel pushed to the wall by superior military powers—might actually attempt to manipulate genetic editing to wreak havoc and gain national security advantage.[54]

The challenge, as with other technology governance issues, will be to get the major powers, especially Washington and Beijing, to agree to impose constraints on biotechnology research and applications. While the battle for AI and 5G dominance has grabbed most of the attention of policymakers, tackling the emerging threat of biotechnology must be made a priority as well—some consider biotech as an even bigger threat than AI.

There are many difficult questions to be addressed: Where do we draw the line between therapies and enhancements? What are the moral and ethical boundaries that we as humans are not willing to cross? How would we govern the mixing of human and animal DNA? What are the penalties the world is ready to put on those who cross certain boundaries? In the case of nuclear weapons, almost twenty-five years elapsed between the first atomic bomb and the agreement on the Nuclear Non-Proliferation Treaty (NPT) between the major nuclear powers. Would we be comfortable taking an equally long time to get to an international treaty on genetic editing and bioweapons? Should international controls precede or follow developments in this technology and its applications?

No wonder that some, like technology futurist Jamie Metzl, have called genetic engineering 'perhaps the greatest foreign policy challenge of our time'.[55] Richard Hayes, former director of the Center for Genetics and Society, has pointed out that social, political and environmental values, historical experiences, and cultural and religious beliefs shape people's views on the genetic engineering debate.[56] Advances in this field will therefore likely challenge and disrupt core, strongly held moral and metaphysical beliefs, and ultimately raise the spectre of deep rifts and conflicts both within and between societies.[57]

The Nuclear Non-Proliferation Treaty (NPT), despite its flaws and limitations, offers useful insights on how to bring major powers together to sign a Genetic Non-Proliferation Treaty (GPT). The NPT, signed in 1970, established standards for non-proliferation by the five nuclear states at the time, but also incentives for non-nuclear states to refrain from developing or acquiring nuclear weapons in exchange for a pledge by the five nuclear states to help them develop peaceful uses of nuclear energy.

Several violations of the NPT have occurred, and exceptions have been made over the years, but the fact remains that we have not had nuclear war. Similar to the NPT, a GPT might oblige states with greater expertise in the field to share it with other countries. A broad representative body of experts would need to continuously evaluate and monitor developments in the field, as well as identify and penalize violations. Nations would need to develop national regulations and standards that comply with these international norms.[58]

Even if nations do manage to negotiate a GPT agreement, the danger from non-state and proxy actors will remain, as it would even with a future International Cyberwarfare Treaty. Yet, such treaties with enforceable norms would mandate nation states to control the actions of non-state actors within their territories. Non-state actors dominate and drive cross-border or global terrorism. Therefore, regimes, tools and strategies utilized to tackle nuclear proliferation and terrorism might end up guiding the world's efforts to govern the proliferation and use of genetic technology.

Meanwhile, even as the world works through the complex implications of genetic technologies and considers various models for global governance of it, other, less controversial parts of the bio-economy are likely to keep pushing forward aggressively. That means you can enjoy your Impossible Whoppers at Burger King, run your cars on bio-fuels, and wear bio-synthetic apparel.

Notes

1. Megan Poinski, Impossible Foods preparing to go public with $10B valuation, Reuters reports, Food Dive (Aprill 2021), https://www.fooddive.com/news/impossible-foods-preparing-to-go-public-with-10b-valuation-reuters-report/598083/, accessed on 1 October 2021.

2. National Academies of Sciences, Engineering, and Medicine, 'Safeguarding the Bioeconomy', (The National Academies Press, 2020),

https://www.nap.edu/catalog/25525/safeguarding-the-bioeconomy, accessed on 1 October 2021.

3. Ibid.

4. Michael Chui, et al., 'How the Bio Revolution Could Transform the Competitive Landscape', McKinsey Quarterly (May 2020), https://www.mckinsey.com/business-functions/mckinsey-digital/our-insights/how-the-bio-revolution-could-transform-the-competitive-landscape, accessed on 1 October 2021.

5. Matthew Porteus, 'An Academic Physician-Scientist's Perspective on Genome Editing, the CRISPR/Cas9 Technology and its Potential Applications to Humans', testimony before the Senate HELP Committee, https://www.help.senate.gov/imo/media/doc/Porteus.pdf, accessed on 1 October 2021.

6. Written statement of US Representative Daniel Lipinski, 'The Science and Ethics of Genetically Engineered Human DNA', Hearing before the Subcommittee on Research and Technology, Committee on Science, Space and Technology, US House of Representatives, Serial No. 114-24 (June 2015), https://www.congress.gov/event/114th-congress/house-event/LC35946/text/?loclr=eacdg, accessed on 1 October 2021.

7. US Representative Bill Foster, 'The Science and Ethics of Genetically Engineered Human DNA', Hearing before the Subcommittee on Research and Technology, Committee on Science, Space and Technology, US House of Representatives, Serial No. 114–24 (June 2015), https://www.congress.gov/event/114th-congress/house-event/LC35946/text/?loclr=eacdg, accessed on 1 October 2021.

8. Nobel Prize website, https://www.nobelprize.org/prizes/chemistry/2020/prize-announcement/, accessed on 1 October 2021.

9. Dr Jennifer Doudna, 'Testimony on the Science and Ethics of Genetically Engineered Human DNA', hearing before the Subcommittee on Research and Technology, Committee on Science, Space and Technology, US House of Representatives, Serial No. 114–24 (June 2015), https://www.congress.gov/event/114th-congress/

house-event/LC35946/text/?loclr=eacdg, accessed on 1 October 2021.

10. Ibid.

11. Richard Hayes, 'Genetics and Other Human Modification Technologies: Sensible International Regulation or a New Kind of Arms Race?', House of Representatives, Subcommittee on Terrorism, Nonproliferation and Trade, Committee on Foreign Affairs, US House of Representatives (June 2008), https://fas.org/irp/congress/2008_hr/genetics.pdf, accessed on 1 October 2021.

12. Ibid.

13. Matthew Porteus, 'An Academic Physician-Scientist's Perspective'.

14. Liang et al., 'CRISPR/Cas9-Mediated Gene Editing in Human Tripronuclear Zygotes', *Protein & Cell* 6 (2015): 363–372, https://link.springer.com/article/10.1007%2Fs13238-015-0153-5, accessed on 1 October 2021.

15. 'World's First Genetic Modification of Human Embryos Reported: Experts Consider Ethics', *Science Daily* (April 2015), https://www.sciencedaily.com/releases/2015/04/150424122312.htm, accessed on 1 October 2021.

16. Ibid.

17. Jon Cohen, 'The Untold Story of the "Circle of Trust" Behind the World's First Gene-Edited Babies', *Science* (August 2019), https://www.sciencemag.org/news/2019/08/untold-story-circle-trust-behind-world-s-first-gene-edited-babies#sidebar, accessed on 1 October 2021.

18. Katherine J. Wu, Carl Zimmer and Elian Peltier, 'Nobel Prize in Chemistry Awarded to 2 Scientists for Work on Genome Editing', *The New York Times* (7 October 2020), https://www.nytimes.com/2020/10/07/science/nobel-prize-chemistry-crispr.html, accessed on 1 October 2021.

19. Jon Cohen, 'The Long Shadow of a CRISPR Scandal', *Science* (August 2019), https://www.sciencemag.org/news/2019/08/untold-

story-circle-trust-behind-world-s-first-gene-edited-babies, accessed on 1 October 2021.

20. Jon Cohen, 'The Untold Story of the "Circle of Trust"'.

21. Matthew Porteus, 'An Academic Physician-Scientist's Perspective'.

22. Jon Cohen, 'China's CRISPR Push in Animals Promises Better Meat, Novel Therapies, and Pig Organs for People', *Science* (July 2019), https://www.sciencemag.org/news/2019/07/china-s-crispr-push-animals-promises-better-meat-novel-therapies-and-pig-organs-people, accessed on 1 October 2021.

23. Jon Cohen and Nirja Desai, 'With Its CRISPR Revolution, China Becomes a World Leader in Genome Editing', *Science* (August 2019), https://www.sciencemag.org/news/2019/08/its-crispr-revolution-china-becomes-world-leader-genome-editing, accessed on 1 October 2021.

24. Sharon Begley, 'Watch: Meet One of the World's Most Groundbreaking Scientists. He's 34.', Stat, https://www.statnews.com/2015/11/06/hollywood-inspired-scientist-rewrite-code-life/, accessed on 1 October 2021.

25. Scott Moore, 'In Biotech, the Industry of the Future, the US Is Way Ahead of China', Lawfare (February 2021), https://www.lawfareblog.com/biotech-industry-future-us-way-ahead-china, accessed on 1 October 2021.

26. Scott Moore, 'China's Biotech Boom Could Transform Lives—or Destroy Them', Foreign Policy, Nov 2019, https://foreignpolicy.com/2019/11/08/cloning-crispr-he-jiankui-china-biotech-boom-could-transform-lives-destroy-them/, accessed on 1 October 2021.

27. Cohen and Desai, 'With Its CRISPR Revolution, China Becomes a World Leader'.

28. Jon Cohen, 'To Feed Its 1.4 Billion, China Bets Big on Genome Editing of Crops', *Science* (July 2019), https://www.sciencemag.org/news/2019/07/feed-its-14-billion-china-bets-big-genome-editing-crops, accessed on 1 October 2021.

29. Ibid.

30. Ibid.

31. Lai et al., 'Genome Editing in Large Animals: Current Status and Future Prospects', *National Science Review* 6, no. 3 (May 2019): 402–420, https://doi.org/10.1093/nsr/nwz013, accessed on 1 October 2021.

32. Ibid.

33. Sayantan Bera, 'Inside India's Genetic Crop Battlefield', *Mint* (June 2019), https://www.livemint.com/industry/agriculture/inside-india-s-genetic-crop-battlefield-1561054298998.html, accessed on 1 October 2021.

34. Ibid.

35. Ibid.

36. Ibid.

37. Biotechnology Industry Research Assistance Council (BIRAC) website, https://www.birac.nic.in/desc_new.php?id=89, accessed on 1 October 2021.

38. 'The India Bioeconomy Report 2021', Biotechnology Industry Research Assistance Council (BIRAC), https://birac.nic.in/webcontent/1615182060_Indian_BioEconomy_Report_2021.pdf, accessed on 1 October 2021.

39. 'Strengthening India's Biotechnology Sector to Prevent Future Pandemics', Carnegie Endowment for International Peace (July 2021), https://carnegieindia.org/2021/07/15/strengthening-india-s-biotechnology-sector-to-prevent-future-pandemics-event-7674, accessed on 1 October 2021.

40. Scott Moore, 'In Biotech, the Industry of the Future, the US Is Way Ahead of China', Lawfare (February 2021), https://www.lawfareblog.com/biotech-industry-future-us-way-ahead-china, accessed on 1 October 2021.

41. Michael J. Ainscough, 'Next Generation Bioweapons: The Technology of Genetic Engineering Applied to Biowarfare and

Bioterrorism', The Counterproliferation Papers, Future Warfare Series No. 14, USAF Counterproliferation Center (April 2002), https://fas. org/irp/threat/cbw/nextgen.pdf, accessed on 1 October 2021.

42. 'DARPA Launches Biological Technologies Office', Defense Advanced Research Projects Agency (DARPA), April 2014, https://www.darpa. mil/news-events/2014-04-01, accessed on 1 October 2021.

43. Sara Reardon, 'The Pentagon's Gamble on Brain Implants, Bionic Limbs and Combat Exoskeletons', *Nature* 522 (June 2015): 142–144, https://www.nature.com/articles/522142a, accessed on 1 October 2021.

44. Elsa Kania and Wilson VornDick, 'China's Military Biotech Frontier: CRISPR, Military-Civil Fusion, and the New Revolution in Military Affairs', *The Jamestown Foundation China Brief* 19 no. 18,(October 2019),   https://jamestown.org/program/chinas-military-biotech-frontier-crispr-military-civil-fusion-and-the-new-revolution-in-military-affairs/, accessed on 1 October 2021.

45. Vivek Wadhwa, 'The Genetic Engineering Genie Is Out of the Bottle', Foreign Policy (September 2020), https://foreignpolicy. com/2020/09/11/crispr-pandemic-gene-editing-virus/.

46. Stephen Rose, 'The Coming Explosion of Silent Weapons', *Naval War College Review* 42, no. 3 (Summer 1989): 6–29, https://www. jstor.org/stable/pdf/44636914.pdf, accessed on 1 October 2021.

47. Doudna, 'Testimony on the Science and Ethics of Genetically Engineered Human DNA'.

48. Dr Jeffrey Kahn, 'Testimony on the Science and Ethics of Genetically Engineered Human DNA', Hearing before the Subcommittee on Research and Technology, Committee on Science, Space and Technology, US House of Representatives, Serial No. 114–24 (June 2015), https://www.congress.gov/event/114th-congress/house-event/ LC35946/text/?loclr=eacdg, accessed on 1 October 2021.

49. Ibid.

50. Jon Cohen, 'Commission Charts Narrow Path for Editing Human Embryos', *Science* (September 2020), https://www.sciencemag.org/

news/2020/09/commission-charts-narrow-path-editing-human-embryos, accessed on 1 October 2021.

51. Ibid.

52. Ibid.

53. Doudna, 'Testimony on the Science and Ethics of Genetically Engineered Human DNA'.

54. Brad Sherman, 'Genetics and Other Human Modification Technologies: Sensible International Regulation or a New Kind of Arms Race?', Testimony before the Subcommittee on Terrorism, Nonproliferation and Trade, Committee on Foreign Affairs, US House of Representatives (June 2008), https://fas.org/irp/congress/2008_hr/genetics.pdf, accessed on 1 October 2021.

55. 'Jamie Metzl, Genetics and Other Human Modification Technologies: Sensible International Regulation or a New Kind of Arms Race?', Testimony before the Subcommittee on Terrorism, Nonproliferation and Trade, Committee on Foreign Affairs, US House of Representatives (June 2008), https://fas.org/irp/congress/2008_hr/genetics.pdf, accessed on 1 October 2021.

56. Richard Hayes, 'Genetics and Other Human Modification Technologies: Sensible International Regulation or a New Kind of Arms Race?', Testimony before the Subcommittee on Terrorism, Nonproliferation and Trade, Committee on Foreign Affairs, US House of Representatives (June 2008), https://fas.org/irp/congress/2008_hr/genetics.pdf, accessed on 1 October 2021.

57. Jamie Metzl, 'Genetics and Other Human Modification Technologies'.

58. Ibid.

16

Whither Human Behaviour, Culture and Values?

'The machine itself, however, is a product of human ingenuity and effort: hence to understand the machine is not merely a first step towards re-orienting our civilization: it is also a means towards understanding society and towards knowing ourselves.'

—Lewis Mumford, *Technics and Civilization* (1934)

Writing in the 1930s, Lewis Mumford, an American historian and philosopher of technology, describes the legend of the monastery and the clock. Benedictine monasteries of thirteenth-century medieval Europe, the legend goes, divided the spiritual and work life of the monks as a way to measure the strength of their religious devotion. This required a mechanism or a device to measure time, which led to the development of the first mechanical clocks. These clocks, according to Mumford, 'helped give human enterprise the regular collective beat and rhythm of the machine; for the clock is not merely a means of keeping track of hours, but of synchronizing the actions of men'. Mumford concluded that the clock, not the steam engine, was the key machine of the industrial age.

The legendary clock has been replaced in the twenty-first century by the smartphone, which is irreversibly impacting and shaping human behaviour and, by extension, our culture. Observing that the human dimensions of technology, in 'their full, rich complexity' had not been explored, Mumford embarked upon his classic treatise of technology and humans, *Technics and Civilization.* 'Isn't there much more to the tale than just the powerful new engines and their contributions to productivity and economic growth?' he in effect asked.

That question could not be more relevant today. And the answer, as it was then, is an emphatic yes. Technology is opening up new avenues for expression, communication, connection and interaction. The benefits, personal and professional, are profound. We just have to see the Instagram feed of an Instagram influencer to be able to peek into the power of the smartphone and the internet. The vision of the founders of the internet as a global village is almost realized. The internet has connected over half of the world with each other, within a few decades. It has never been easier for a small business or individual in any part of the world to connect with potential customers thousands of miles away.

But if the legendary clock had worked to synchronize the actions of men, the overuse of technology today is distracting from our ability to focus and engage fully. Technology is reshaping our values, transforming various aspects of our behaviour, dictating many aspects of our decision-making, and fundamentally altering, in complex ways, how we think. As these new technologies solve many of our problems, it is important to understand and acknowledge that they also create new ones—and we haven't had much time to adapt or learn how to deal with the new problems. Even as we have knowledge and information at our fingertips like never before, the barrage of information, news feeds, emails and tweets is often overwhelming and numbing. The constant window into the 'happy, fun, and exciting' lives of others on social media is lonely, depressing and anxiety-inducing.

While it might be too early to assess its full and varied impact on different aspects of our culture, our values and way of thinking, the impact will be no less than the cultural impact of the agricultural revolution, the Gutenberg press, the European industrial and the American capitalist eras. The current technological revolution is similar to the Gutenberg Revolution in its impact on the diffusion of information and knowledge, and the consequent impact on established institutions of authority. Yet, it is also similar to the Industrial and Capitalist Revolutions in its drive towards greater productivity and efficiency in economic activities, the accumulation (and concentration) of resources, wealth and technology, and the resultant inequalities within society.

Moreover, unlike previous revolutions or historical forces that originated in certain regions of the world, today's technology is actually being designed and shaped differently in multiple parts of the world, from the US to Europe to India to China. Therefore, the cultural responses to the impact of technology will vary across regions, and will need to be studied as such.

Finally, the skills—mental, physical, emotional—required to adapt to these technologies will need to be much better and more fully understood, not to mention widely discussed and taught. As we teach our kids to swim or read, we must teach them to use technology smartly, wisely and sustainably so that they do not drown in it. Again, here, we will need to keep in mind the cultural and regional differences. The skills required by the teenager in London will be different than the skills required by the teenager in a remote rural village in India, for example. But before we can teach them, we must ourselves learn how to navigate these new waters.

Technology is changing how we live, communicate and think

Writing in 1964 in his landmark classic, *Understanding Media: The Extensions of Man,* Marshall McLuhan argued that whenever a new medium of communication comes along, people get caught up in the content being delivered through that platform—whether it was news in the newspaper, music on the radio, the shows on TV or conversations over the phone. [1] Similarly, today, we are undergoing this infatuation with content on the internet, whether it be YouTube and TikTok videos, Twitter and Facebook and Instagram feeds, or Netflix originals.

McLuhan argued that new communication technologies do not necessarily change our opinions or concepts, but rather they alter how consumers perceive and understand issues. Every new medium changes us, and the content of a medium is just 'the juicy piece of meat carried by the burglar to distract the watchdog of the mind'. More than the content itself, the technology medium acts on our nervous system itself and changes what's going on inside our heads.[2] This insight remains equally powerful today, as social media platforms and online content platforms, for example, are having deep effects on our psyche and state of mind, even as we remain focused on the content of the feeds.

The founders could not have conceived how the internet would keep us hooked, with not a moment to catch our breath between checking our phones for emails, messages and feed updates. Unlike the television, the smartphone is everywhere, in our homes, bedrooms, bathrooms, offices and cars. It is with us at all times of day and night. And it is not, as the television or radio was, for passive viewing or listening. It has become an all-purpose device, for working, communicating, shopping, dating and pretty much anything else you can think of.

Mary Aiken, a prominent cyber psychologist, has likened the phase we're going through today with the Enlightenment. It's not often in history, she argues, when a seismic shift in how we live and think is underway. The pervasive use of technologies in our daily lives has fundamentally changed the way we work, speak and communicate, interact and socialize, shop, eat and entertain, and almost everything else.[3] As Carr has argued, 'It is so much our servant that it would seem churlish to notice that it is also our master.'[4]

The internet is no longer just a medium. Rather, it has become a distinct place or environment that you travel to. Once you are online, your awareness, your consciousness, your emotions, your responses and your behaviour are often transformed.[5] Just like you might behave differently in a foreign country or someone else's home than when you are at your own home, people tend to often behave differently on the internet. And it can take time to adjust and adapt to the norms of the new environment, depending on one's age, education and other factors.[6] New concepts, such as online disinhibition, cyber-stalking and cyber exhibitionism, are entering the field of psychology derived specifically from human behaviour in cyber space, and populating the research in the field of what is now known as cyber psychology.[7]

Humans are communicating differently now than we did a couple of decades ago. Face-to-face and voice-based conversations increasingly feel like a luxury today, as most communication has moved to email, text, WhatsApp chats and Twitter. Anything else seems too time-consuming, or too direct without the protection of the technology layer in between.[8] Similarly, even our language—spoken and written—is changing. New modes of expression have evolved, such as emojis and GIFs and TikTok videos.

The Digital Impact Framework

A useful framework for thinking about the impact of the internet on our behaviour is to closely examine digital deficits, addictions, divisiveness, duress and dangers.[9] Digital deficits largely refer to the decline in people's cognitive capabilities such as memory, focus, reflection and introspection. Digital addictions refer to the tools designed to hook users to digital products, often by using dopamine-inducers. Digital divisiveness is being driven by algorithms and filter bubbles, taking away our personal agency. Digital duress, driven by information overload and smartphone addiction, is being manifested as higher levels of stress, anxiety, loneliness and insomnia. And finally, the digital dangers involve the technology-driven loss of security, privacy and work, which we have discussed in detail in previous chapters.[10]

Digital deficits: Addictions, cognitive capabilities and tacit wisdom

Our social interactions have become more fleeting now. Sharing updates on Facebook or Instagram Stories, and articles and jokes via WhatsApp, give you a sense of connectedness with more people than you otherwise might have been able to.[11] But the same obsession and pervasive use of the mobile phone and social media platforms have made deeper conversations and connections scarcer. We view and experience intimacy differently; somehow, intimacy has started to seem problematic. To make and hold eye contact seems more difficult, riskier and just more awkward.[12] Teenagers prefer texting their friends since it allows them to talk to a lot of people at the same time, keeps them busy and allows them to easily move in and out of relationships, conversations and problems.[13] The smartphone is the gateway to participate in an always-on digital conversation, 'a constant invitation to engage in whatever is going on in the digital space'.[14]

Distraction is not new to humans. Philosophers, yogis and Buddhist monks have all considered distraction a part of the human condition. Yet, technology is making distraction ubiquitous. Nir Eyal, author of *Indistractable*, has argued that our brains are not yet equipped to handle so much distraction, and therefore get manipulated into wasting time on various diversions.[15] We continue to be misguided by the romanticized idea of multitasking (many research studies have now shown multitasking to be cognitively suboptimal.) This 'crisis of inattention' might ultimately hamper our ability to attain wisdom, achieve intimacy and drive creativity.[16]

The pervasiveness of communication technologies makes it hard to find any place with respite.[17] We are experiencing a 'loss of personal priority': regardless of the significance of the incoming calls or messages, we prioritize our smartphones over whatever else we might be engaged in at that moment.[18] Instead of soaking in the natural beauty, during a mountain hike we are more inclined to post photos and videos on Instagram.

As a WEF report points out, connectivity and all the distractions it brings—checking social media updates, non-work emails, videos and games—offset to varying degrees the productivity-enhancing potential of the technology.[19] Studies conducted by University of Texas professor Adrian Ward concluded that even when people do manage to avoid the temptation to constantly check their phones, the mere presence of the devices actually diminishes the cognitive capacity available at that time.[20]

For many people, the connectivity and the mobile phone in particular is adversely impacting not just their work output, but also their quality of life: persistent phone calls, constant emails, and WhatsApp messages seem to add more stress than pleasure for many.[21] Prof. Stewart Friedman, an organizational psychologist and the founder of Wharton's Work/Life integration project, believes that the rise of mindfulness and wellness is an outcropping of the fact that people are looking for peace in their lives to fight the barrage of disturbance.

Our cognitive ability to focus and concentrate has declined, as have our attention spans. We tend to read less, not more. We prefer reading short articles (or really, just tweets and hashtags) and shorter videos (movies seem like five-day cricket test matches). Books are harder to read entirely, while a long article in a newspaper is considered an achievement. Younger people tend to know a lot about many things, but not deeply about anything. Focusing long enough for an in-depth conversation seems hard.[22] Not surprisingly, students today are mistaking information for wisdom.

As Prof. Henrich has argued, humans are a cultural species, and we have a high ability to learn from others. But with the pervasive use of technology, our cultural ways of learning are changing—who we are learning from, what we are learning (or thinking we should learn), and how we are learning.[23] This itself has implications for how and what kinds of cultural learning will be passed on. Henrich talks about the idea of a cumulative cultural evolution, a process that selectively filters and inculcates beliefs, practices, and techniques driven over generations. This process shapes human learning but also generates increasingly sophisticated technologies, languages, rituals and protocols. We don't give much thought to these, but as Henrich argues, they are much smarter than we individually are, because they have been refined over such a long time.[24]

Large parts of this tacit knowledge and wisdom, I believe, could be lost as people immediately turn to technology-driven modes of learning. Earlier, if we would turn to adults or experts when we needed to learn something, we now turn to Google, for example. We are now watching how-to videos on YouTube. The design (and the designers) of these platforms will therefore greatly shape how we learn, what we learn and who we learn from. These platforms could very well actually improve the passover of this tacit knowledge. For example, the tacit knowledge of many communities is being documented better and becoming more easily accessible through technology and digitization.

Not just our learning, these platforms are shaping how we spend our time. Critics have argued that Big Tech firms have been consciously 'hacking our minds' and tricking us into staying hooked. As McLuhan had presciently warned, the increasingly sophisticated technologies are often underpinned with the use of consumer psychology. These technology platforms are exploiting the consumer's constant yearning for social and peer validation, and feeding the consumer with novelty (think Instagram stories and Facebook feeds) to keep them hooked.[25]

To explain today's smartphone addiction, parallels have been made with psychology researcher B.F. Skinner's famous experiment, conditioning pigeons, in the 1950s. Skinner trained pigeons to peck at a box of plastic every time they wanted food but then rigged the system to reward them randomly—sometimes after one peck, sometimes after three or five. The pigeons became addicted and kept pecking impulsively for hours. William Wan sees us today as 'pigeons pecking at our iPhones'.[26]

The implications of such addiction and usage are immense but vary for different demographic groups. A Pew Research Center's Internet & Life Project, for example, found that for people under the age of 35, hyper-connected lives lead to a thirst for instant gratification and quick fixes and 'loss of patience'.[27] Gary Small, author of *iBRAIN: Surviving the Technological Alteration of the Modern Mind*, has highlighted that the aged are actually able to maintain better connections with distant family and cousins with technology. For them, technology is often a tool for managing and researching health issues, but also a way to increase brain activity. Aged people can feel less isolated, and more mentally active as a result. Small and his colleagues conducted a study for adults aged 55-76 and found that those using the internet actively had more neural activity compared to those who didn't. Technology, Small concludes, can therefore increase life effectiveness for seniors and help them function longer.[28]

Digital divisiveness and duress: Our mental health and socio-political well-being

Many of these behavioural changes are having ill effects on our physical, mental and emotional health. Our digital addictions are leading to increased depression, loneliness and even promoting suicidal behaviour amongst teens and young adults.[29] Productivity at work seems to be falling (experts do not seem to be sure why), and stress, anxiety and depression are commonplace now.[30]

The future of our well-being is at stake. Moreover, the current trends of technology, driving greater isolation, loneliness, inability to focus and concentrate, will worsen. For children growing up with so much screen time, the long-term effects, though not quite fully understood yet, include poor attention spans, anxiety, depression and lack of personal social connections. The net result could be a greater number of teenagers who are addicted as well as dysfunctional adults. (Parents have been worried about the threat of excessive screen time with earlier technologies also, such as the television or the Xbox.)[31]

Noreena Hertz has, in fact, termed this '*The Lonely Century*'. She argues loneliness is on the rise across the world, driven by various reasons, including technology. But it is her articulation of the impact of loneliness that is most striking. She argues:

> The contemporary manifestation of loneliness goes beyond our yearning for connection with those physically around us, our craving for love and being loved, and the sadness we feel when we consider ourselves to be bereft of friends. It also incorporates how disconnected we feel from politicians and politics, how cut off we feel from our work and our workplace, how excluded many of us feel from society's gains, and how powerless, invisible and voiceless so many of us believe ourselves to be.[32]

Loneliness, Hertz has argued, is fuelling divisiveness and extremism across the world. In fact, she believes that loneliness and right-wing populism are close bedfellows. While most arguments for the rise of populism have been economic, I find the linkage that Hertz posits quite intriguing.

In any case, we increasingly live within filter bubbles and echo chambers, enabled and furthered by the personalized algorithms that decide what we see, read and watch, and the cookies that follow and track you wherever you go on the web.[33] This often leads to a state of intellectual, ideological and socio-economic isolation, and leaves us vulnerable to propaganda and manipulation. (Some researchers, though, have argued that social media as a source of news increases the likelihood of incidental exposure to a wider diversity of news sources than an offline reader of news would be exposed to.)[34]

Though, obviously, the technology platforms do not make it impossible for anyone to actively seek them out, alternative viewpoints, ideologies and ways of thinking become that much harder to come by.[35] As a result, we might overestimate the pervasiveness of our own perspective (the so-called reinforcement bubble). The digital divisiveness, ideological segregation and polarization of society that results from such bubbles have increasingly started to become evident from the rising incidence of fake news, disinformation campaigns and manipulated opinions.

Rob Reich, professor of political science at Stanford University, has argued that despite the enormous, indisputable benefits of digital life, it is likely to, on balance, harm people's well-being in the next decade.[36] The ways in which we are being harmed have already started to become evident, and the trend line is likely to grow stronger. Pervasive surveillance and tracking, the consequent loss of privacy and security, the addictive technologies that have monopolized the attention and mind-space of the young, and the ideological segregation enabled by personalized algorithms, will all collectively threaten our economic, social, political and mental well-being.

Is there a way to swim across, and not drown in, the sea of technology?

We must learn how to swim and navigate these new waters. We cannot ignore these new waters, or wish them away. As tempting as it might be for some to occasionally want to turn the clock back on this new world, the impulse to say goodbye to it permanently is not translatable into action as a viable option.

Societies and people need time to adapt to new technologies, and the pace of technological advancement is making things tougher. Still, people are trying to adapt through strategies such as digital detoxes such as ten-day Vipassana retreats or 'digital sabbaths' over weekends, apps that lock your phone after a certain amount of usage in a day, and even deletion of social media accounts. Some are giving up smartphones altogether. Others are coming up with personal productivity tools and techniques that can help them be more productive in an increasingly hectic environment of knowledge work.[37]

Still, others are passing the baton to the tech firms, asking them to live up to their 'duty to cater to our more complete selves' rather than just our narrow, superficial interest in maximizing convenience and minimizing discomforts.[38] (Indeed, Apple's Screen Time and Google Android's Digital Wellbeing apps are intended to help users deal with screen addiction, but initial research indicates these apps induce little or no change in behaviour.[39]) Some are trying to reduce their email-induced misery and anxiety through new, less invasive communication tools.[40]

But ultimately, a re-think of our approach to life and a reassessment of what we value the most is essential. We must question the very industrial-era idea of a constant pursuit of maximizing production and productivity. Regardless, these hacks, tools and techniques to limit smartphone use will not be sufficient by themselves to prevent these new technologies from depleting our cognitive capacities and squeezing out our productive output.

Instead, we must develop our own individual 'philosophy of technology use'.[41] Much in the way we learn the intricacies of swimming and the rules of the road, we must develop our rules of engagement with technology. The rules of the Great Game, it turns out, are needed not just for better global governance, but for the ability of individuals, especially children, to purposefully and consciously consume technology.

The parallels with the conscious consumption movement are obvious. Conscious technology consumption would entail turning to digital technology only when it would be the most efficient method of achieving your objective in that moment. Similarly, we must practise mindfulness. As artist and critic Jenny Odell argues, attention is our most precious resource, and we must mindfully choose how we spend it.[42]

These principles would apply as much to professional use as they would to personal use. In fact, the ability to think critically about the impact technology is having on your productivity and cognitive capacity might itself become a source of competitive advantage. Individuals who use technology in ways that are compatible with the existing nature of the human brain will benefit more from the technological future.

Will Technology Fundamentally Transform How We Think? (Or, How Does This Matter in the Long Run?)

How does this all matter in the long run? Haven't we been hooked by television and other such technologies before? Haven't we been distracted by vices before? Haven't we been jealous of the lives of others before?

Many argue that the current crop of technology platforms have gone further and deeper than anything that came before them. Today, as Yuval Harari has cautioned, we are letting even our choices be determined by algorithms, and are therefore losing our ability to make fully informed decisions. Then there are the second- and third-order consequences of this lack of focused attention, such as inflexible thinking driven by the constant multitasking, diminished availability of cognitive capacity, declining productivity and increased stress from distraction-rich days. With a lowered ability to listen or care for those around us, what will happen to our ability to resolve conflicts, establish common ground and pay attention to averting the next financial or environmental or diplomatic crisis?

Nicholas Carr has noted that there is an increased sense that the brain's neural circuitry is getting remapped and memory is getting reprogrammed. He worries that the mind is not being able to think the way it used to. Immersing oneself in a lengthy article or book has become nearly impossible; one's concentration starts to wander within a few minutes and loses the plot. He attributes it, as McLuhan did, to the medium—the internet. Quick Google searches, and the urge to continuously click on hyperlinks and follow them into a rabbit hole, have contributed to making us scatterbrained.[43]

There is no doubt that Google, and its ability to organize the world's information, has been an incredible boon. But this innate behaviour change—for example, from the earlier process of doing research in a library, poring over books and having in-depth conversations, to clicking on links to search for information—is shaping the very process of human thought today. It is chipping away at our ability to engage in-depth. As Carr describes it, 'Once I was a scuba diver in the sea of words. Now I zip along the surface like a guy on a Jet Ski.'[44]

The brain's capacity is limited. Patience, perseverance and concentration are needed to evaluate, weigh and process the information, but these qualities are in short supply when browsing the internet. A brain overburdened by stimuli makes for more superficial and impulsive, less reflective or contemplative, thinking and, by implication, decisions.[45] Similarly, Georgetown professor Cal Newport has described the knowledge worker's mind as the Hyperactive Hive Mind. The hyperactive hive mind's workflow, he explains, structures the work-day around tending to the unscheduled and unstructured messages received throughout the day via email and messaging apps. Research has shown that the frequent switches in attention and context takes a heavy toll: it reduces cognitive performance, reduces efficacy and productivity, and drains you mentally.[46]

There is a counterview to this dismal judgement of the internet's impact on how we think. Some researchers have argued that this new way of researching has actually enhanced our creativity, improved our ability to scan a lot of information on the web, and expand and expose our mind to much more. They have noted the 'intellectual intoxication' people feel when fluttering across the web (I am definitely guilty of this), and their brain lighting up and feeling smarter as they seemingly absorb all this information. Being able to read short snippets of books and articles online, saving links of interesting articles for later reference, making easier connections, and being able to constantly discover new thoughts and research has actually made us smarter. They argue that this 'networked thinking process'—measured against our traditional 'linear thought process'—might actually be superior, but we just don't recognize it yet.[47]

The rise of the 'creative class' could be seen as a sign that creativity is actually on the rise. As David Eagleman and Anthony Brandt have argued in their book, *Runaway Species*, 'creativity is just connecting things.' And potentially, the networked thinking process might help people make more connections and synthesize new things.[48] In 2011, technology thinker Clay Shirky had argued that digital technology would unleash a wave of creative production and collaboration, driven by the cognitive surplus – the time freed up by technology for the world's educated classes.[49] Russian-born American author Isaac Asimov had predicted something to this effect, back in 1988:

> As computers take over more and more of the work that human beings shouldn't be doing in the first place—because it doesn't utilize their brains, it stifles and bores them to death—there's going to be nothing left for human beings to do but the more creative types of endeavor.[50]

More research will be needed to understand the trade-offs between these two modes of thinking and learning, but it is clear that our thought processes are being impacted by the internet in subtler and deeper ways than perhaps we comprehend today. We seem to be 'at an important juncture in our intellectual and cultural history, a moment of transition between two very different modes of thinking'.[51] The Gutenberg press had made book reading a popular pursuit and led to the development of the linear literary mind, the scientific and rational mind of the Enlightenment, and the inventive mind of the Industrial Revolution.[52] This mind might soon be 'yesterday's mind,' and the networked, hyperactive mind might be 'tomorrow's mind'.

The Impact on Us, Our Society, Our Nations and Our Future

How are these changes in human behaviour relevant in a book about technology, geopolitics, economic growth, society and the world order? It is, in fact, the most important shaping factor. Just like the Baby Boomers changed the destiny of the US (and the world), current generations that have been shaped by their use of technology will, in turn, shape the destiny of their respective nations and the world. While much has been written about how technology is changing human behavioural traits, not enough has been written about the impact those changed behavioural traits will have on our values, societies, economies, nations and the world order.

This zipping along on a jet ski will ultimately shape the way our society—and our leaders—process information and make their policy decisions. These impacts on human behaviour, our ways of thinking, and making choices and decisions are likely to shape how we, in turn, shape our societies, manage our relationships and envision our world in the coming decades.[53]

If Mahatma Gandhi's and Martin Luther King's reading of lengthy treatises such as Leo Tolstoy's *War and Peace* shaped their views on non-violent resistance, what do we expect our leaders to be influenced and shaped by in a decade or two from now? Will it make a difference that our decision-makers will have access to loads of information on their mobile phones but not the ability to engage in-depth with an issue or intractable problem? Will history or the top-ranking search results on Google serve as our guide when we encounter a new problem? Will the 'impatience with anything nuanced, poetic, or less-than-obvious' lead to more Trump-esque leaders in our world?

Ultimately, all that we do as humans is driven by our innate human traits, skills and values: whether we have a tendency to want to go to war, or have a predilection for peace; whether we build diplomatic channels of communication or emphasize surveillance and espionage; whether we tend to believe in the richness or diversity of human life or believe that uniformity is most important; and so forth. And if short-term thinking replaces long-term pattern recognitions, if our cultural memories are limited to the digital data that we can easily access, if our relationships are shallow and fleeting, if we have short attention spans, if we believe life is only about maximizing productivity, consumption, comfort and convenience,[54] and if our decision-makers are lonely, anxious and depressed, then we will definitely live in a different world in the future than what we have known in the past.

Various scientific studies have linked delayed gratification with more prosperity, better educational and economic outcomes, not to mention better government and social institutions around the world. In fact, as Henrich points out, 'inclinations to defer gratification may be even more important for economic prosperity where the formal economic and political institutions operate less effectively'.[55] On the other hand, Maggie Jackson has warned that our distraction epidemic could lead to a 'cultural dark age'. She acknowledges that such an argument might seem misplaced, given the techno-miraculous era we seem to be living in. But she draws upon historical examples of the dark Middle Ages in Europe where, despite technological advances, the civilization declined with the emergence of a feudal society.

People have much less time now to reflect on the world around them, let alone their future. Kids are compulsive multitaskers today, and often overestimate their own abilities for synthesis of information, expression of complex ideas and analytical thinking. These skills form the foundation for a well-informed citizenry but also for scientific and technological progress. With an increasing overload of information, these skills have become that much more valuable today. We must therefore question whether all this technological progress actually constitutes or even lays the foundation for societal and human progress. Or does this pervasive lack of time for reflection, solitude and pause increase the risk for cultural and societal decline?[56,57]

We must not view technology tools as a utopian mechanism for progress and prosperity. They are that, but they are also more. And they are constantly evolving. Therefore, amidst all the distractions of our technology-enabled lives, we must, as individuals and as a society, find the time and mind-space to reflect deeply on how these technologies and tools are affecting us, our values, our culture and, ultimately, our destiny and our future.[58]

Notes

1. Nicholas Carr, *The Shallows: How the Internet Is Changing the Way We Think, Read and Remember* (Atlantic Books, 2010), Kindle.

2. Ibid.

3. Mary Aiken, *The Cyber Effect: A Pioneering Cyberpsychologist Explains How Human Behaviour Changes Online* (John Murray Press, 2016), Kindle.

4. Carr, *The Shallows*.

5. Aiken, *The Cyber Effect*.

6. Ibid.

7. Ibid.

8. Julia Hobsbawm, *Fully Connected* (Bloomsbury Publishing, 2017), Kindle.

9. Janna Anderson and Lee Rainie, 'Concerns about the Future of People's Well-Being', Pew Research Center (April 2018), https://www.pewresearch.org/internet/2018/04/17/concerns-about-the-future-of-peoples-well-being/, accessed on 1 October 2021.

10. Ibid.

11. Hobsbawm, *Fully Connected*.

12. Ibid.

13. Maggie Jackson, *Distracted* (Prometheus, 2018), Kindle.

14. C.G. Prado, ed., *How Technology Is Changing Human Behavior: Issues and Benefits* (Praeger, 2019), p. xv.

15. Nir Eyal, *Indistractable: How to Control Your Attention and Choose Your Life* (Bloomsbury Publishing, 2019). Kindle.

16. Jackson, *Distracted*.

17. Ibid.

18. Prado, ed., *How Technology Is Changing Human Behavior*.

19. Jeffrey Frankel, 'Is New Technology Hurting Our Productivity?', WEF (March 2018), https://www.weforum.org/agenda/2018/03/is-technology-hurting-productivity, accessed on 1 October 2021.

20. Adrian F. Ward et al., 'Brain Drain: The Mere Presence of One's Own Smartphone Reduces Available Cognitive Capacity', *Journal of the Association for Consumer Research* 2, no. 2 (2017): 140–154, https://

www.journals.uchicago.edu/doi/suppl/10.1086/691462, accessed on 1 October 2021.

21. Frankel, 'Is New Technology Hurting Our Productivity?'.

22. Hobsbawm, *Fully Connected*.

23. Henrich, *The Weirdest People in the World*.

24. Henrich, *The Weirdest People in the World*.

25. Jackson, *Distracted*.

26. William Wan, 'Rebel Developers Are Trying to Cure Our Smartphone Addiction—With an App', *The Washington Post* (June 2018), https://www.washingtonpost.com/national/health-science/rebel-developers-are-trying-to-cure-our-smartphone-addiction--with-an-app/2018/06/17/153e2282-6a81-11e8-bea7-c8eb28bc52b1_story.html, accessed on 1 October 2021.

27. 'Millennials Will Benefit and Suffer Due to Their Hyperconnected Lives', Pew Research Center (February 2012), https://www.pewresearch.org/internet/2012/02/29/millennials-will-benefit-and-suffer-due-to-their-hyperconnected-lives-2/, accessed on 1 October 2021.

28. Alicia Matsuura, 'How Social Media and Technology Are Changing the Lives of the Elderly', Deseret News (July 2017), https://www.deseret.com/2017/7/23/20616274/how-social-media-and-technology-are-changing-the-lives-of-the-elderly, accessed on 1 October 2021.

29. Anderson and Rainie, 'Concerns about the Future of People's Well-Being'.

30. Hobsbawm, *Fully Connected*.

31. Jane Vincent and Leslie Haddon, eds., *Smartphone Cultures* (Routledge, 2017), Kindle, loc. 320.

32. Noreena Hertz, *The Lonely Century: Coming Together in a World That's Pulling Apart* (Hodder & Stoughton, 2020), Kindle.

33. Eli Pariser, *The Filter Bubble: What the Internet Is Hiding from You* (Penguin, 2011).

34. Dr Richard Fletcher, 'The Truth Behind Filter Bubbles: Bursting Some Myth's', Reuters Institute at the University of Oxford (January 2019), https://reutersinstitute.politics.ox.ac.uk/risj-review/truth-behind-filter-bubbles-bursting-some-myths, accessed on 1 October 2021.

35. Kevin J. Delaney, 'Filter Bubbles Are a Serious Problem with News, says Bill Gates', Quartz (February 2017), https://qz.com/913114/bill-gates-says-filter-bubbles-are-a-serious-problem-with-news/, accessed on 1 October 2021.

36. Anderson and Rainie, 'Concerns about the Future of People's Well-Being'.

37. Cal Newport, 'The Rise and Fall of Getting Things Done', *The New Yorker* (November 2020), https://www.newyorker.com/tech/annals-of-technology/the-rise-and-fall-of-getting-things-done, accessed on 1 October 2021.

38. Tim Wu, 'Technology Gets Better, Will Society Get Worse?', Annals of Technology, *The New Yorker* (February 2014), https://www.newyorker.com/tech/annals-of-technology/as-technology-gets-better-will-society-get-worse, accessed on 1 October 2021.

39. Yudhijit Bhattacharjee, 'Smartphones Revolutionize Our Lives—But at What Cost?', *National Geographic* (January 2019), https://www.nationalgeographic.com/science/article/smartphones-revolutionize-our-lives-but-at-what-cost, accessed on 1 October 2021.

40. Cal Newport, 'E-mail Is Making Us Miserable', Annals of Technology, *The New Yorker* (February 2021), https://www.newyorker.com/tech/annals-of-technology/e-mail-is-making-us-miserable, accessed on 1 October 2021.

41. Cal Newport, *Digital Minimalism: Choosing a Focused Life in a Noisy World* (Portfolio-Penguin, 2019).

42. Jenny Odell, *How to Do Nothing: Resisting the Attention Economy* (Melville House, 2019).

43. Andrew Sullivan, 'I Used to Be a Human Being', *New York Magazine* (September 2016), https://nymag.com/intelligencer/2016/09/

andrew-sullivan-my-distraction-sickness-and-yours.html,   accessed on 1 October 2021.

44. Carr, *The Shallows*.

45. Ibid.

46. Cal Newport, *A World Without Email: Reimagining Work in the Age of Overload* (Penguin, 2021).

47. Carr, *The Shallows*.

48. David Eagleman and Anthony Brandt, *The Runaway Species* (Canongate Books, 2016), Kindle.

49. Clay Shirky, *Cognitive Surplus: How Technology Makes Consumers into Collaborators* (The Penguin Press, 2010).

50. Isaac Asimov on the Thrill of Lifelong Learning, Science vs. Religion, and the Role of Science Fiction in Advancing Society, https://www.brainpickings.org/2014/04/07/isaac-asimov-bill-moyers-education-science-religion/, accessed on 1 October 2021.

51. Carr, *The Shallows*.

52. Ibid.

53. Jackson, *Distracted*.

54. Tim Wu, 'As Technology Gets Better, Will Society Get Worse?', Annals of Technology, *The New Yorker* (February 2014), https://www.newyorker.com/tech/annals-of-technology/as-technology-gets-better-will-society-get-worse, accessed on 1 October 2021.

55. Henrich, *The Weirdest People in the World*.

56. Jackson, *Distracted*.

57. Odell, *How to Do Nothing*.

58. Jackson, *Distracted*.

Conclusion

'Each age tends to have only a meagre awareness of its own limitations.'

—Pope Francis, *Laudato Si'* (2015)[1]

The changes technology is bringing to our world—to our politics, our economies and our lives—are so large that it can often be difficult to fix their impact. Technology is making us freer than ever, and more monitored. It has made it easier to love, and easier to hate. Around the world, it has supported democratic revolutions and undermined confidence in democracy itself. It has made vast new classes of wealth, and destroyed industries and firms that once seemed permanent. For these reasons, the common positions of tech-optimism and tech-pessimism can feel to me like fixed ideological commitments rather than realistic assessments of the changes we are facing.

Personally, I prefer to call myself a tech-realist. This means acknowledging the scale of the changes technology is bringing us, and the mix of opportunities and challenges that we—as individuals, societies, and institutions—will face as we navigate those changes. It means recognizing that tech will play a fundamental role in determining our species' course in the coming centuries—that, where nations once played the Great Game, we are now all playing the Great Tech Game. Most of all, though, it means recognizing that while vast changes are inevitable, the outcomes of those changes are not written in stone—they will depend on the choices we make as we navigate this new era, and on whether we are able to shape technology's impact on our world in accordance with our central human and social values.

The Great Tech Game is already causing seismic shifts in the economic, political and societal structures of the world. But unfortunately, as I argue in this book, we do not fully understand these fundamental shifts. So the first order of business is to fix that. Hopefully, the earlier sections have given you a series of frameworks within which to place current developments in technology—whether it be technology's place in history, its impact on economies, how it is shaping world politics, or how it is transforming our societies and, potentially, humanity itself. This holistic understanding of the Great Tech Game is crucial, for without a clear grasp of its dynamics, we will find it impossible to choose our moves wisely.

In building this understanding, history offers many clues for understanding our present and anticipating our future. What we think is new or novel is not. Though technology is shaping our current trends, many earlier forces have also transformed the world in profound ways. Studying how—and how deeply—the earlier trend-shapers impacted the world helps us place into historical context the seismic changes technology is unleashing today.

The battle for economic dominance, particularly, has been an age-old one. Countries with the ambition for economic leadership, through history, have worked to identify the contours of the game and play it masterfully. But these games can change: periods defined by agriculture and trade gave way to those defined by colonization and industrialization. Now, with technology emerging as the new game, many countries seem to be still thinking in terms of the previous games. The relative importance of the different factors of production is changing, with technology—backed by capital—becoming the major determinant for economic growth. Data is driving an increasingly large chunk of the digital economy, and therefore control over and access to data is becoming a major source of competitive advantage.

The second order of business, then, is that countries must prepare themselves to play that game with a clear strategy tailored to their existing positions, endowments, and aspirations. The digital economy is fast replacing the industrial economy of the last two centuries, and the digital giants that are being born today across various sectors of the economy might end up dominating the economic landscape for as long as the industrial giants did. Catching up is possible, despite it currently seeming that the forces for economic divergence are greater than the ones for convergence.

But countries and people must meet the moment with urgency. Nations that leverage technology intelligently may remove the current constraints to their economic growth and well-being, and position themselves for future opportunities. A country that does not have a strategy to find its own niche within the Great Tech Game, meanwhile, will struggle to compete. Perhaps most painful, though, will be the fates of countries that remain preoccupied with earlier games.

Nations must understand that the nature of not just economic competition but also the geopolitical battles in the world is changing. For much of our memory, territories, trading routes and critical resources such as oil have driven geopolitical tensions and conflicts. Today, technology—specifically the quest for technological dominance—is driving geopolitical competition. Today's new battles are not over pipeline routes, but over control of internet infrastructure, access to and dominance of digital markets and emerging technologies, and cyberespionage and cyberwarfare have become the new battlefronts. A nation's capabilities have to accordingly evolve if it wants to be able to win these new geopolitical battles. And today's new alliances are being formed based not on strategic geographical locations but technological resources, capabilities, and appealing digital markets. Nations that hope to prosper in these new geopolitical alignments must, accordingly, develop new capabilities in order to compete.

Just as the US and China contest a great power rivalry for technological dominance, though, a battle of similar scale is being fought between Big Tech firms and the state. For millennia—likely since the emergence of history's first governments—states have been in a tug of war with private players. The twenty-first-century avatar of this battle is probably the most profound challenge that has been mounted by any private players against governments. As Big Tech firms have grown to a global scale considered too risky and uncontrollable by national governments, states are leveraging all the tools and strategies in their arsenal to fight back. Fearful of being broken up, Big Tech firms are presently complying (willingly or otherwise) with the first wave of pushback they are experiencing. While governments seem to be winning the first round of these battles in many countries, this is likely to be a multi-stage battle, and Big Tech firms are not likely to easily give up their influence, power and wealth. Both they and the governments seeking to control them will need to evolve rapidly as well. Governments, by the end of the twenty-first century, will likely look very different than they did at the beginning.

Governments and existing institutions may find themselves disrupted by the trend towards greater disintermediation. As leading tech thinker Don Tapscott has argued, the world has often oscillated between the two countervailing forces of centralization or concentration, and disintermediation or decentralization. Traditionally, powerful intermediaries such as banks, governments and even Big Tech firms have played a critical role in establishing trust and maintaining integrity of transactions. But now, much like the internet, technologies such as blockchain and web 3.0 offer alternatives to the current institutional infrastructure of the world. As Joichi Ito, director of the MIT Media Lab, has explained, 'the blockchain is to trust as the internet is to information'.[2] Underlying these disruptive trends is a popular desire to take back some of the control and power that has been appropriated by institutions over time.

Global governance itself is likely to be challenging during such a period of transition. There are worries about a twenty-first-century technology cold war. All the major powers want to leverage all the time they can get to prepare their capabilities before norms, rules, and even laws emerge to govern their behaviour. Amid that urgency, the incentives for the global powers to cooperate even as they compete have not been emphasized enough. But these incentives may require new frameworks. The global governance institutions that have dominated the twentieth century might not be the institutions of choice in the twenty-first century. The battle between different institutions trying to assert their legitimacy and authority, especially on issues related to technology, will become an increasingly contentious one. Yet, it is evident that the world will need fundamentally new and different institutions for better technology governance. The values and objectives at the foundation of the new institutional architecture will require serious, in-depth conversations at the global, national and societal levels.

These conversations, in turn, will require deep study of the impact technology is having on our society, our polities, humanity, and on all of us as individuals. Technology—and the economic and geopolitical battles accompanying it—are driving a fear of the second Great Divergence in recent history. This inequality is manifesting itself between nations, but also within nations, as a new group of tech elites (venture capitalists, tech founders, engineers and senior executives) accumulate wealth and power at a global scale. These new titans are replacing the old industrial elites—and stirring similar resentments.

The challenges posed by tech-inequality are amplified by the imminent irrelevance of many industries, jobs and sectors in the new economy. Even dominant energy sources like oil may see their economic and geopolitical importance waning rapidly. These large structural transitions, combined with rising inequality and great power rivalry, will likely lead to major social, political and economic movements. As waves of communism and fascism followed the great economic disparities within European nations and the great power rivalry around the two world wars, major political changes may follow the turmoil created by technological change. We are already seeing emerging signs of such movements in the rise of populism and aggressive nationalism in many countries around the world.

As we face those changes with past parallels, we may find ourselves haunted by the consequences of past choices. The industrial era's dependence on carbon-intensive energy sources and lack of emphasis on environmental sustainability and ecological balance have had significant implications for the world over the last two centuries. We now live in the Anthropocene era, in which humans have become the biggest shaper of our environments. The loss of biodiversity, climate change, loss of livelihood, and a declining quality of life in many large cities—especially in the emerging nations—have become matters of political as well as humanitarian concern.

As we enter another major energy transition in the twenty-first century (from fossil fuel sources to cleaner energy sources), we have an opportunity to make some critical decisions again. Will we choose our energy sources wisely this time around? What role will outer-space exploration play in the coming decades? Will we leverage technology to reduce the adverse impact of human activity on our planet? And will we take the difficult decisions to ensure ecological balance on planet Earth?

Choices will have to be made, too, about certain emerging technologies—especially biotech and genetic engineering technologies such as CRISPR—which have put us in the throes of a genetic or a biotech revolution. We might, for the first time in history, have the potential to change our genetic makeup in ways that could transform the future of humanity. Along with emerging technologies such as AI, genetic editing technology poses ethical and governance issues of grave import. The paths we choose on these technology-driven issues will shape the future of humanity.

As we make these decisions, we must recognize that technology is already impacting us as individual humans in ways that we do not yet fully comprehend. The rising crisis of attention driven by the mass addiction to smartphones is shaping our ways of thinking and decision-making, not to mention our relationships. We might be seeing a transition from our minds being driven by linear thought processes to minds driven more by networked thought processes. Increasing stress, anxiety and depression—often due to these digital addictions and their impact on our emotional, mental and physical well-being—is likely to shape our interpersonal and societal relations. Ultimately, these changes in human traits will shape the decisions our leaders (and we as people) take on matters of war and peace, diplomacy and espionage, privacy and surveillance, and other such critical policy matters.

From amidst changes of such scale, it is difficult to fathom that the wide-ranging impact of technology on our economy, our politics, our world order, our societies, and the future of humanity is just in its early days. Its impact will likely continue to evolve, complicate and accelerate in the coming years and decades. In fact, it will be the convergence of various trends with the juggernaut of technology intensify many of the changes we are already seeing.

If we don't grasp technology's impact fully even today, the chances of us being able to do so in the future are even bleaker. Therefore, it is absolutely essential that we start to engage in much broader conversations about the impact of technology. If our conversations remain narrowly focused on the size and scale of Big Tech firms, or the amount of venture capital funding raised by start-ups in our respective nations, then we will have missed the point.

It is hard to make accurate predictions about geopolitical and other developments that rely on the motivations and actions of so many different actors. Yet, some key questions are already evident: Will we see a Second Great Divergence among nations, or will the laggards be able to catch up? Will there be a Cold War between the US and China and an accompanying polarization of the world? How will the nation-state evolve to meet the onslaught of Big Tech firms? Will power devolve in a more centralized or de-centralized manner in the coming decades? Will technology lead to greater inequality and chasms in society, or will the rising tide raise all boats? Will climate and bio-technology change the great game again in the coming decades? Will we as humans fundamentally be transformed by emerging technologies, or will we continue to shape the technologies to serve our purposes and values? And probably, the most important of the question of all, underlying all the ones above: what values will we hold dear as a society and race? And will we have the imagination, foresight, wisdom and courage to ensure that those values shape the design and impact of technology?

It is in response to all these questions that I have become a techno-realist, seeking to strike a balance between the techno-optimists and techno-pessimists of the world. Technology has solved some of the core problems that have bedevilled human history. The connections it has engendered in recent decades have fundamentally improved our ability to communicate, collaborate and solve problems. Yet, technology cannot solve all of these problems alone. Technology, for example, will not be able to solve our climate problem unless we make changes in behaviour, restructure our systems and institutions, rethink our priorities, and recalibrate our values.

The central urgency of these values is what makes so many of today's conversations about technology inherently political. Just as trade, industrialization and other world-shapers were enmeshed with politics, so too is technology. We must, then, work to better design technology, so it aligns with what we value most as humans. As we create more technology, we must ask, as Langdon Winner exhorts us to: 'What in the world are we making here? Do our impressive technical "things" express our best impulses and commitments, or something entirely different? How can we think about such matters in a fruitful way and respond appropriately?'[3]

The alternative is hard to imagine. Each of the chapters in this book has implicitly outlined the scenarios that result if we do not understand the Great Tech Game and make wise choices on the options that we are faced with. Countries, and vast populations of the world, could end up lagging behind others. The rising divides could result in massive socio-economic and political backlashes around the world. The world may become more divided than before, and the spectre of the clash of civilizations might become real, yet again. The magnitude of the climate problem, or the consequences of genetic editing, might move beyond our control altogether. The future of our societies and humanity might not reflect the values we believe we hold dear.

Transforming nations, firms, societies and our political, economic and social systems will be very hard, but it is possible. This requires that we do not view technology within a narrow paradigm of progress. The focus of technology must not be confined to the economic, political and environmental models propagated by the trade, industrial, or capitalist eras. Rather, we must view technology in the context of societal progress and a healthier, sustainable future for humans. Only then will technological progress start to equate with societal and human progress.

We must seek to better understand the gravity and scale of the changes afoot. We must take tough decisions as individuals, families, nations, societies, and as a race, so that we do not repeat past mistakes. And as we make these decisions, the human and societal values that we hold dear must be invoked and embodied first, and not as an afterthought.

We must prepare ourselves for this new age of technology. This is our destiny, and it is up to us to shape it.

Notes

1. Pope Francis, *Encyclical Letter Laudato Si'*.

2. Don Tapscott and Alex Tapscott, *Blockchain Revolution: How the Technology behind Bitcoin and Other Cryptocurrencies is Changing the World*, Penguin (2016), Kindle.

3. Langdon Winner, *The Whale and the Reactor: A Search for Limits in an Age of High Technology* (University of Chicago Press, 2020), p. ix.

Afterword

A Game Plan for India

In such a fast-evolving game, what grand strategy or game plan should a country like India adopt? For India, a few priorities emerge clearly out of the analytical exercise I have undertaken in this book. As history suggests, India—and its policymakers, strategic thinkers, businessmen and entrepreneurs—must understand the contours of the Great Tech Game and ensure that it does not miss the boat this time. India has no choice—and neither does any other country, really. A successful strategy to compete successfully in the Great Tech Game can transform the socio-economic prospects of over a billion Indians. Failure to compete, on the other hand, will have equally serious adverse ramifications.

India must therefore focus its energy on building out its digital economy rapidly—and that means not just the tech sector, as we discussed in Chapter 4. Technology and data—as factors of production—must permeate all sectors to boost productivity. India must adopt a mix of approaches and strategies to create its own defensible competitive positioning within the global ecosystem. A globally competitive India will need to maintain global leadership in higher value-added IT services as well as excellence in software-enabled manufacturing. Identification of SaaS products and other, deeper layers of software, and doubling down on tech innovation in sectors such as agriculture, education and healthcare can form the foundation of its global niche.

Development of digital entrepots within India—along the lines of Singapore or Estonia—can help attract talent and capital, as can timely adaptation of its governance, rules and institutions for the tech era. Most excitingly, the expansion (and potentially, global export) of its digital public infrastructure ecosystem, the IndiaStack, offers a unique opportunity for India to design—and benefit strategically and economically from—the creation of the world's digital commons.

India must also keep an unstinted focus on the future, and not just reactively attempt to compete in existing large technology ecosystems such as consumer internet. Even as it finds niches within the existing tech markets, it must seek to pro-actively build a strong foundation for leadership in the next big set of transformative technologies, whether it is climate tech or biotech or others. Focusing on these clusters of emerging technologies could help India leapfrog into the 'big league' of technology nations in the coming decades.

India must become a tech nation, not just a talent nation. A strategy of labour arbitrage will not suffice; we cannot only rely on providing cheap talent to the world. We must also develop a strategy of technology arbitrage. India has to develop a culture—and a well-funded ecosystem—of fundamental scientific and technological research and build core tech IP across sectors. Even if it takes several years or a couple of decades—as it most likely will—India must take calculated bets and increasingly seek to be in the 'Circle of Five' for several strategic technology sectors. Only then will greater value accrue to its companies and its people.

Geopolitically, it must ensure security of its digital and tech infrastructure—whether it is the underwater fibre optic cables connecting India to the world, or the multitude of data centres and cloud networks hosted within India. It must use the traditional tools of diplomacy and foreign policy to further its domestic economic objectives. The right partnerships and alliances can help secure critical supply chains, but more importantly, they can bring the right mix of technology and capital to supplement India's talent. This pooling of talent, technology and capital will be critical to solve for the specific binding constraints that currently hinder India's economic growth. The focus of India's foreign policy must span not just its geopolitical goals, but also, increasingly, its economic and technological objectives.

Rules- and standards-setting organizations can further facilitate India's economic objectives and, therefore, it is imperative to have a clear vision of what it wants from global tech governance institutions. For this, it must ensure that domestically, its various ministries and groups are strategically aligned. Securing a seat at the right tables this time around should also be a strategic priority. Domestically, balanced relationships—most importantly between citizen and state, but also the state and Big Tech firms—will be critical.

Militarily, India must continue to build its strengths in the emerging domains of cyber and space. Building strong cyber-defence and offence capabilities will help secure and deter any crippling attacks. As the nature of war, and the tools required to win, evolve, India must accordingly evolve its capabilities and military doctrines.

Finally, it must seek to better understand how the new technological revolution is shaping its own societal structures, values, identities and preferences. The current technological revolution will—much like the others that preceded it—unleash forces that threaten to upend the existing political, social and economic order. Like earlier Great Games, the Great Tech Game shall also create a new set of opportunities and winners, but also challenges and losers. Managing this transition will be one of the biggest challenges facing government and society.

Public debates around the core values that society holds dear—such as freedom, privacy, openness, transparency, equitable and sustainable development—must be encouraged. The design and use of technology, as I've argued through this book, must be in sync with those values. Adapting our socio-economic policies and institutions to uphold these values will require a whole-of-society effort, not just a whole-of-government one.

Acknowledgements

This book is based on over my two decades of personal and professional engagement with technology. Bringing many perspectives—the historical, the economic, the geopolitical, the societal and often even philosophical—into one book meant that I had to lean heavily on the work of giants in each of these disciplines.

The first section—the peek back into history—was shaped by the work of many historians, and in particular economic historians and technology historians. I am most grateful to William Bernstein and Daniel Headrick, two stalwarts who have each written several books that have transformed my understanding of history. Bernstein's book, *The Splendid Exchange: How Trade Shaped the World*, does for trade what I have attempted to do for technology. Both were kind enough to spend many illuminating hours over Zoom with me.

For the economic competitiveness section, I benefitted from conversations with many incredible thinkers, fellow entrepreneurs and venture capitalists, policymakers, economists, and international development specialists. Professors Robert Ayres and Philippe Aghion from INSEAD, Professors Oliver Hart and Ricardo Hausmann at Harvard, Prof. Bart Hobijn from Arizona State University, Prof. Karthik Muralidharan from UC San Diego, Prof. Frank Nagle from

HBS, Professors David Hsu and John Zhang at the Wharton School, Jeffrey Wong at Spring Gate Capital, Shailesh Lakhani at Sequoia Capital, Shreyas Shibulal at Micelio, Ganapathy Venugopal at Axilor Ventures, Craig Wing, Ronak Gopaldas at Signal Risk Africa, Matt Tilleard at Crossboundary Africa, Hema Vallabh, Tobias Adrian at the IMF, William Maloney and Indermit Gill at the World Bank, Zia Qureshi and Landry Signé at Brookings Institution in Washington DC, were all extremely generous with their insights on the complex relationship between technology and economic growth.

My years at McKinsey have shaped much of my thinking, and I remain immensely grateful to my colleagues there. Conversations with Gautam Kumra, Noshir Kaka, Anand Swaminathan, Alok Kshirsagar, Jonathan Woetzel, Eric Hazan, Nomfanelo Magwentshu, and Kartik Jayaram—all from McKinsey—gave me incisive insights and global perspective. Martin Reeves and Arindam Bhattacharya from BCG's Henderson Institute, Hermann Simon of Simon-Kucher & Partners, Prof. Bhaskar Chakravorti and Ravi Chaturvedi at Tufts, and Prof. Arun Sundararajan at NYU helped provide a practical perspective on how laggard nations could devise niche strategies for enhancing their competitiveness in the digital economy.

S.D. Shibulal, one of the founders of Infosys, took valuable time to share a historical perspective on India's IT services journey but, more importantly, provided an extremely balanced, thoughtful perspective on how technology is shaping our lives. Sharad Sharma, founder of the iSPIRT Foundation in Bangalore, has a deep understanding of history and an even deeper understanding of the technology world. His insights have not surprisingly permeated many sections of the book. Pilar Fajarnes Garces, the author of the UNCTAD Digital Economy Reports, provided especially valuable insights into the nature and structure of global digital value chains, and the role digital services is likely to play in the economic development strategies of nations, especially India. Jessica Nicholson and her colleagues at the US Bureau of Economic Analysis (BEA) were kind enough to share their insights on the issue of measurement of the digital economy.

On the geopolitics, world order and governance sections, I am grateful for the time and insights I got from Prof. Chris Foster at the University of Manchester, Prof. Nick Couldry at the LSE, Tim Strong at TeleGeography, Tim Rühlig at the German Council on Foreign Relations (DGAP), C. Raja Mohan, Sithu Ponraj and Drew Thompson at the National University of Singapore (NUS), Manuel Muniz, former secretary of state for Global Spain and now Provost at IE University in Madrid, Spain, Nitin Pai and Pranay Kotasthane at the Takshashila Institution, Lt. Gen. Panwar, Prof. Susan Landau from Tufts, Prof. Jonathan Winkler at Wright State University, Manish Maheshwari, Matt Ferchen at the Mercator Institute for China Studies, Zhao Hai at the China Academy of Social Sciences, Prof. Bruce Schneier at HKS, Danko Jevtović of the Board of Directors of ICANN, Tong Zhao at the Carnegie-Tsinghua Center for Global Policy, Klon Kitchen at the American Enterprise Institute (AEI), Parminder Singh from IT for Change, Dr Farzaneh Badiei of the Internet Governance Project, Carl Gahnberg at the Internet Society (ISOC), Gaurav Keerthi at the Cyber Security Agency of Singapore (CSA), and Johanna Weaver at the Australian National University.

The last section on society was, in many ways, the hardest. Some brilliant work has been done in this field, but so much more is needed. Many people helped me think broadly about the impact tech is having on society. Many thanks to Pratap Bhanu Mehta (former vice-chancellor of Ashoka University), Prof. Devesh Kapur at Johns Hopkins University School of Advanced International Studies (SAIS), Prof. Debora Spar at HBS, Dr Jane Vincent from the London School of Economics, Prof. Mauro Guillen (Dean at the Cambridge Judge Business School), Luis Miranda (founder of the Indian School of Public Policy) and Reshma Saujani (founder of Girls Who Code) for helping me consider the impact of tech on society from multiple perspectives. On climate and energy matters, I benefitted greatly from the perspectives of Nobuo Tanaka (former executive director of the International Energy Agency), Ranjan Mathai (former foreign secretary of India), Nitin Prasad (chairman of Shell companies in India), shared during an online panel discussion. On the impact of technology on human behaviour and values, I must acknowledge the fascinating work that has been done by Nicholas Carr, Prof. Cal Newport, Prof. Mary Aiken, Julia Hobsbawm, among others.

Many former professors have considerably enhanced the quality of the book. Adam Grant, my professor at Wharton, was extremely generous with his learnings and insights (not to mention a big dose of encouragement!), and for that, I am immensely grateful. He is genuinely a 'giver'. Similarly, Professors Kevin Werbach, David Hsu and John Zhang all took out time despite hectic teaching schedules to share their insights with me. Prof. Sunil Gupta at HBS provided valuable ideas and leads; Prof. Bruce Schneier at the HKS and a prominent cybersecurity expert helped make sense of this new world; Prof. Dwight Perkins at HKS shared valuable insights about the East Asian miracle, while Prof. Mauro Guillen helped me understand how future trends are likely to converge.

Many close friends, partners and mentors helped shape the overall set of arguments in the book. My partner in my venture capital and entrepreneurship journey, Nihal Mehta, and his wife, Reshma Saujani, have been big pillars of support throughout. My friend, guide and mentor, Rajan Anandan, with whom I have shared the ups and downs of the last decade of the Indian tech ecosystem, has always gently encouraged me at every step. His energy and enthusiasm for start-ups and innovative ideas have been infectious.

George Perkovich at the Carnegie Endowment for International Peace provided immense intellectual and moral support, not to mention the brutal editing that I had gotten used to as a Junior Fellow at Carnegie. Ashley Tellis has been an incredibly kind and supportive mentor since my Carnegie days. His strategic insights for the book were, as always, astute and helped me ask the right questions. C. Raja Mohan's incisive insights and his ability to see the big picture have always motivated me to look deep and broad. Gurcharan Das, with whom walks in Jor Bagh and Lodhi Gardens are filled with intellectual and reflective conversations, provided me with a broad, long-term perspective. C.V. Madhukar, whose guidance and kind encouragement I have benefitted from since my HKS days, shared many unique insights into the public digital ecosystems of India given his work at Omidyar.

Debjani Ghosh, president of NASSCOM, has done more than anyone else to bring industry, government and entrepreneurs together for a truly Digital India. Various sections of the book have benefitted from her inputs. Former colleagues and friends in the Government of India, especially at the ministry of electronics and IT ('MeitY'), were extremely gracious with their time and insights, especially my dear friend, former colleague and now CEO of India's National E-Governance Division (NeGD), Abhishek Singh.

Several senior former and current members of the Government of India have helped ensure this book is grounded in reality. K. VijayRaghavan, principal scientific advisor to the Prime Minister of India, provided me with a valuable glimpse into India's scientific and technological vision, while highlighting the unique layered complexities of India. I am also extremely grateful to Mr Amitabh Kant, CEO of India's NITI Aayog, for his deep insights and vision for India as a tech nation. Few combine a mastery of vision, articulation and execution as he does, and India has benefitted immensely from that. Jayant Sinha, former minister of finance in the Government of India, has been a mentor and guide. His foresight on strategic issues—including most recently on climate change—has always inspired me. He pushed me to aim for deeper insights, which has greatly improved the quality of this book. Sanjeev Sanyal, principal economic advisor, Government of India, helped me better frame the guiding principles for India's game plan. His ability to analyse current policy problems from a historical perspective is exceptional.

Shivshankar Menon, former National Security Advisor of India, has been one of India's best diplomats on the global stage. His intricate understanding of the changing world order dynamics—which he was kind enough to share with me—greatly informed this book. Arun Singh, India's former ambassador to the US and France and now a member of India's National Security Advisory Board (NSAB), provided a valuable expert view on how technology is reshaping or reinforcing alignments in the evolving world order. Vijay Gokhale, former Indian foreign secretary, has thought deeply about the impact of technology on diplomacy, and shared his views on how geo-politics, geo-economics and geo-strategy are merging today. Sanjeev Arora, former secretary in the ministry of external affairs (MEA), helped me immensely in gauging the path forward for India's diplomacy, especially on the techno-commercial front. Anupam Ray, joint secretary, public policy and research in the MEA provided me with a candid view of how foreign policy was evolving in the age of technology, and the need for a whole-of-society effort for India to adapt and compete effectively in it.

I'd like to acknowledge the consistent support provided by Swati Chopra, my editor at HarperCollins, to nudge me into writing a book. In particular, I owe special gratitude to Corley Miller, whose editing prowess was an incredible boon to me, especially in the last stages of the finalization. Aditi Rukhaiyar from Columbia (SIPA) and Ankith Pinnamaneni from my alma mater, Haverford College, provided valuable research assistance. Many fellow Harvard alums who have been successful authors helped guide me in the early stages of the book, including Ravi Agrawal (now editor-in-chief at *Foreign Policy*), Dr Abhinav Chandrachud and Apurva Chamaria.

Many friends from around the world pitched in, often fielding my repeated calls and messages at odd times of the day and night. Pranav has always been a brother, friend and a rare poet-intellectual, and his early inputs helped shape the arc of the book. Ankur, thank you for reviewing the manuscript and being my sounding board on the various ideas contained in the book. Many friends—Aarti, Pritika, Simran, Vinay, Laurel, Afreen, Vikas, Suraj, Divya, Parisa, Suhair, Natasha, Mariana, Shailesh and Manuel—from around the world shared their time, connections, insights, feedback and constant encouragement.

In the midst of finishing the book, I lost one of my biggest supporters and cheerleaders, my father, Shiv Suri. He had, through his own love of newspapers and books, inspired me to read extensively as a child. That love for reading and writing has kept me whole. He was delighted when I started writing my first book and would have been immensely proud to see my book on the shelves. My mother prodded me along to complete the book despite our loss. Her unstinted love, quiet strength, and strong values have shaped me in more ways than I could explain. My brother, Shikhil, has always pushed me to do better, but has also kept me grounded. In fact, this book is partly due to his constant prodding—a late-night conversation with him nudged me back into writing after a hiatus of several years.

My loving wife, Gursimran, put her heart and soul into this project right alongside me. She was not just patient and generous with her time and intellectual contributions to the book, but was equally forgiving when I disappeared, sometimes weeks at a time, into my writing shell. This book wouldn't have been completed without her.

And, of course, my deep love to both my lovely daughters, Mira–Sophia and Kirat–Nafisa. Knowing that their father was writing a book about it, they learnt how to pronounce the word 'technology' properly. They were surprisingly understanding and patient, though one day, my older daughter quipped: 'If you keep writing more, Papa, the book will not fit into any bookstore.' To both of them, I hope I can pass on the love for writing and reading (even if it is on Kindle).

Index

509

About the Author

Anirudh Suri is the managing partner at India Internet Fund, a technology-focused venture capital fund based in India and the US. Previously, he has worked with the Government of India in Delhi, McKinsey and Company in New York, the Carnegie Endowment in Washington, DC, and Goldman Sachs in London.

He has written extensively on foreign policy, geopolitics, technology and entrepreneurship in publications such as *The Indian Express, Foreign Policy, The New Republic* and *Asia Times*. An alumnus of the Wharton School and the Harvard Kennedy School, he studied economics and politics at Haverford College and the London School of Economics, and learnt Mandarin at the Beijing Foreign Studies University in China. Named a Goldman Sachs Global Leader, he has also served on the board of the Harvard Alumni Association.

He lives in Delhi with his wife and two daughters.

Twitter @AnirudhSuri